Contents

The following units are available online at **www.hoddereducation.co.uk/hscdiploma**:

Unit HSC 2013 Support care plan activities 2 credits

Unit HSC 2032 Working as part of a team in health and social care or children and young people's settings 2 credits

Unit HSC 2029 Meet food safety requirements when providing food and drink for individuals 3 credits

Additional resources

Go to **www.hoddereducation.co.uk/HSCDiploma** to access a range of additional resources to support you through your study of the Level 2 Health and Social Care Diploma!

HEALTH & SOCIAL CARE LEGISLATION UPDATES

Keep up to date with all the important information on Health & Social Care assessment, regulation and legislation.

Watch this space - stay informed...

Up-to-date Legislation
Legislation is always changing. To make sure that you are up to date with the latest changes and developments, simply click on the Legislation updates link which will guide you through all you need to know.

LEVEL 2 ADDITIONAL OPTIONAL UNITS

Access additional optional units for the Level 2 Health & Social Care Diploma:

Unit HSC 2013 Support care plan activities
Unit HSC 2032 Working as part of a team in health and social care or children and young people's settings
Unit HSC 2029 Meet food safety requirements when providing food and drink for individuals

Additional units
Access the additional units: HSC 2013 Support care plan activities, HSC 2029 Meet food safety requirements when providing food and drink for individuals, and HSC 2032 Working as part of a team in health and social care or children and young people's settings.

HEALTH & SOCIAL CARE DIPLOMA
Caroline Morris

E-UPDATES

Keep up to date with new publishing, curriculum info and special offers.

SIGN UP

E-updates
Sign up to e-updates for all the latest news on the curriculum as well as our new publishing.

Also available:
A comprehensive glossary, grids to clarify the different unit names/numbers across the different awarding bodies, additional activities and a range of other resources to guide you through the Diploma.

LEVEL 2

HEALTH & SOCIAL CARE DIPLOMA

Fiona Collier
Belinda Goode

HODDER
EDUCATION
AN HACHETTE UK COMPANY

FSC
www.fsc.org
MIX
Paper from
responsible sources
FSC® C110418

Orders: please contact Bookpoint Ltd, 130 Milton Park, Abingdon, Oxon OX14 4SB. Telephone: (44) 01235 827720. Fax: (44) 01235 400454. Lines are open from 9.00 – 5.00, Monday to Saturday, with a 24-hour message answering service. You can also order through our website www.hoddereducation.co.uk

If you have any comments to make about this, or any of our other titles, please send them to educationenquiries@hodder.co.uk

British Library Cataloguing in Publication Data

A catalogue record for this title is available from the British Library

ISBN 987 1 471 80660 5

Impression number   10 9 8 7 6 5 4 3 2 1

Year   2018 2017 2016 2015

Cover photo © Jupiterimages/Brand X Pictures/Thinkstock

Typeset by Integra Software Services Pvt. Ltd., Pondicherry, India

Printed in Slovenia

Author biographies

Fiona Collier is a registered nurse with extensive experience of delivering services in Health and Social Care. In addition to her clinical skills Fiona has also worked as an assessor, trainer and internal moderator within Further Education providing work based training and education to health and social care workers. More recently, Fiona has worked in Regulation within health and social care. Throughout her career Fiona has worked as a Consultant in Education and Training for the Health and Social Care sector. This role involves designing, delivering and evaluating training as well as writing educational material for publishers and awarding bodies. Fiona has written the underpinning knowledge and assessments for a number of awards and qualifications.

Belinda Goode is a registered social worker with varied experience of working as a manager in both Mental Health and Social Care services. In addition to her social work Belinda has also worked in service development in the Department of Health. Belinda has worked in Mental Health services for the past 10 years and is currently supporting the development of new mental health liaison services into acute hospitals in North Yorkshire. She has a particular interest in Dementia, delivering education and awareness sessions to both health and social care staff. She is also a Dementia Champion. Belinda has co-written a text book on Dementia for the QCF as well as academic articles.

How to use this book

This book is your constant companion and covers all the mandatory and 10 optional units you need to master the knowledge and skills for the Level 2 Diploma in Health and Social Care. An additional 3 optional units are available online at **www.hoddereducation.co.uk/HSC Diploma**.

Key features of the book

What are you finding out?

This unit is about identifying ways you can communicate with individuals on difficult, complex and sensitive issues.

A summary of what will be covered in the unit.

Some learners may be working towards their L2 Diploma in Health and Social Care after achieving units from the L2 Certificate in Preparing to Work in Adult Social Care. The units across both qualifications share some of the same knowledge content. The table at the beginning of each mandatory unit identifies the assessment criteria that are shared between both qualifications.

SHC 22 Assessment Criteria	Unit PWCS22
AC1.3	AC1.3
AC3.1	AC3.3

LO1 Understand why communication is important in the work setting

AC 1.1 Identify different reasons why people communicate

Understand all the requirements of the qualification fully with clearly stated learning outcomes and assessment criteria fully mapped to the specification.

Key term

Communication is a means of sending or receiving information.

Understand important terms.

Time to think

1.1 Communication

Make a note of all the times you communicate with people throughout the course of your working day.

Learn to reflect on your own skills and experiences.

Research and investigate

4.1 Confidentiality in your workplace

Find a copy of your organisation's confidentiality policy and identify the main points of the policy.

Enhance your understanding of topics with research-led activities encouraging you to explore an area in more detail.

Case study

1.1 Mr Cross

Mr Cross is a 79-year-old gentleman who lives in a care home. He has become unwell and the doctor has been called out to see him.

See how concepts are applied in settings with real life scenarios. See how concepts are applied in settings with real life scenarios.

Evidence activity

1.3 Reactions

Explain why it is important to take into account an individual's reaction when you are communicating with them.

Test your knowledge with questions linked to assessment criteria to help you generate evidence as well as short tasks to help enhance your understanding of assessment criteria, and apply your knowledge in the work setting.

Legislation

Data Protection Act 1998

Equality Act 2010

A summary of the legislation relevant to the unit.
Go to **www.hoddereducation.co.uk/HSC Diploma** for updates to key legislation.

Useful resources

Websites
Deafblind UK
www.deafblind.org.uk

Includes references to websites, books and other various sources for further reading and research.

Acknowledgements and photo credits

Fiona Collier

I would like to thank my parents, Mick and Jackie, for having belief in me and giving me the encouragement and opportunity to fulfil my childhood dream of becoming a nurse. It is through my experience as a nurse that I developed a strong desire to strive to improve care for people using health and social care services.

I would also like to thank my husband Rob and my children Aimee and Sam for their continued support and encouragement whilst I have been writing this book. They have been there when I have needed them and have also given me space to write when I have needed that too.

I would like to remember my grandma Alice, who died in a care home whilst I was writing this book, aged 94 years. It is for people like grandma Alice that I want health and social care workers to be as knowledgeable as they possibly can be.

Belinda Goode

Thank you to all my colleagues in health and social care and to those people using our services who teach us so much.

Photo credits

Mandatory
Group A Units

Introduction to communication in health, social care or children's and young people's settings

This unit is worth 3 credits

What are you finding out?

Communication is a basic human need and something that we do in everyday life. However, because it is something we do every day, it can be easy to forget how important it is. Effective communication is essential within any health or social care environment.

People communicate in different ways and for a range of reasons. This unit will therefore introduce you to the reasons why people communicate and the different methods they use. It will also highlight why communication is important within health and social care settings.

By the end of this unit you will:

1 Understand why communication is important in the work setting
2 Be able to meet the communication and language needs, wishes and preferences of individuals
3 Be able to reduce barriers to communication
4 Be able to apply principles and practices relating to confidentiality at work.

Links to Level 2 Certificate in Preparing to Work in Adult Social Care

SHC 21 Assessment Criteria	Unit PWCS21
AC1.1	AC1.1
AC1.2	AC1.2
AC1.3	AC1.3
AC3.1	AC3.1
AC3.4	AC3.4
AC4.3	AC4.3
AC4.4	AC4.4

LO1 Understand why communication is important in the work setting

AC 1.1 Identify different reasons why people communicate

Health and social care workers are required to provide a range of information to people who use services to enable them to understand the support that is available to meet their needs.

Key terms

Communication is a means of sending or receiving information.

Service users are those that use health and social care services. They are often referred to as individuals in this book.

Communication constantly takes place within the health and social care services. **Service users**, staff and other adults interact and communicate with each other for a variety of reasons in your health and social care workplace. For example, people communicate in order to:

- make and develop relationships
- obtain and share information
- express thoughts and ideas
- give and receive support
- express feelings, wishes, needs and preferences.

Making and developing relationships

Communication is an effective way to make new relationships. In health and social care settings these relationships may be with service users, visitors or colleagues. Positive **verbal communication** such as talking to someone using your voice, and **non-verbal**

Figure 1.1 Good communication can help you to create a good impression

communication skills, such as being friendly, smiling and shaking hands when greeting the person, are needed to make a good first impression in a relationship.

Members of staff working in a health or social care environment develop relationships with service users, their relatives or carers and with colleagues by maintaining a friendly, supportive approach, and by being interested in what other people are doing and feeling. This enables service users to feel comfortable and secure, and to feel that they can trust and rely on the professionals who are supporting them.

Obtaining and sharing information

Members of staff working in a health or social care environment may need to obtain and share information about service users with colleagues and other professionals in order to co-ordinate care and to ensure the rest of the team are kept fully informed. Health and social care workers will also need to communicate with service users or their families about the care and support they receive, or about the kinds of services and facilities that are available in the **care setting**. You may find it useful to refer to HSC 028 for more information on handling information.

Expressing thoughts and ideas

Members of staff working in health and social care services may also need to share their own thoughts about care issues or aspects of practice with other colleagues. Effective communication skills are also needed to encourage service users to express their thoughts and ideas.

Giving and receiving support

Service users and their relatives often seek reassurance from care staff as a way of developing their self-confidence. In response, care staff often use the following methods when supporting and reassuring them:

- praise
- touch
- time
- attention.

Some health or social care settings also use support groups, staff meetings and appraisals as ways of providing staff with their own support and reassurance about their work performance.

Expressing feelings, wishes, needs and preferences

It is important that people using health or social care services are encouraged to express their feelings and to talk about how they wish to be treated, as well as to say what they like and dislike. People will communicate in this way if they trust and have a secure relationship with care staff.

Key terms

Verbal communication is spoken communication, and this can be face-to-face, by telephone, television, radio or other spoken means.

Non-verbal communication is a means of communicating without using words. It includes the use of facial expressions, body language, eye contact and posture.

A care setting is any place where a person receives health or social care. Some examples of care settings include care homes, hospitals, dentists and GP surgeries.

Time to think

1.1 Communication

Make a note of all the times you communicate with people throughout the course of your working day.

Who did you communicate with?

How did you communicate with them?

What was the reason for the communication?

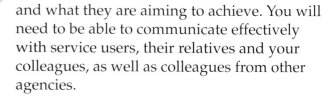

AC 1.2 Explain how effective communication affects all aspects of own work

As we have discussed, effective communication is a central part of the work that must happen in the health sector. You will need to develop a range of communication skills and be able to use those skills effectively to carry out the various aspects of your work role. You will establish many different relationships across the sector – some will be formal and some will be informal.

Two-way communication is required to form relationships and establish boundaries. This will help to ensure that all parties understand the purpose of the relationship and what they are aiming to achieve. You will need to be able to communicate effectively with service users, their relatives and your colleagues, as well as colleagues from other agencies.

The relationships between workers and service users, and also between colleagues, have a significant impact on the ability to provide effective care and support. Respect for each other can be developed through communication. Getting to know different people by talking and listening to them will enable you to develop awareness and understanding, which will lead to stronger relationships in the long term.

Being respectful, consistent in approach and patient in the way you listen and respond to people within your organisation will encourage them to trust and communicate with you.

The communication cycle

In order to communicate effectively, we have to go through a process known as the communication cycle. This process is called the communication cycle because in order for it to be effective, it creates a continuous cycle.

The communication cycle happens subconsciously, but consists of the stages shown in Figure 1.2 on the following page.

When communicating, this process is repeated as many times as necessary to continue the communication.

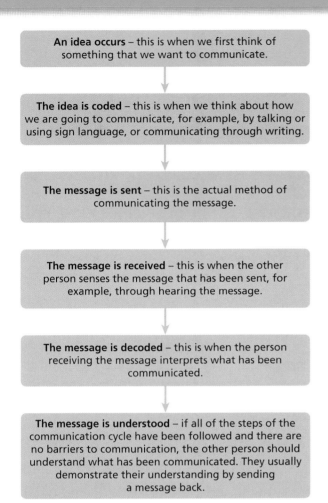

An idea occurs – this is when we first think of something that we want to communicate.

The idea is coded – this is when we think about how we are going to communicate, for example, by talking or using sign language, or communicating through writing.

The message is sent – this is the actual method of communicating the message.

The message is received – this is when the other person senses the message that has been sent, for example, through hearing the message.

The message is decoded – this is when the person receiving the message interprets what has been communicated.

The message is understood – if all of the steps of the communication cycle have been followed and there are no barriers to communication, the other person should understand what has been communicated. They usually demonstrate their understanding by sending a message back.

Figure 1.2 The Communication cycle

Knowing about the communication cycle and being able to send and receive messages appropriately is the key to understanding how to communicate well. In general, you will use communication effectively as part of your work role if you can:

- attract the other person's attention before you begin communicating with them
- speak clearly and directly so that you get your message across
- adapt the way you communicate so that the other person is able to understand you
- use empathy to try to understand the other person's point of view or the way the other person might be feeling throughout communication
- actively listen to what the other person is communicating to you

Evidence activity

1.2 Effective communication
Explain how effective communication affects all aspects of your work.

- use your own non-verbal communication skills effectively
- observe the other person's non-verbal communication
- summarise what the other person has said as a way of checking and confirming your understanding of what the person means.

Your communication skills will develop and become more effective as you gain experience in your work role. You will learn by observing more experienced colleagues. Learning from others, seeking advice and using support are all part of this process.

AC 1.3 Explain why it is important to observe an individual's reactions when communicating with them

Because communication is a two-way process it is important to be mindful that all communication will have an effect on the person you are communicating with. It is therefore essential that you are observant of the other person's reactions when you are communicating with them. Being an effective communicator involves observing how other people respond to your communication. This involves looking at the person's non-verbal communication, otherwise known as body language.

Non-verbal communication refers to the messages we send out to express ideas and opinions without talking. When we interact with other people, we continuously give and receive wordless signals. Non-verbal behaviours include the following:

- gestures we make
- the way we sit

- how close we stand to a person
- how much eye contact we make.

These all send strong messages that we need to be observant of. For example, observing non-verbal communication can help to assess the person's:

- understanding of what is being communicated
- feelings about what has been communicated.

It is often easy to see whether a person is happy or upset, but there are more subtle elements of body language that you should look out for.

The way the person listens, looks, moves and reacts can tell you whether they are upset or happy, whether they are interested or not, or whether they have understood what you have said. These non-verbal signals can help you to sense whether there is trust and desire for connection or whether the person is uninterested, distrusting or confused. Sometimes a person's body language may communicate something different to what the person communicates verbally. For example, a person may state they are not in pain, however, their body language may indicate otherwise. It is especially important to be aware of this when supporting people who have a condition such as dementia.

Figure 1.3 By looking at this person's body language, how do you think they feel?

Evidence activity

1.3 **Reactions**

Explain why it is important to take into account an individual's reaction when you are communicating with them.

LO2 Be able to meet the communication and language needs, wishes and preferences of individuals

AC 2.1 Find out an individual's communication and language needs, wishes and preferences

It is important to be aware of the fact that not all people communicate in the same way. It is therefore essential that you communicate with people who use health and social care services in a way that best suits them.

There are a wide range of factors that can affect a person's ability to communicate, including:

- language
- **sensory ability**
- **culture**
- learning ability
- self-confidence.

Effective communication can take place only if the right method is used, and is received and understood by the person you are communicating with. It is therefore important to be aware of a range of methods for communicating. Health and social care services are used by people

Key terms

A person's sensory ability relates to their ability to see, hear and speak.

Culture refers to the ideas, customs and behaviours of particular people or society.

Evidence activity

2.1 Communication and language needs
Explain how you can find out about different people's communication and language needs, wishes and preferences within your place of work.

Key terms

Beliefs are an acceptance for things you feel to be true.

Values are the importance or regard that is given to something, or what someone judges to be important.

from a diverse range of backgrounds and each person will have their own way of communicating. Finding out about each person's methods of communication and their preferences is an essential part of your role. You can do this by:

● directly asking people about their language or communication preferences and needs
● accessing information from service users' support plans
● being aware of each individual's culture and any aspects of their nationality that might affect their language preferences and needs
● speaking with specialists such as speech and language therapists about the best way to support people who have special communication requirements.

AC 2.2 Demonstrate communication methods that meet an individual's communication needs, wishes and preferences

In order for effective communication to take place, the right method has to be used, so that messages can be received and understood. As a health or social care worker you will need to know about a range of communication methods. You should also know about the importance of communicating with people in a way that meets their language needs, wishes and preferences.

Preferences may be based on:

● **beliefs**
● **values**
● cultures.

People who use health and social care services will come from a diverse range of backgrounds and many people will have differing methods of communication. You can find out about a person's language needs, wishes and preferences by:

● asking people about their preferred method of communication or, where communication is difficult, asking their relatives about their particular language and communication needs
● familiarising yourself with the service user's care plan relating to communication – this care plan should highlight any preferences or specific support that might be required to make communication easier
● being aware that the individual's culture, ethnicity and nationality might affect their language preferences or needs
● observing people within your workplace to establish their language and communication skills
● discussing individuals' communication preferences and needs with other professionals such as speech and language therapists who may be able to advise on how best to support people who have specific communication needs.

Non-verbal communication
Non-verbal communication includes facial expressions, the tone and pitch of voice, gestures displayed through body language and the distance between the people who are communicating. These non-verbal signs can give clues and additional information over and above spoken verbal communication.

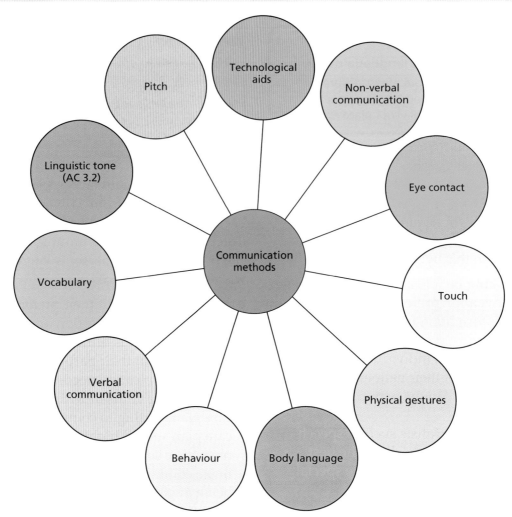

Figure 1.4 Communication methods

Eye contact

Eye contact is a type of non-verbal communication. The eyes can give a lot of information about what is being communicated. This is especially important when a person cannot verbalise their needs and feelings.

Touch

Touch is an essential element of communication. Touch can take a number of forms, for example, holding a hand, giving a hug, placing an arm around a person's shoulder or stroking a person's hair. It is important to establish whether a person feels comfortable with touch prior to using this form of communication. It may be more acceptable in some cultures than others.

Physical gestures

The gestures we make can be very effective in making our feelings known when we are unable to use words to express how we are feeling. Waving hands or arms can be an effective way of attracting attention as well as signalling distress. As a health or social care worker you can use gestures to convey messages. For example, pointing or demonstrating an action can be helpful when a person finds instructions difficult.

Other communication methods are covered throughout this unit.

2.2 Communication methods

Undertake a case study to explain different times when you have used different methods of communication to meet the communication needs, wishes and preferences of individuals within your place of work.

Ask your supervisor to observe your interactions and methods with one or two individuals (but ensure you have gained their consent first). You need to see feedback about how you have ensured that your communication methods are understood.

AC 2.3 Show how and when to seek advice about communication

There may be times when you need to seek further advice to enable you to effectively support people to communicate within your place of work. For example, you may need to seek further support when:

- a person has specific communication needs
- a person speaks a different language
- communication is not effective
- you are not sure how to deal with a situation.

In situations like this, you can seek advice and guidance from:

- the person themselves or their family and friends
- your manager
- communication and language support specialists such as teachers, psychologists or speech and language therapists.

2.3 Advice and guidance

Explain who can offer advice and guidance to ensure communication needs are met within your place of work.

LO3 Be able to reduce barriers to communication

AC 3.1 Identify barriers to communication

Despite your best efforts, you may sometimes find that you are unable to communicate effectively with another person in your work setting. There are a number of possible reasons why this might happen. Knowing about different barriers to effective communication will enable you to avoid potential difficulties and adapt your communication approach where this is necessary.

Barriers to communication are things that interfere with a person's ability to send, receive or understand a message. These may include:

- environmental barriers
- individual/personal barriers
- cultural differences
- language barriers
- sensory impairment
- speech impairment
- factors affecting health
- conditions affecting the brain
- learning disabilities.

Environmental barriers

As well as your own actions and choice of words, careful consideration must be given to the environment in which the communication takes place. This does not just relate to the physical layout of the environment but also to other factors that can impact on communication, for example, lack of privacy and distractions from other people.

3.1 Barriers

Make a list of as many barriers to communication as you can think of that have affected you this week.

Environmental barriers could include the following:

- **Lack of privacy** – private conversations should never be held where other people can hear them, as this is very disrespectful. Privacy is an essential component of confidentiality, and conversations that can be overheard may impact on the way in which the person communicates with you. In addition, interruptions from other people can make a person feel intimidated and unimportant. Lack of privacy can be a problem within a hospital environment particularly, especially when discussions take place at the bedside. Even when the area is screened by curtains, it is important to be aware that this does not make the area soundproof.
- **Poor lighting** – a person who does not see very well may struggle to read written information in a dimly-lit room. Equally, flickering lighting could distract a person, making communication difficult.
- **Distractions** – these may include ringing telephones, televisions, other people talking or even other members of staff seeking your attention.
- **Inappropriate fixtures and fittings** – an uncomfortably furnished room which is poorly set out (for example, chairs too far apart or at differing heights) could make communication difficult. A person in a wheelchair may find it impossible to communicate with the person in reception if the desk is at such a height that the person in the wheelchair cannot see above it.

Individual/personal barriers

There are a number of individual or personal factors that can influence how people communicate with each other. People differ in their ability to communicate. Some people have better communication skills and listening skills than others. We all process and interpret information differently based on our unique experiences. The level of trust between the individuals who are communicating can also influence the communication process. Communication is more likely to be difficult when people don't trust each other. Finally, **stereotypes** and **prejudices** can also impact on communication.

Cultural differences

Cultural differences can influence communication. Culture is much more than the language spoken – it includes the way people live, think and how they relate to each other. Because different cultures have different communication 'rules', this can sometimes make effective communication difficult. For example, it is regarded as polite and respectful to make eye contact when speaking to someone in Western culture; however, in some cultures this could be seen as rude and defiant. Within other cultures, children are not allowed to speak when certain adults are present, and within some cultures, women are not allowed to speak to men they do not know.

Language barriers

The United Kingdom is a multicultural country with a mix of different **ethnic groups** and language communities. English may be a second or even third language for some people and it may not be spoken or understood at all by others. Communication in written and spoken English may not be easy or even possible for people who do not understand the language. Similarly, people from different cultural groups may interpret non-verbal behaviour in different ways, misunderstanding messages.

Even with people who speak English as their first language, careful thought and consideration must still be given to ensure

Key terms

A **stereotype** can be defined as well-known ideas or beliefs about a person or a group of people.

Prejudice refers to opinions that are formed about a person or a group of people in the absence of facts.

effective communication. **Medical jargon** and abbreviations only make sense to people with specialist knowledge. A person who doesn't have this specialist knowledge may not understand the message.

Sensory impairment

Sensory impairment is a term that is used when a person has a problem with their eyesight or hearing. People who have a hearing or visual impairment have different communication needs. A visual impairment may reduce a person's ability to see faces or read written signs and leaflets. A hearing impairment may affect a person's ability to hold a conversation because of the inability to hear. People who have a visual impairment may require spectacles, while a person who has a hearing impairment may require a hearing device.

Deafblindness is a serious visual and hearing impairment, where often a person has difficulty seeing or hearing. In more extreme cases they can be totally deaf and blind. These impairments can be of any type or degree and are sometimes called multi-sensory impairments (MSI). Some people who are deafblind may also have impaired speech.

Speech impairment

Speech impairments, caused by an accident or a stroke for example, can impact on a person's ability to communicate. The individual may have very good understanding but may find it difficult to make themselves understood.

Conditions such as cerebral palsy, cleft palate, Down's syndrome and **autism** can also affect a person's ability to communicate, both verbally and non-verbally. Difficulties interpreting non-verbal communication may also affect communication if a person has autism.

Factors affecting health

Illness may affect a person's ability to communicate. This could be temporary, for example, if a person feels unwell due to infection. He or she may feel tired and weak or may even lose the ability to speak, especially if they have a sore throat. Other conditions have longer lasting effects, for example, multiple sclerosis – a condition that affects the nervous system and in some cases speech.

Learning disabilities

A **learning disability** can affect or delay a person's intellectual development, including language and social skills. Many people with profound and multiple learning disabilities

Case study

3.1 Barriers to communication

Mr Singh does not speak English. Verity, a care worker, is attempting to communicate with him. She is talking to him in English but is trying to gesture to see if he would like a cup of tea. He is hard of hearing but refuses to wear a hearing aid. He is sitting in the lounge area where people are talking. The television is on and Mrs Cooper is listening to the radio in the corner. There are also workmen in the home fixing a shelf to the wall.

Make a note of all the barriers to communication within this scenario.

What could Verity do to minimise the barriers you have identified?

Key terms

Ethnic groups are groups of people who share common characteristics such as culture, religion and language.

Medical jargon refers to the use of technical or medical terms that may not be understood by members of the public.

Autism is a developmental disability that affects how a person communicates with and relates to other people. It also affects the way in which the person makes sense of the world around them.

Key term

A **learning disability** is a term used to refer to people who have a reduced intellectual ability and who experience difficulty with everyday activities.

Evidence activity

3.1 Barriers to communication

Think about three service users within your workplace and identify any barriers that could affect their communication.

Time to think

3.2 Barriers to communication

Think about a time when you have experienced a barrier when communicating.

How did this make you feel?

How do you think this made the person you were trying to communicate with feel?

What steps did you take to overcome the barrier?

(PMLD) do not communicate using formal communication like speech, symbols or signs. But this does not mean that they cannot communicate. If you work with a person who has a learning disability you will need to be aware of their preferred way of communicating in order to fully support the person.

Conditions affecting the brain

People who are living with the symptoms associated with Alzheimer's disease, or indeed any form of dementia, will have problems with their short-term memory. These people may be unable to make sense of their environment and the people who surround them. They may forget recent events, and this will certainly impact on the way in which they communicate.

AC 3.2 Demonstrate how to reduce barriers to communication in different ways

Having learned about the barriers that can affect communication, it is vital that you develop skills to help you to overcome these barriers if people are to receive the care and support they need.

Communication difficulties can isolate a person, making them feel cut off from others. So it is particularly important that staff work to overcome these difficulties within the

health sector. Barriers to communication should be minimised as much as possible.

Adapting your approach to overcome communication barriers

You must give careful consideration to your approach when communicating with other people.

Timing

Speaking clearly, slowly, repeating and, if necessary, rephrasing what you say can make communication more effective with some service users, their relatives and colleagues. Speaking a little more slowly can help if a person has:

- a hearing or visual impairment
- a learning disability.

This can also help if they are:

- anxious
- confused.

The pace of communication may need to be slower to give the person time to understand what you are saying to them. It is also important to allow time for the person to respond. This can mean being patient and allowing for silences while the person thinks and works out how to reply.

Listen carefully

Active listening is important to ensure effective communication. It is important to show not only that you are listening to the individual but that you have actually heard and understood what has been said. Responding to what they have said will reassure the person and encourage them to be more open. See AC 3.3 for more information on active listening.

Look interested

Using open body language, smiles and eye contact will reassure the individual that you are interested in what they are saying. Leaning towards the individual when communicating with them shows interest and commitment to what is being said. It can also help you both to listen to what is being said. You do however need to be careful that you do not invade the individual's **personal space**. Showing interest will help to develop a trusting relationship, which over time can improve communication.

Respect cultural differences

It is important to develop your knowledge and understanding of different cultures. Cultural differences include social customs regarding dress, beliefs and values about family life, morals and religion. It is therefore important to be respectful of differences and avoid projecting your own culture or background onto others.

Language differences can occur when the individual and members of staff do not speak the same language. Language may be misinterpreted or it may not be understood at all. You may need to engage the services of an **interpreter** or a translator. Written information should also be presented in a language that the individual understands.

Key terms

Personal space is the physical area that surrounds someone or that they feel comfortable or safe with.

An **interpreter** converts spoken material from one language to another while a translator converts written material from one language to another.

Use appropriate language and words

It is important to think carefully about the words you use when communicating. Your choice of words should be appropriate to the person you are communicating with and to the situation. In order to help people understand what you are saying, it is important that you speak clearly. Face the other person while speaking and avoid:

- covering your mouth with your hands
- eating at the same time as speaking
- shouting
- speaking too fast.

It is also important to be aware that **accents** and **dialects** can impact on understanding when communicating with others. This is because the meaning of words can vary across different regions of the country. The **pronunciation** of some words can also make them difficult to understand, especially where an individual's accent is very strong.

Avoid the use of **jargon**. Service users may not be familiar with terminology used in the health sector but may feel afraid to ask what you mean.

Slang words must also be avoided. Certain slang words may be acceptable when communicating informally with friends outside of work. However, it would be considered unprofessional to use slang words when communicating with service users and other professionals within the health sector.

Tone of voice

The pitch and tone of voice will tell a person a lot more about how you are feeling than the choice of words you use. If you are feeling irritated, annoyed or rushed, other people could pick up on this through your tone of voice. This could seriously impact on how a person communicates with you.

Key terms

An **accent** is a way of pronouncing language, or the way a person sounds when they speak. We all have different accents depending on where we come from.

A **dialect** is a particular form of language which is particular to a specific region or social group.

Pronunciation is the way that people say words or speak. This can include their manner of speaking or accent or the way they deliver speech.

Jargon involves the use of certain (complicated) words that otherwise are meaningless to other people.

Slang is a type of language consisting of words and phrases that are thought of as being informal.

Adapting the environment

Careful consideration must be given to the environment and how this can affect communication. This can be done in a number of ways. For example, you can:

- ensure the layout of the room is appropriate for the communication to take place
- reduce background noise to a minimum – switch off the television or radio and move away from areas where other people are talking
- avoid interruptions – divert telephone calls and make sure other members of staff are aware that you should not be disturbed.

The environment must also be accessible for everyone. Health care environments can be adapted in ways that help specific groups of people. For example, lifts can be installed with sensors that indicate when the doors are opening or closing or indeed which floor the lift is on so that people with a visual impairment can hear these messages. Ramps can be placed so that people who are in a wheelchair can access areas where steps are a problem. Reception desks can be lowered and signs placed lower down on walls so that wheelchair users can access the people and information they need.

Using support services, specialist devices and alternative methods of communication

If you work in the health sector, you should understand the language needs and communication preferences of the people you work with. If an individual has difficulty communicating in English, or has sensory impairments or disabilities that affect their communication skills, specialist communication support may be needed. Learning a few words of another person's language or developing some basic sign language skills could help you to establish positive, supportive relationships with service users, their relatives or colleagues.

We will now look at all the tools that may help you support people in this area.

British Sign Language (BSL)

Sign language is a visual means of communication, using gestures, facial expressions and body language. These signs are made up of the shapes, position and movement of the hands, arms or body and facial expressions to express a speaker's thoughts. Within Britain, the most common form of sign language is known as British Sign Language (BSL). BSL is a recognised method of communication for individuals who have a hearing impairment.

Lip reading

Lip reading is a technique used by some individuals who have a hearing impairment to interpret the movement of a person's lips, tongue and face. It is therefore essential that when you communicate with a person who has a hearing impairment you look directly at the person who is lip reading and place yourself in a well-lit area when speaking.

Makaton

Makaton was first developed in the United Kingdom in the 1970s. It is a method of communication using signs and symbols and is often used as a communication process for

Figure 1.5 Makaton in action

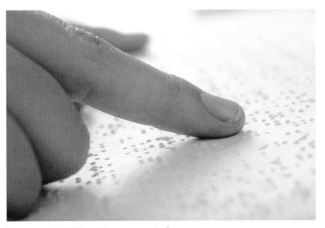

Figure 1.6 Braille materials

those who have learning difficulties. Unlike BSL, Makaton uses speech as well as actions and symbols. It uses picture cards and ties facial expressions in with the wording in order to make it easier for people with learning difficulties to recognise the words.

Braille

Braille was devised in the 1800s by a French man called Louis Braille. Braille is used to communicate written information to people who have a visual impairment. Information leaflets and books can be produced in Braille. Each Braille character is based on six raised dots, arranged in two columns of three dots. There are variations of the six dots which represent all the letters of the alphabet, numbers, punctuation marks and commonly occurring groups of letters. Braille is simply designed to be read by fingers rather than eyes.

Remember, when communicating with someone who is visually impaired, it is important to emphasise your expression through your tone of voice and use of language rather than through gestures and facial expression. Using touch to communicate certain emotions may be more appropriate.

Picture boards and symbols

There may be times when you are required to support an individual who may be unable to communicate verbally. There may be a number of reasons for this. For example, the individual may have had a tube inserted into their throat, or may have had an illness that has weakened their voice muscles. The individual may have suffered a stroke or other trauma and/or be living with one of a number of **neurological diseases** (see page 18 for definition). These are all reasons that verbal communication skills may be limited. In such cases, non-verbal communication replaces speaking, and communication boards are one common tool to help individuals communicate non-verbally.

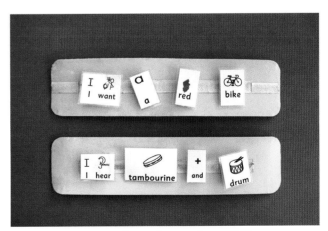

Figure 1.7 Picture boards used in HSC setting

Assistive technology

Assistive technology is used to support people with their daily living, including their communication needs. There is a range of equipment, including large keyboards and touch screens that may spell or sound out words. Some people may use word or picture boards to support their speech. Others may use **speech synthesisers**, which replace speech either by producing a visual display of written text or by producing synthesised speech that expresses the information verbally through a robotic voice. Hearing aids, **hearing loops**, text phones, text messaging on a mobile phone and magnifiers are examples of assistive technology.

Human aids

Human aids are people who help in the process of communication. Examples include interpreters, translators and **signers**. Interpreters are people who communicate a conversation, whether spoken or signed, to someone in a language they will understand. There are many organisations that can provide interpreters for people who do not speak English, or for those who rely on sign language – these include social services, local communities, voluntary organisations and charities. When communicating through an interpreter, it is important to ensure you speak directly to the individual and not to the interpreter.

Figure 1.8 Sign language

AC 3.3 Demonstrate ways to check that communication has been understood

Effective communication in health and social care settings is essential to maintain effective **partnership working**. It is easy to assume that everything is alright and that people have understood if they do not speak out or question what is happening, but this may well be because they have not heard or understood what is happening or they simply do not want to make a fuss. Sometimes communication can break down because the person has not fully received or understood what has been communicated. There are a number of ways to check whether what you have communicated has been understood by the person receiving the communication. Active listening and clarifying or repeating techniques are useful for checking this.

Key terms

Neurological diseases are those that affect the nervous system, the brain and the spine.

Speech synthesiser is a computer system that helps to produce sound and speech artificially. This is used by people who are unable to use their vocal chords due to illness or disability for example, Stephen Hawking the famous physicist is famous for using a speech synthesiser.

Hearing loop This may also be known as an induction loop. It consists of a microphone and amplifier which sends a signal through a wire or loop around the perimeter of the building or room. People using a hearing aid can 'tune in' by switching on a 'T' switch or their hearing aids.

Signers are people who communicate using sign language.

Partnership working is about developing inclusive relationships that are beneficial to both parties, and improve the quality and experience of care. Partnership working involves working with everyone involved in a person's care, including the person at the centre of their care.

Active listening

Active listening involves paying close attention to what the other person is saying while observing the non-verbal messages they are communicating to check their understanding. Active listening involves listening with all senses. As well as giving full attention to the speaker, it is important that the 'active listener' is 'seen' to be listening, otherwise the speaker may think that what they are talking about is uninteresting to the listener.

Interest can be conveyed to the speaker by using both verbal and non-verbal messages, such as maintaining eye contact, nodding your head and smiling, agreeing by saying 'Yes' or simply 'Mmm' to encourage them to continue. By providing this 'feedback', the person speaking will usually feel more at ease and therefore will communicate more easily, openly and honestly with you.

Clarifying

Clarifying or repeating can also be helpful in establishing whether the other person has understood what has been communicated. This involves repeating back, summarising or rephrasing aspects of what has been discussed throughout the conversation. Phrases such as 'Can I just check that you meant …?' or 'Do you mean …?' are examples of ways of clarifying what has been communicated.

Remember, sometimes even a simple 'thumbs up' can be useful to check understanding. It is, however, important to remember that in some cultures such as in some parts of the Middle East, this may not be acceptable.

Evidence activity

3.3 Has communication been understood?

How can you demonstrate ways to check that communication has been understood?

Ask your supervisor to observe your interactions with one or two individuals (ensure you have gained their consent first). You need to seek feedback about how you have ensured that your communication methods are understood.

AC 3.4 Identify sources of information and support or services to enable more effective communication

It is important that every service user is supported in communicating their needs and is able to understand what is being communicated to them. As we have seen earlier in this unit, we know that difficulties with communicating can happen for a number of reasons.

As a health or social care worker you should always seek support if you identify a communication problem with any service user, their visitors or your colleagues. There will be lots of different types of support services you can tap into to help you and the people you support to communicate effectively. In the first instance you should speak to your manager, who should be able to guide or support you with accessing services such as:

- specialist practitioners such as speech and language therapists or psychologists
- interpreters, sign language and lip speakers
- advocacy services
- specialist organisations.

Always remember that the relatives of service users can be a valuable source of information and support to enable effective communication.

LO4 Be able to apply principles and practices relating to confidentiality at work

AC 4.1 Explain the term 'confidentiality'

Key term

Confidentiality is not about keeping secrets, it is about protecting an individual's right to privacy. At its simplest, confidentiality can be defined as 'protecting information from unauthorised disclosure'. This simply means that as an employee within the health service, you must strive to keep service user and business information private.

Throughout your working day you will come across private and personal information relating to service users. This information may come from service users, their families or other professionals that you work with. As a health or social care worker, you have a duty to:

- maintain confidentiality by keeping personal information about people who use your services private
- only share information about service users with those who have a right to know
- obtain permission from people before sharing information about them.

Your employer will have a confidentiality policy that sets out the procedures that must be followed when sharing information. It is important that you read this policy and that you follow it throughout your daily practice.

AC 4.2 Demonstrate confidentiality in day-to-day communication, in line with agreed ways of working

Maintaining confidentiality is a very important aspect of building trust between people working in the health sector and people using services within the health and social care sector. This trust is dependent on the service user being confident that personal information they disclose will be kept private. Your workplace should have a confidentiality policy which sets out the procedures that should be followed in order to maintain confidentiality. This does not only relate to verbal communication, but it also relates to written information. People who work in health and social care environments have a duty to protect confidential information. In addition, there is a legal requirement to keep personal records confidential under the Data Protection Act 1998.

The right to confidentiality means that personal and medical records must be kept secure and that information stored on a computer is password protected.

There will however be many occasions in your day-to-day work when you will need to share information about service users in order to ensure they receive the support and care required. This information can be shared with your work colleagues without breaching confidentiality because it is shared on a need-to-know basis. This means that everybody in the team knows what they need to know about each service user.

Nevertheless, in your day-to-day work you can promote and demonstrate confidentiality by:

● not talking about service users in areas of the organisation where you can be overheard by non-staff members
● not disclosing confidential information about one service user to other service users
● using service users' initials only when discussing or writing up your observations about them
● storing written records about service users securely and making sure they are put back correctly after using them
● password protecting computers that contain information about service users
● ensuring personal records can be accessed only by people who are authorised to access them
● referring relatives to the service user's key worker when they request information relating to their relative
● not giving out personal information over the telephone
● not sending personal information via fax or email
● ensuring the person you are sharing information with is authorised to access it.

It is just as important to maintain confidentiality outside of work as inside. If you are not careful, you could breach confidentiality without realising it. One of the most common ways this can happen is by chatting about work with friends and family. You can ensure you maintain confidentiality outside of work by not talking, gossiping or complaining about the people you work with when you are at home or when you are

socialising with your friends. This is a serious breach of confidentiality, which could lead to disciplinary action by your employer.

Evidence activity

4.2 Demonstrating confidentiality

Using your knowledge of confidentiality and what you have learned from the confidentiality policy of your workplace, demonstrate how you protect confidentiality and follow the confidentiality procedures of your work setting in your day-to-day communication with others.

Ask for feedback on your ability to maintain confidentiality from your mentor or manager.

AC 4.3 Describe situations where information normally considered to be confidential might need to be passed on

Even though you have a duty to maintain confidentiality you must never promise that you will keep information secret if a person wants to tell you something. If you cannot guarantee confidentiality it is important that you let the person know before they begin to disclose the information.

Disclosure of information to people other than your immediate colleagues normally only happens with the consent of the service user or, where the individual has been assessed as lacking capacity, their **next of kin**. However, there are exceptions to this rule.

There may be times when you have to share what you have been told or have seen to a more senior person at work or to an external organisation. A request to keep information confidential can be broken if:

● a person has disclosed that they are going to harm themselves
● a person has disclosed that they are going to harm someone else
● a person has been engaging in or is likely to engage in criminal activities

- the information is ordered by a court or a statutory organisation, such as a Mental Health Commissioner
- a **tribunal** asks for specific information about a person.

Key terms

Disclosure of information is when you inform others of, or make known, new or secret information.

Next of kin is the individual's closest living relative or relatives but could also include friends or anyone that the individual has assigned as the person to contact in case of emergencies.

A **tribunal** is where a dispute is settled.

Case study

4.3 Confidential information

Emily is a 48-year-old lady who suffers with multiple sclerosis. She has been admitted to your unit for management of her symptoms as her mobility has deteriorated and she is experiencing severe pain. Her condition is getting worse and she depends on carers to help her with her personal hygiene requirements.

You are supporting Emily with her personal care and she tells you she has had enough and that she wants to die. She feels she has nothing to live for. Emily is self-medicating, which means she can take care of her own medication.

Emily tells you that she has had thoughts about taking an overdose to bring her suffering to an end. She tells you that you mustn't tell anyone and that she has told you this in the strictest of confidence.

- Should you keep this information confidential?
- Explain the answer you have given.

Evidence activity

4.3 When information needs to be passed on

Describe three situations that could occur, or that have occurred in your workplace when information normally considered confidential needs to be passed on.

AC 4.4 Explain how and when to seek advice about confidentiality

As discussed earlier, it is a requirement that all organisations supporting people with health or social care have a confidentiality policy and that procedures relating to the recording and reporting of information are clearly detailed.

Confidentiality is an important part of providing care for people accessing health or social care services.

It is best to treat everything you come across within your workplace as confidential information. However, if you are in a situation where you are unsure about maintaining confidentiality, then you must discuss it with your manager before you pass on confidential information.

Similarly, it is always best to tell your manager if you receive any information that concerns you. If someone says they want to tell you something 'in confidence', you should let them know that you may not be able to keep the information to yourself because part of your job involves safeguarding the welfare of adults and children. As we have already discovered, there are some pieces of information that cannot be kept confidential.

Evidence activity

4.4 Seeking advice

Explain who or where you would seek advice from in relation to concerns about confidentiality.

Explain the circumstances in which you may need to seek advice about confidentiality.

Legislation

Data Protection Act 1998

Equality Act 2010

Useful resources

Websites

Deafblind UK
www.deafblind.org.uk

Talking Point
www.talkingpoint.org.uk

I CAN
www.ican.org.uk

Alzheimer's Society
www.alzheimers.org.uk

Mencap
www.mencap.org.uk

The National Autistic Society
www.autism.org.uk

The Royal National Institute for Blind People (RNIB)
www.rnib.org.uk

Introduction to personal development in health, social care or children's and young people's settings

This unit is worth 3 credits

What are you finding out?

Personal development is very important in health and social care because in your role you not only have to complete practical tasks but you also have to interact in a professional and caring manner with the individuals you support. You have a responsibility to always think carefully about the way you work, how you respond to others and how you can continue to improve your skills and knowledge.

This unit aims to provide the knowledge, skills and understanding of concepts of personal development, reflective practice and ways to implement these.

These are fundamental to those who work in health or social care settings, or with children or young people in a wide range of settings.

By the end of this unit you will:

1 Understand what is required for competence in own work role
2 Be able to reflect on own work activities
3 Be able to agree a personal development plan
4 Be able to develop knowledge, skills and understanding.

Links to Level 2 Certificate in Preparing to Work in Adult Social Care

SHC 22 Assessment Criteria	Unit PWCS22
AC1.3	AC1.3
AC3.1	AC3.3

LO1 Understand what is required for competence in own work role

AC 1.1 Describe the duties and responsibilities of own role

Key term

Competence means having the skills and knowledge that enable you to do your job in the correct manner to a high standard and in a way that is expected from your organisation.

There are many different roles within the health and social care sector. These include people who support care workers, for example, team or ward secretaries, receptionists and office staff. However, here we will focus on the job roles that provide care and support. These include:

- social workers
- personal assistants
- social care workers/health care assistants/ support workers.

The exact duties and responsibilities are different for each role. Even roles with the same name might have some different duties and responsibilities, depending on exactly what your job involves (your job description) and the organisation you work for. However, there are some duties and responsibilities that are the same for everyone because they relate to the basic principles of the way in which we should provide care and support to the individual. We can break down the duties and responsibilities of a job role into those required by the employer and those required by law or by the governing body of the role. For example, nurses must abide by a code of practice set down by the Royal College of Nursing.

Duties and responsibilities outlined by the employer

The duties and responsibilities that your employer places on you might be stated in your contract of employment. There might be a **job description** that was given to you when you applied for the job, or that forms part of your contract. You may have had an **induction** in your first few weeks of work, which would also have given you guidance as to what your employer wants you to do. During your induction, you will have covered topics such as the structure of the workplace, the people who will be managing and supervising you, and the policies and procedures you will need to follow.

The kinds of duties and responsibilities that an employer will state might include:

- personal qualities such as honesty or kindness
- qualifications
- arriving at work on time and working a certain number of hours per week, including start and finish times

- wearing the correct clothes or uniform while you are at work
- reading and writing reports and taking part in staff meetings
- assisting the service user with personal care, which may for example include getting up and getting dressed, providing support with going to the toilet, eating and drinking.

Standards of conduct

Beyond your employer, you have other duties and responsibilities. A role in the health and social care sector means that you are working with, and caring for, some of the most vulnerable people in society. There are various standards of conduct or behaviour, discussed in AC 1.2, that you must be familiar with, and you should always act and behave in line with their recommendations. These standards vary between the different countries in the UK and their detailed content can change over time too. However, the current Code of Conduct in England includes the following themes, which provide guidance as to what your additional roles and responsibilities are:

1 Be accountable by making sure you can justify/explain your actions or omissions.
2 Promote and uphold the privacy, dignity, rights, health and well-being of people who use health and care services and their carers at all times.
3 Work in collaboration with your colleagues to ensure the delivery of high quality, safe and **compassionate** health care, care and support.
4 Communicate in an open and effective way to promote the health, safety and well-being of people who use health and care services and their carers.
5 Respect a person's right to confidentiality.
6 Strive to improve the quality of health care, care and support through continuing professional development.
7 Uphold and promote equality, diversity and inclusion.

Source: http://www.skillsforcare.org.uk/Standards/Codes-of-practice/Codes-of-practice.aspx

For more details on standards relevant to your roles and responsibilities, see AC 1.2 (page 27).

Evidence activity

1.1 Duties and responsibilites

Find your job description and list the duties and responsibilities that your employer places on you. Now compare them to the seven themes in the Code of Conduct in England (page 26).

Make a second list of what you think your overall roles and responsibilities are.

AC 1.2 Identify standards that influence the way the role is carried out

In general, standards include:

- Codes of Practice
- rules and regulations
- minimum standards
- National Occupational Standards.

England

Codes of Practice

Codes of Practice are a set of statements that describe **best practice** for somebody working in a particular role within health and social care. In 2013 a new Code of Conduct was published by Skills for Care, which applies to adult social care workers (including personal assistants, residential and **domiciliary care workers**) and health care support workers.

The Code is based on the idea that you can help to protect people by promoting best practice for the workforce. Following the Code means that you will be providing high quality, compassionate health care, care and support. The following is quoted from the Code:

'The Code describes the standards of conduct, behaviour and attitude that the public and people who use health and care services should expect. You are responsible for and have a duty of care to ensure that your conduct does not fall below the standards detailed in the Code. Nothing that you do, or omit to do, should harm the safety and wellbeing of people who use health and care services, and the public.'

> ### Key terms
>
> **Best practice** is working to the standards that are set out as the most appropriate, professional and compassionate in meeting the needs of the individual.
>
> **Domiciliary care workers** are care workers who support people in their own homes. This might include personal care, shopping or cleaning or helping them to socialise.

Putting the code into practice

By using the Code, you can be sure of exactly what is expected of you – even if your employer has not talked about some of the topics covered in it with you. If you are not meeting all of the standards in the Code then you know you have to change some things about the way you do your job. It is your responsibility to make these changes – you need to talk to your line manager and discuss how these changes might fit in with your professional development. It is very important that your manager is made aware of any possible changes in the way you carry out certain elements of your role. By following the Code you can be sure you are doing a good job and providing the best possible care for your clients.

The Skills for Care website states: 'Skills for Care and Skills for Health will [continue to] review the code to ensure the language is readily understood and that there is synergy with the Social Care Commitment.' There are a lot of changes in the health and social care sector at the time of writing, so you must visit the Skills for Care website regularly to keep up to date with the latest guidance and codes.

National Minimum Training Standards (NMTS)

Currently, for adult social care workers and health care support workers there is a set of minimum training standards that defines the minimum you should know when working in the sector. Meeting these standards does not mean that you are fully competent to do your job – there are things you will need to show you can do as well as know. But you will certainly need to meet these standards, as you will not be competent if you do not meet them.

Common Induction Standards

At the time of writing there is a set of Common Induction Standards (CIS) that people working in health and social care must achieve before they are allowed to work unsupervised. Staff should undertake induction training that meets these CIS within 12 weeks of beginning their role. (If you have already been working in the sector but have a new job, you may not have to meet the CIS, although you might still need an induction, particularly if you move to a different area of the service or to a new organisation.) The CIS relate directly to the National Minimum Training Standards.

Care Certificate

From 2014 a new Care Certificate is being created which replaces both the National Minimum Training Standards and the Common Induction Standards. It has been designed in response to a report commissioned by the government, so that workers in the health and social care sector are better prepared for their roles. It will cover both knowledge (what you need to know) and competencies (what you need to do/the skills you need to demonstrate), and it will be assessed. If you are beginning a new role, you will be given training and assessment as part of this certificate within 12 weeks of starting your job.

Care Quality Commission (CQC)

The CQC is a **regulatory body** (see page 29 for definition) that inspects and regulates health and social care settings to see whether they meet the required national standards. So this is the body that will check whether, for instance, the staff and management of a care home are providing the right care in the right way.

Research and investigate

1.2 Standards

Visit the following websites and conduct some research to learn more about them.

Codes of conduct:

www.skillsforcare.org.uk/Document-library/Standards/National-minimum-training-standard-and-code/CodeofConduct.pdf

National Minimum Standards

www.skillsforcare.org.uk/Document-library/Standards/National-minimum-training-standard-and-code/Nationalminimumtrainingstandards.pdf

National Occupational Standards

nos.ukces.org.uk

Scotland

You must be registered to work in care home services for adults. Registration is with the Scottish Social Services Council (SSSC) and must be within six months of your start date. Employers need to check that their staff are registered. They would be committing an offence if they were found to be employing unregistered staff. The SSSC website has full details.

In order to register you must either have a relevant qualification or be working towards a relevant qualification. The details of qualifications that are relevant for each role are here:

Research and investigate

1.2 Your role

Research and investigate any requirements for your current post. This includes training and qualifications. Look at how these requirements correspond with your role, and discuss with your supervisor or line manager what further training will help your role.

Regulatory body – the organisations who create the rules and standards and ensure that they are obeyed, for example, CQC.

The Care Inspectorate (formerly known as SCSWIS) is a regulatory body responsible for regulating social services. It developed the National Care Standards, which cover provision of care at all ages. The standards are written from the point of view of people using the services – i.e. your service users – and outline what they should expect from you and your organisation. This is useful as it gives you first-hand information of what the individuals you care for expect from you.

Codes of Practice

The Scottish Social Services Council (SSSC) publishes a Code of Practice for social care employers and employees. Within the Code it states:

'As a social service worker you will have criteria to guide your practice and be clear about what standards of conduct you are expected to meet. You are encouraged to use the Codes to examine your own practice and to look for areas in which you can improve.'

The SSSC expects registered employees to meet this code and may take action if they do not. See the Key terms box above for information on Scotland's National Care Standards and its Care Inspectorate.

Research and investigate

1.2 SSSC

Explore the following website to learn more about the SSSC Codes of Practice and **National Care Standards** in Scotland:

www.sssc.uk.com/doc_details/1020-sssc-codes-of-practice-for-social-service-workers-and-employers

Wales
Code of Practice

The Care Council for Wales (CCW) is a body that regulates the health and social care sector in Wales. It has a Code of Practice for social care workers, which is expected to be replaced with a revised version in 2015. This Code 'sets out the standards all practitioners should work to and what is expected of them by individuals who use services, the public and employers'.

The Council hold a register of social care workers. The register is not mandatory for adult care home workers, but you are allowed to register if you wish. In order to register you must:

- have the necessary qualifications – newly-appointed staff, not yet qualified, must have completed the Social Care Induction Framework for Wales
- be physically and mentally fit
- be of good character
- agree to comply with the Code of Practice for Social Care Workers.

The CCW publishes a Code of Practice that lets social care workers know what is expected of them. If an employee breaks the Code, it may lead to an investigation and action by their employer and the CCW.

Social Care Induction Framework for Wales (SCIF)

The CCW has produced an induction framework that outlines what an employee needs to know and be able to do in their first 12 months of work. There is a certificate upon completion.

Care and Social Services Inspectorate Wales (CSSIW)

This body inspects the health and social care services.

Northern Ireland

Some of that workforce must be registered with the NISCC in order to work, including social care workers in adult residential homes. There are no qualifications or training requirements for a social care worker to become registered, but you must have completed and met the NISCC Induction Standards.

NISCC Code of Practice for Social Care Workers

As with the Codes for the other regions of the UK, this Code sets down what is expected of a social care worker. Meeting the standards of this Code is one of the requirements of registration. Another requirement is that you commit to completing 90 hours of training and learning within each registration period.

UK

National Occupational Standards (NOS)

This is a comprehensive set of standards covering all aspects of all job roles within health and social care, at all levels, across the UK. While the various induction programmes mean that all staff have a certain level of knowledge and competency to work in the sector, the NOS state exactly what it means to be fully competent in any role. The qualification you are undertaking and which this book is written for – the Level 2 Diploma in Health and Social Care – is based on the NOS.

AC 1.3 Describe ways to ensure that personal attitudes or beliefs do not obstruct the quality of work

What do we mean by 'attitudes' and 'beliefs'?

If we have an attitude about or towards something we might not realise that our way of thinking, or our feelings, are not the only valid point of view. This can sometimes mean we fail to understand another person's point of view.

An attitude is often an expression of values and beliefs. Values are the things we think are important in life, while beliefs are ideas and values that we think are true and can form part of our own code of behaviour.

How do attitudes, values and beliefs develop?

Values and beliefs are formed as we learn through encountering new situations and ideas as we develop. We learn from our families and friends, and from the experiences we have during our life. Attitudes and beliefs develop over time and influence the way we behave. Has anyone ever told you to 'change your attitude' or that someone had a 'bad attitude'? Perhaps you wondered how someone could make that change.

Our values and beliefs can form a big part of who we are and can be quite difficult to change, although it is not impossible. Our attitude towards certain things is a result of our values and beliefs which we have learned throughout our life and have become a part of our personality and makeup. Whenever we are faced with a choice or decision to make we will look to what we value the most. Consider your attitude to shoes. If you value comfort and practicality over having the latest fashion, you will choose a more sensible shoe; if you value fashion over comfort, then your choice of shoes will be different. That is a simple example. Things become a little more demanding when we think about more important examples.

Changing attitudes and beliefs

Within your family you may have been brought up in a particular way and therefore grown up with certain views about how you should live your life. However, as you have become an adult you may have started to question some of those views and values. By paying more attention to how you think and feel about something, or by reflecting upon experiences and being truthful to yourself about how you feel, you can start to become a more self-aware person. This process can help you to start to actively choose your own values.

Time to think

1.3 **Personal values**

Think for a moment about a personal value – something you think is really important to the way you live your life.

Try to trace back to your very first experience of it. How did you first experience it?

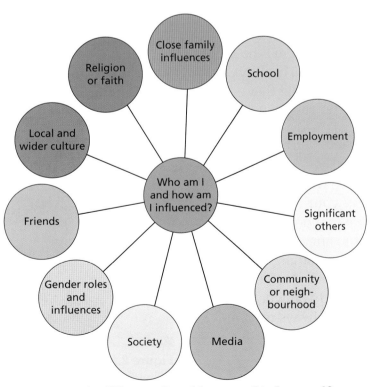

Figure 2.1 Who am I and how am I influenced?

It is important to know what it is that you value and believe in because this can have an effect on how you work. For example, if you value honesty, then in your work you will always take that quality with you and it will impact positively upon the way in which you deal with people in your care and with your colleagues. Part of this quality is to treat all people with respect and compassion whatever their age, background, or disability, for example.

Disagreements

Other people do not always share our beliefs about what are important values and attitudes in life. Our lives are shaped differently as we grow up and we do not all experience the same things. We can begin to see that having different sets of values and beliefs means that we will not always think about issues in the same way as others. This may lead to problems. For example, perhaps you value your health and believe that only you are responsible for it. This may mean that you find it difficult to understand people who smoke or engage in other risky health behaviour; you may feel so strongly that you object to the way they live their lives. Yet they may have a firm belief that 'what will be will be'. In other words, they take the view that there is no point in giving up smoking or having a healthy lifestyle as fate will dictate whether they become ill, and you both disagree.

Ensuring personal attitudes and beliefs do not obstruct work

As a health and social care worker, it is your responsibility and one of your main duties of care to make sure that you do not allow your values and beliefs to affect your work. Just because you believe something to be true and valuable you should not base the way in which you care for somebody on what you feel to be right. You should always remember that individuals have choices and only they can make decisions about how they should live their lives. This is good practice and part of ensuring that you follow a person-centred approach where the needs and preferences of the individual are at the centre of the service you provide.

Person-centred approach

You need to work in ways that respect clients' wishes in order to demonstrate how much you value them as people. If you try to impose your own values and attitudes on the people you work with, they may feel that you are judging them in a negative way. Clients need to be able to make decisions based on their own values and attitudes and you need to leave your personal values out of the workplace. Feeling strongly about something may cloud our judgement and lead to a negative decision being made, which can harm the client/care worker relationship. It is therefore best to be aware of these stronger feelings you have and not allow them to affect your daily work lives.

Organisational values

It is equally important to remember that you are a small part of an organisation that will in itself have a set of values – this might be called a mission statement or code of practice. There is an expectation that you work within these values as they will help to support your work ethic.

It can be easy to influence clients in subtle ways. Simple things like body language, gestures, the way you say something or even actions can give

Figure 2.2 It is important to respect the individual's wishes and not impose your own values and attitudes

Evidence activity

1.3 Personal attitudes and beliefs

Answer the following questions and then think about what values and beliefs your answers show. In each case, what led you to have those values and beliefs?

1 Do you agree with the smoking ban, which stops people from smoking in public places like restaurants and bars?
2 Do you think that eating meat is wrong?
3 Would you prefer it if people had the choice as to whether they wear seatbelts in cars?

Give two examples of values or beliefs you hold.

For each one, think about how these values or beliefs affect a normal day at work.

How might you need to change your attitude so that your values and beliefs do not affect the way you carry out your role?

Key terms

Knowledge is facts or information that you know or need to know. These are the building blocks for your practice, for example learning about health and safety or how to record information correctly.

Skills are how well you are able to perform a task. This is how you apply your learning, so you know how to bath an individual, ensuring their health and safety, for example.

Practice is how we behave. This means that you also adopt the right attitude – so that you know how to help an individual to have a bath in a safe and dignified way, for example.

Objective means to not be influenced by emotions or any personal prejudices. In this context you should think objectively about your own practice and listen to advice without taking it as an insult but rather as constructive comments to help you improve your practice.

a client the impression you agree or disagree with their values or beliefs. This can obstruct or hinder the relationship that you may need to develop with the individual, in order to support them in the most appropriate way.

LO2 Be able to reflect on own work activities

AC 2.1 Explain why reflecting on work activities is an important way to develop knowledge, skills and practice

Reasons for reflective practice

'Reflective practice' means that you think **objectively** about a particular situation – this could be one that involved mistakes, but equally it could be a situation that had positive outcomes. We can learn from both.

Reflection is an important skill for health and social care professionals. This is because it is only after reflecting or thinking back on a situation that you can identify if you need to change the way they act or behave.

The process of reflective practice should include you thinking about the following so that you can learn and develop:

● situation – what happened? How did you approach it? What was your role?
● background – what led up to the situation?
● assessment – think about the issues in the situation. How did your interactions affect the others involved, for example the individual you provided support to, and colleagues? How did you perform? Make sure to include the things you did well as the things you didn't.
● recommendation – what could you change, improve or even continue to do?
● decision – agree conclusions and future actions. How will you improve the things you have outlined? What support will you need in order to do this?

In Learning Outcome 1 (LO1) you learned about your roles and responsibilities. It is important to reflect on these and ensure that your attitudes and beliefs do not prevent you from carrying out your role effectively. You can meet these requirements by reviewing your **knowledge**, **skills** and **practice** at work and then thinking about which of these need to change, and how. Some changes may be things you need to implement or put in place straightaway; others may be aspects that will take time to change. These may form part of a **personal development plan** (PDP).

Reflection as part of personal development

Beyond the very important duties and responsibilities of your role, reflection also allows you to develop as a person. With regular reflection you can begin to discover more things about yourself and better understand why you behave in particular ways at certain times. The benefit of this will continue to be felt in your work role, but it will also help you in all aspects of your life and in your relationships with family and friends, as well as with colleagues and the individuals you support.

Reflecting on work activities

Reflecting on work practice often means reviewing a particular activity you have completed, or the manner in which you approached a particular situation or individual. By reviewing, you can think about how, when and where the activity was completed, and how well it was done. You should go on to consider whether there was something else you could have done to make it better, or safer. From all this you can plan how you would deal with a similar activity in the future, and then implement that plan at the next opportunity. This can help to develop your knowledge

Key term

A **personal development plan** is usually written with your manager or supervisor when you meet to discuss your progress, learning needs and plans for your further development and learning.

by leading you to further reading or training about different issues. It can help to develop your skills by giving you the opportunities to practice them more often or to observe a more experienced colleague. It improves your practice by helping you think about why you performed a task or an intervention in a particular way. You can talk the issues through with experienced colleagues or more senior staff.

Some of the things you need to consider when reflecting on your working practice with the individual are:

- What was the outcome for the individual – was there a positive outcome?
- Was my practice safe and in line with policies, procedures and working guidelines?
- If there are things that did not go well, what led up to this?
- How could I improve this situation?
- How do I share my learning with others?

Reflection is *not* a description of your working practice. Many learners fall into the trap of describing an event rather than evaluating it or 'making a judgement' about it, so you need to get into the habit of asking the right questions. **Gibbs' reflective cycle** is a useful tool to help you reflect on what you have done (see figure 2.3). There are six stages of reflection:

1 Description: what happened in the work task or situation?
2 Feelings: what did you think or feel about it at the time?
3 Evaluation: what worked well and what did not?
4 Analysis: what is your understanding of what happened and why?
5 Conclusion: what else could have been done?
6 Action plan: if this happened again, how would you deal with it next time?

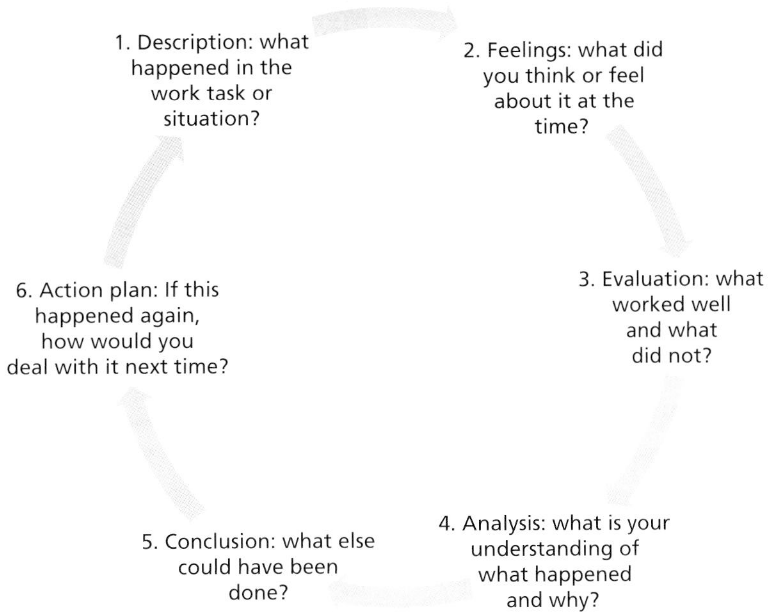

1. Description: what happened in the work task or situation?

2. Feelings: what did you think or feel about it at the time?

6. Action plan: If this happened again, how would you deal with it next time?

3. Evaluation: what worked well and what did not?

5. Conclusion: what else could have been done?

4. Analysis: what is your understanding of what happened and why?

Figure 2.3 Gibbs' reflective cycle

Evidence activity

2.1 Reflecting on work activities

Explain why you think reflection on your knowledge, skills and practice at work is a good idea. What benefits do you think it will bring to:

a) your clients?

b) to your colleagues?

c) yourself?

Think about a time at work when you had a disagreement with a colleague. Use Gibbs' cycle and spend 10–15 minutes thinking about and answering the questions for stages 1–6.

How will you deal with a situation like this again in the future?

AC 2.2 Assess how well own knowledge, skills and understanding meet standards

One of the things you need to continually reflect upon is the standard of your work practice and whether or not you are working in a competent and safe manner. To be able to assess how well you are performing you need to understand where you are now. This can be termed

the 'baseline' and measure how well you are doing, you need someone who is experienced and skilled in your area of work to explain what you are doing well and where you may need to improve your practice. Compliments from the individual or their families are helpful, but in fact you need an objective opinion about your practice. it is important to have a very clear understanding of the standards to work to so that you can be sure to follow best practice.

Standards relate both to the way you perform a task and to the attitude you have in doing so. Standards are in place to help you work in a safe, competent and caring way. As an example, the NHS has published 'Our culture of compassionate care – the vision of strategy for nurses, midwives and care staff' which explains how the NHS sees nursing staff working in a compassionate way.

Staying up to date

It is important that health and social care workers keep up to date with developments in their own area of work. Your organisation might send out information in bulletins or newsletters. You can read articles in health and social care journals or log on the NHS website or the .gov website. You could talk to colleagues and managers and if in doubt ask for information and advice. There is a steady stream of developments in health and social care – often reported in the media. Ensure that you check these reports out and consider doing more research if they concern your own area of work.

There are six areas of action:

- Helping people to stay independent, maximise well-being and improve health outcomes.
- Working with people to provide a positive experience of care.
- Delivering high quality care.
- Building and strengthening leadership.
- Ensuring we have the right staff, with the right skills, in the right place.
- Supporting positive staff experience.

You can see that most areas of action refer to setting standards of positive practice that require well trained staff who have the right skills to deliver high quality care. In your own organisation, standards are usually defined by national guidelines. To assess how well you are meeting those standards, you must first familiarise yourself with them and then use different methods of assessment. This might include supervision and appraisal with your line manager or supervisor, and feedback from service users.

You can measure your own skills and knowledge by asking for feedback from colleagues and managers about your performance. Knowledge is sometimes measured by tests where there is an expectation that you achieve a certain mark. Appraisals (assessments) of your work with your manager should also be held on at least a yearly basis. This is an opportunity for you to understand how well you are doing. You should also ask for feedback from the users of your service and their carers.

Evidence activity

2.2 Meeting standards

1 What standards are you working to? What will you need to do to ensure that your knowledge, skills and understanding meet these standards?
2 Reflect on a recent activity in which you were shown how to carry out part of your role. How did you know it was meeting the standards to which you are expected to work? Go through the reflective process shown in the Gibbs diagram on page 35.

AC 2.3 Demonstrate the ability to reflect on work activities

Reflection is an important activity and should not be regarded as 'separate' from your work role. We can develop our working practice only if we constantly think about the quality of our performance. It is a good idea to keep your reflective accounts in a 'learning journal' that forms part of your development and on-going learning. Discuss this with your manager or supervisor as your organisation may have policies in place and can support you with this. Journals or portfolios can be hand written or electronic but should be treated in a confidential manner. Avoid naming the individual in accounts of interventions with service users.

Reflecting on work practices can feel quite threatening, particularly if you are looking at a situation where things did not go well for either yourself or the individual. In these situations you should ask for some support from a more senior member of staff. Reflective practice is a skill in itself and therefore needs time and support to develop. Neil Thompson, in his book *People Skills*, says there are six stages to consider when developing reflective practice skills:

1 **Read** about the topics you are learning about.
2 **Ask** others about the way they do things and why.
3 **Watch** what is going on.
4 **Feel** – by paying attention to your thoughts, feelings and emotions.

5 **Talk** – share your views and opinions.
6 **Think** – it is vital to spend time thinking about how and why you behave and perform at work.

Evidence activity

2.3 Reflecting on work activites

Think about a recent work activity. Describe the activity and the impact of the activity on yourself and others.

Did you work according to laid down standards?

What would you do differently and why? Explain how you used reflective practice to demonstrate (show) your learning.

LO3 Be able to agree a personal development plan

AC 3.1 Identify sources of support for own learning and development within and beyond the organisation

Professional and personal development is about developing all staff in the organisation, in order to meet standards. Health and social care services focus on the people who work within the service to develop quality care. As such there is a need to ensure that all staff are given the opportunity to develop their roles further. Your own organisation may have developed 'peer support' groups or networks so that people who do the same job are able to meet together to discuss issues, for example.

Your role and the organisation

Success in the health and social care sector is therefore linked to the capabilities and attitudes of the staff who work within it and to the development of their knowledge and skills. Your learning and development are an essential part of your organisation's success. You are a representative of the organisation and the way you behave will have an effect on the individual. If they have a negative experience they may also have a negative feeling towards the organisation that employs you. There will also be an expectation that you work in line with the values of the organisation – for example, working to promote dignity and independence. Your personal development plan therefore needs to have in mind the needs of the organisation. You must remember that the organisation will support only those learning needs that are relevant to your role and the service. You may be interested in the history of art but you will not be supported to study this as it has no value for your service users or your employer.

Formal and informal support

In order to promote and sustain good practice it is important that staff have access to support for their learning and development. This can include informal and formal support. Informal means learning as you go along, or on the job, through, for example, day-to-day observations and feedback. It might also include advice from colleagues, all of which may help you to build your knowledge. Formal support might include more planned training and development sessions such as supervision and appraisals and staff meetings. This is discussed below.

We all learn in different ways – some of us respond better to practical demonstrations while others prefer to discuss a situation. The following contains methods of learning to suit all types of learners:

● **Supervision** – once you have joined an organisation and undergone an induction or introductory period, it is important that your support continues with supervision sessions. These are opportunities to meet with your manager or supervisor to discuss your progress and think about your training and development needs. The sessions should be held on a regular basis and planned in advance so you can prepare for them. They can also be used to discuss situations or problems. Your manager will also help you to work within the values and objectives of the organisation and to support you in developing your role.

- **Appraisal** – this will usually occur once a year. It is more focused around your role, practice and progress in achieving agreed goals and training that may be required in order to achieve them. Once you are in a job, and as your experience and knowledge of your role develop, an appraisal is the point where you and your manager consider:
  - Where you are now
  - How well you are doing
  - Where you want to be
  - How you will get there
  - What you and your manager think of your progress so far
  - How your training and development needs can be met both within and outside the organisation, e.g. in-house or external development and training.
- **Mentoring** – it can be helpful to ask for a more experienced colleague who can support you in your personal and professional development. You can have meetings to share problems and practice issues as well as work together to address your needs.
- **Group discussions** – these can be useful when looking at new practices and processes because they help health and social care workers develop consistent practices. The sessions may be 'closed', where confidentiality is respected and staff feel safe to explore difficult issues and situations.
- One to one **'shadowing'** – 'look and learn' is a helpful way of developing skills and knowledge, so long as you shadow a person who is known to demonstrate excellent practice. For example, you may

Key term

Shadowing means to work alongside someone, perhaps a colleague to understand their role.

Evidence activity

3.1 Sources of support

Think about your work placement.

Have you had an induction and are there processes in place for regular formal and informal support sessions?

Make a list of the opportunities and sources of support available to you and show it to your manager or supervisor. Discuss whether there are other options available.

Agree an action plan for future learning and development opportunities that are both formal and informal.

have 'champions' in your workplace who have expertise in particular areas.

- **Coaching** – this is a method of directing, instructing or training people to help them improve their practice or learn a new skill.
- **E-learning** – you can obtain more knowledge by accessing courses on the internet, but bear in mind they will cover theory only and you must apply this theory to practice properly to ensure high standards. You should also check with your manager or supervisor that any e-learning you access independently is approved by your organisation. Most large organisations also provide their own 'in-house' e-learning.
- **Courses run by your own or other organisations** – take advantage of courses. You have the opportunity to meet other like-minded people and often you will receive a certificate that you can add to your portfolio, which is evidence of your new learning. Books, journals, DVDs and web links are also helpful sources of information. All of this can improve both your knowledge and practice.

AC 3.2 Describe the process for agreeing a personal development plan and who should be involved

A personal development plan can have other names, but it should contain a record of:

- your current record of achievements
- future agreed plans and deadlines for achieving your goals and the overall plan for your role and career
- what you need to learn/aims or objectives for training and development that you and your manager have agreed
- how you are going to achieve this learning (e.g. activities, shadowing, reading, attending a course)
- your own assessment of where you are in your learning and development
- your manager's assessment of the situation
- an assessment of how well you are working to the aims and values of your organisation.
- time scales of when you will review the plan.

Setting up a personal development plan is usually done with your manager or mentor and they will support you in planning your learning. Others such as the individual, carers, advocates, and other professionals may also be involved in this process. If you have a time set aside for supervision or appraisal then this is when you can start to discuss your plan. It is important to set aside time as you need the opportunity to carefully consider your progress and learning needs in an uninterrupted and quiet session.

The plan should be a flexible document in that it must be reviewed on a regular basis and updated to include any new areas for learning that might be of benefit. The Social Care Institute for Excellence (SCIE) identifies a format that might be of help (see the table on page 40).

Evidence activity

3.2 Process for agreeing a PDP

List the steps involved in drawing up a PDP and who should be involved. Think about the kind of issues and learning needs you might want to consider.

AC 3.3 Contribute to drawing up own personal development plan

In the last activity you should have developed the personal development plan by yourself before approaching the line manager with your plan. Reflect on the following – did you gather all the information needed for the plan?

- Did your plan include statements and an action plan highlighting your personal goals showing what you wanted to achieve in your career?
- Did you include areas such as education? You might want to take training courses and perhaps self-improvement plans.
- Did you set up a meeting with your line manager to discuss the plan and to check whether the goals meet the needs of the organisation?
- Did you arrange another meeting to discuss your progress with the plan?

Your PDP can be formatted as a table with the following headings:

- Topic to look at – e.g. promoting dignity.
- Areas that need development – supporting the individual to go to the toilet.
- What action is needed – learning how to transfer the individual from a wheelchair to the toilet while maintaining their dignity.
- What is your target? To be able to complete this task in a safe way while maintaining the dignity of the individual.
- Date for completion of the target – agree this; ensure it is realistic, especially if you first have to access training.

- Resources needed – practical demonstrations, i.e. someone to show you how to do this.
- Input from staff – coaching from supervisor, working with experienced colleagues.
- Achievement – whether you were able to complete the task successfully without support.
- Explanation or a reason if the goals were not achieved.

The following are suggestions for topics that you can discuss with your line manager. They may be a helpful way to break down objectives into manageable goals:

- Short term – you can think about your current knowledge and things you still need to and learn so that you can carry out your job safely and effectively. This may include considering training opportunities.
- Medium term – things that you can do once you have learnt the basics of your job safely. This may include applying your learning to new skills that enhance your role so that

you are able to work more independently or try new ideas.
- Long term – this includes thinking about your future personal development and might include working towards a qualification, for example, or your long term career ambitions.

SMART Targets

Remember that your aims and targets should be SMART.

- Specific – goals should be clear and say exactly what it is you want to achieve.
- Measurable – so you can understand when you have reached the target. You might want to consider milestones or markers that tell you when you have reached a certain goal. For example, this may be when you can complete a certain task unsupervised, or have attended a particular training course.
- Achievable – they should not reflect something that is outside either your job description or your competence.

Evidence activity

3.3 Drawing up a PDP

Use the following table and set out four areas for your own learning. Set up a meeting with your manager and/or mentor to discuss what you intend to do, but explain you would like to draw up the plan independently first. Keep evidence of the meeting and the plan in your portfolio. You should

refer to the plan on a regular basis. You may also wish to keep a record of the people who may be able to support you. These might include managers, senior care staff, colleagues, service users and carers and academic staff.

What do I need to learn?	How will I learn?	How will this help at work?	Review/completion date

Source: http://tinyurl.com/onhwkc6

Now work with a colleague and look at a personal development plan. Give each other goals and targets and discuss learning outcomes by giving feedback.

Concentrate on one area of practice you would each like to improve. Use the SMART process to help you.

Discuss the result of your planning with your manager or supervisor.

- Realistic – ensure goals can be met and that goals can be achieved in that time and that you are not being expected to achieve something that is outside your role or ability. For example, as a health care assistant you should not be expected to give injections.
- Time based – there should be an achievable date/deadline. You should think about the milestones you will need to hit in order to achieve your goal. That way, you can think about this in terms of development and milestones.

Reviewing your plan

Once you have put your plan together, you can start to think about the training and development opportunities you can take up in order to achieve the goals you have outlined. Remember you should also make sure you keep your plan updated and record any changes you make with your manager. Reviewing and evaluating your plan is also a good way of keeping track of your progress. You can look at your goals, the milestones and time frames that you had outlined and whether you were able to achieve these. This will also help you to work out whether you will need to revise your targets and goals.

LO4 Be able to develop own knowledge, skills and understanding

AC 4.1 Show how a learning activity has improved own knowledge, skills and understanding

Every day in your job, you continue to learn and increase your knowledge and practice through your duties and tasks that you carry out. You should therefore look for opportunities to ask questions or discuss problems. A learning activity is helpful only if you can evidence (prove) that it has improved our practice (the way you do your job). The activity should be evaluated by the trainer and the person receiving the training so that any room for improvement can be noted and acted upon. This will enable you to increase your knowledge of the subject, improve your skills and understanding so that you can apply your new skills.

Key term

Evaluate – this is a way to measure how effective and useful your learning is.

Evidence activities

4.1 Learning activities

Consider the following scenario written in a personal development plan:

'I attended a Dementia Awareness day. The topics covered were:

- What is dementia?
- How does it feel to live with dementia?
- How can we best support a person living with dementia?
- Future ideas for training.'

You can show whether and how this learning activity has improved your knowledge, skills and understanding by asking yourself these questions:

1 Was the study day useful?
2 What were the good ideas gained? Why were they 'good'?
3 What did I learn from the course?
4 What questions for me remain unanswered following the study day?
5 What else can I do to improve my knowledge and skills?

By answering these questions you gain a more in-depth knowledge of how useful this study day really was because you are asked to analyse your reaction to the training. When you return to look at the reflection it is more useful because it will give examples of what you gained from the activity and how this has moved you forward in your learning.

4.1 A recent activity

1 Write about a recent activity where you were taught something new. By using the above questions and putting together what you already know about reflective practice, show how this activity has improved your knowledge, skills and understanding.
2 Hand the finished piece to your mentor and/or tutor and ask for some feedback on what you have written.

AC 4.2 Show how reflecting on a situation has improved own knowledge, skills and understanding

In this section we consider how thinking about our practice improves our knowledge, skills and understanding. We are constantly learning in our job. This is because the policies, laws and procedures that govern the way we work change. They change because as a society we are constantly developing and changing the way we think about supporting people. If you compare the way we supported vulnerable people 50 years ago and how we work today you will see huge differences. Today there is a big emphasis, for example, on helping people to remain as independent as possible to live a fulfilling life in society, rather than to keep them in institutionalised care. Our working practices have therefore had to change.

In your work setting, reflecting on a situation should include asking yourself:

- How do your personal views and beliefs affect your work, and how appropriate are they in your work setting? Do you need to question some of your values, for example?
- Your attitude to and relationship with other people at work. Do they impact on your practice? Do you need to 'rethink' any of your attitudes, for example because they are not helpful in promoting good practice?

Your skills and work practices – are they up to date and do they still reflect the values of your organisation? Learning from your mistakes and your successes

Mistakes are a way of learning as long as you understand what went wrong, why and how to do things differently to avoid the mistakes again. We all celebrate success but it is equally important to learn from the success and not be complacent. Rather you should consider why things went well, how you could carry this on in the future and how you could have improved and done something better still.

Training

Think about the opportunities for training. Your organisation will send out information and your manager will also be able to give you more information. Some training will be compulsory and it is likely you will be expected to attend this as a priority. Mandatory or compulsory training might include safeguarding, or health and safety, for example.

Prepare for training by doing any suggested reading or gathering materials you may need to take with you. You will gain most benefit if you participate in the training if that is expected. Some people feel shy and uncomfortable speaking in groups. In those situations, you might find it easier to write any questions or comments about the subject and read them out to the group.

Remember to take any hand-outs so that you can look back on them to refresh your memory and you may also be expected to feedback information to your colleagues as well as reflect on what you learnt and how you can apply it to your practice.

Personal and professional development

Reflecting on practice helps you to identify how training, shadowing, reading, and attending courses for example has supported your learning and how well you are able to apply it to your every day job. Thinking about your personal and professional development can also help to prepare you for further training as well as set milestones and targets for yourself.

Evidence activity

4.2 Reflecting

You decide to challenge a colleague who you think is not behaving in line with the policies and values of your organisation. You have noticed they do not act in a person-centred way, do not work according to the individual's care plan and do not use approved techniques when moving the individual.

How has your reflection on your own practice helped you to understand that you need to 'whistle-blow' about your colleague's behaviour?

AC 4.3 Show how feedback from others has developed own knowledge, skills and understanding

Types of feedback

Feedback is a method of showing us other people's opinions of how we are performing and it can be both positive and negative. It can be in written or verbal form. The feedback you obtain at work could range from a word of praise – a 'well done' – to a more formal discussion during a supervision session. It might be a grade for a piece of work with comments and suggestions for improvements. Although we may feel that some feedback is negative because it is a criticism, it is important to remain objective. Think about any negative feedback – if it is simply a negative comment you should ask for clarification. If it is supported by an explanation you should think about this carefully and consider whether the criticism is reasonableand ask for support so that you can improve your practice. Do not allow this to lower your confidence. Use it to improve your practice.

Importance of listening to feedback

To increase our learning and to improve the way we do something it is important to listen and think about what might be gained from the feedback. A small change to the way we do something may make a huge difference to our learning and performance and as a result to the quality of life of the individuals we support. It can feel uncomfortable to be criticised, but it can have very positive effects if we take the suggestions on board. We might disagree with the feedback at first, but we need to take a deep breath and listen in order to gain a better understanding about what is needed from us. It is important to hear feedback clearly and understand it.

How feedback can improve knowledge, skills and understanding

Feedback should be summarised so that you can see your assessed strengths and weaknesses. You should discuss it with your manager or supervisor and agree ways of addressing the weaknesses and building on the strengths. If you disagree with the feedback you should discuss this with the person who gave feedback and ask for examples. Try not to be defensive or make excuses but listen carefully and think about how your actions may have been seen 'from the outside', even if they were not what you intended. For example, you may be told that you were joking too much with a service user and there was a possibility that, as they have a learning disability, they might have misunderstood the joke, leading to **professional boundaries** becoming blurred. This may not have been your intention – you may have been trying to put the individual at ease. Feedback like this can help you to understand that others can misunderstand your intentions. (See evidence activity 4.3)

> **Key term**
>
> **Professional boundary** This is to understand the limits of your job role. For example although you should be friendly towards the individuals you support, your professional boundary is that you do not become a 'friend' as this compromises your professional relationship with them.

Figure 2.4 Feedback is important

AC 4.4 Show how to record progress in relation to personal development

Your personal development plan should reflect an on-going record of your strengths and weaknesses and your learning and development goals. It will therefore be an on-going record of your progress in your place of work. The record may include notes, certificates of achievement or attendance, and summaries of evidence.

Why record progress?

It is important to keep a record of these activities because:

- it may be a requirement of your professional body or organisation
- it helps to build up a picture of your achievements, which will help you write a personal profile (curriculum vitae, or CV)
- it proves that you have achieved a particular level of competence.

In LO3 we looked at how you might plan your personal development by using the table on page 40.

You might already have a portfolio or file in which you keep various records of your work setting training and learning.

The purpose of a PDP

A personal development record will mean you can keep track of all your learning experiences and any training activities you undertake and will also help you to:

- take responsibility for your own learning – be aware of your limitations and learning needs
- identify the strengths you already have and the experience and skills you have developed to date
- identify the areas in which you need to develop – this might be due to a professional interest in a particular subject or because you or another person have identified a learning need
- use learning opportunities within your area and ensure you participate in any others outside of the setting – for example, you may wish to gain experience in a different part of the sector in which you work and can therefore ask to shadow somebody in another setting for a while to learn their role
- describe what you learn from these opportunities
- set targets and goals for future learning and development; this could include for example how you can be more organised, or manage your time better
- identify how you can achieve your goals and who can support you.

When you document your learning activities it is most important to write reflectively about what you gained and learned from the activity you took part in.

You might like to use the following templates to record your future learning:

Development Record

Date:

xxxxxxx

Name:..

Setting: ....

Mentor/Manager's name: ....

Dates	Activity undertaken What did I do?	Reflective account What did I learn?	What next? How have/will I use this? Any further action

Figure 2.5 Personal development record

Evidence activity

4.4 Recording

Compile a portfolio of work using the above template to record the activity you have undertaken and the developmental plan to show what you wish to do.

Legislation

The Data Protection Act 1998

The Care Standards Act 2000

The Health and Social Care Act 2008

The Care Act 2014

Useful resources

Care Quality Commission
www.cqc.org.uk

National Health Service
www.nhs.uk

Skills for Care
www.skillsforcare.org.uk

Social Care Institute for Excellence
www.scie.org.uk

Local Authority Commissioners

Introduction to equality and inclusion in health, social care or children's and young people's settings

This unit is worth 2 credits

What are you finding out?

Equality and inclusion is an essential aspect to consider for any person working in health or social care. This is because it is so important to ensure all people accessing services are treated equally. This does not mean that all people have to be treated in the same manner. Rather, it means that people are given the same opportunities to access health and social care services.

This unit will enable you to understand the importance of ensuring you work in a way that enables people to access and use services. You will

also learn about how discrimination can impact on people and how you can ensure you can work in a way that is inclusive.

By the end of this unit you will:

1 Understand the importance of equality and inclusion
2 Be able to work in an inclusive way
3 Know how to access information, advice and support about diversity, equality and inclusion.

Links to Level 2 Certificate in Preparing to Work in Adult Social Care

SHC 23 Assessment Criteria	Unit PWCS23
AC1.3	AC1.3 (equality, inclusion)
AC2.1	AC2.1 (equality, diversity, discrimination)
AC3.1	AC3.1 (diversity, equality, inclusion)

LO1 Understand the importance of equality and inclusion

AC 1.1 Explain what is meant by:

- diversity
- equality
- inclusion
- discrimination.

Equality

Equality does not mean that everybody has to be treated the same. Rather, it is about treating people fairly, regardless of their differences, by ensuring they have access to the same opportunities as others. Some people may need extra help to access opportunities, for example having a **physical** or **sensory disability** can impact on a person's ability to use services. For this reason, equality is also about ensuring people get the appropriate help in order to ensure they can access services and that they are not disadvantaged or treated any less fairly than anyone else.

Diversity

Diversity is about variety. For example, your local high street or shopping mall has a diversity of shops, restaurants, banks and bars; football teams have a diversity of roles, including goalkeeper, centre forward and winger. We live in a diverse society where people vary in many ways, including their height, weight, age, gender, sexual orientation, skin colour, ability, personal experiences and personal characteristics such as values, activities, attitudes, cultures, beliefs, skills and life preferences.

Key terms

Diversity is concerned with **respecting** differences and valuing everyone. Diversity includes visible and non-visible individual differences and is about respecting those differences.

Equality is about having equal status, rights and opportunities.

Inclusion is concerned with ensuring that people are treated equally and fairly and are included as part of society.

People may **discriminate** as a result of prejudice or stereotyping. Whether this behaviour is intentional or unintentional does not excuse it. It is the perception of the person discriminated against that is important.

Respect means having due regard for other people's feelings, wishes or rights.

Physical disability limits the way a person functions physically.

Sensory disability is a disability of the senses. It may for example, affect vision or hearing.

Care settings reflect the diversity of the population at large. Residents in a care home for elderly people – men and women, heterosexual and homosexual – may range in age from 60 to well into their ninth decade. Each will have their own set of personal experiences and, especially in locations with an immigrant community, may come from a variety of countries. Preferences, for example for food and music, will vary from one person to another. Attitudes will also differ, for example to staff and fellow residents, beliefs, political ideas and religion, health status and physical and intellectual ability. The same goes for child care settings and hospital wards – a nursery caters for children and a hospital ward for in-patients, but the children and the patients using the service will have a wealth of different – diverse – characteristics, experiences and personal qualities.

Apart from differences in age, sex and gender, physical characteristics, ability, experiences and personal attributes, people also differ in respect of their:

- diet – for example, different health conditions mean that some people have specific dietary needs, and vegetarians and vegans can't take medication that is derived from animals
- religious faith – for example, some religions have specific requirements with respect to diet and method of worship, others require the use of running water to maintain personal hygiene, the right hand for eating and the left for personal cleansing after using the toilet, and so on
- need for modesty and dignity – for example, some people aren't comfortable being touched or seen undressed by someone of the opposite sex or who they don't know, and different people have different ideas about how to be addressed when being spoken to
- communication – for example, different physical and mental health conditions require the use of different methods of communication; some people express their fear, pain and grief freely and openly while others are more reserved, and different people have different ideas about the extent of their personal space.

Working with and getting to know a diverse range of people – service users, patients, their friends and family, colleagues and other professionals – enables health and social care workers to develop their knowledge and understanding of different ways of thinking and living and the reasons for different behaviours. As a consequence, tolerance of and respect for others develop, both of which are essential for meeting diverse – and individual – needs. Having their differences acknowledged and understood helps people to develop a sense of belonging.

Inclusion

Inclusion is about accepting people regardless of their differences. Inclusion can help with a person's sense of well-being and confidence in their abilities. It also ensures that everyone is given the opportunity to reach their full potential. Having our individual differences acknowledged and understood helps us to develop a sense of belonging, or inclusion, and to understand that disadvantaging people because they are different in some way leads to their becoming excluded. It follows, then, that inclusion is about accepting everyone, regardless of difference. It is also about getting rid of intolerance of differences and providing help and support where appropriate.

Any organisation or institution – including local authorities, health service providers, educational establishments, the police service, voluntary organisations and workplaces – that supports and promotes inclusion demonstrates that it values everything about the people involved within it. Inclusion nurtures a sense of well-being and of confidence in your own identity and abilities. And it ensures that everyone can achieve their potential and take their rightful place in society.

Research has shown that certain factors reduce the likelihood of developing a sense of belonging and living a happy and productive life.

Discrimination

Discrimination is when a person is viewed and treated in a negative way because of a particular characteristic – for example their gender, the way they look or their race. A **prejudice** is an attitude or way of thinking based on an unfounded, unreasonable pre-judgement of an individual, particular group of people or situation, rather than being based on facts. Discrimination happens when we act out our negative prejudices. Discriminatory behaviour can therefore result in unfair, unjust treatment.

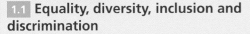

AC 1.2 Describe ways in which discrimination may deliberately or inadvertently occur in the work setting

Prejudices can be positive or negative. If we are **positively prejudiced** towards someone, we think well of them. On the other hand, if we are **negatively prejudiced** against someone, we tolerate them less. Mainly, negative prejudices develop against people who are different in some way. Discrimination happens when we act out our negative prejudices.

Discriminatory behaviour results in unfair, unjust treatment. The people most likely to be discriminated against are those who are different in respect of their:

- **Age** – age discrimination, or ageism, isn't only targeted at elderly people – young people can also be on the receiving end of bullying, harassment and undeserved criticism.
- **Gender** – men and women continue to be treated unfairly in certain walks of life, in particular in the workplace. Discrimination based on gender is known as sexism.
- **Nationality, ethnic background, religion** – some people consider themselves superior to those from different backgrounds and faiths. The victimisation, or bullying, or

harassment of people for such reasons is known as racism.

- **Ability** – barriers that prevent disabled people from accessing the same opportunities as able-bodied people and the ignorant acting out of negative prejudices against physically or intellectually disabled people, for example through name calling and damage of their property, is known as disablism.

- **Size** – some of us are guilty of judging people by the size of their bodies and treating them unfairly as a result. This behaviour is known as sizeism.

- **Financial status** – discrimination against people on the grounds of their income, for example treating people living in poverty as inferior, is known as povertyism. See more about changes for people and places in poverty at: **www.jrf.org.uk**

There are two main types of discrimination: **direct discrimination** and **indirect discrimination**.

Discrimination can take place in a variety of settings, such as schools and colleges, where learners who have a disability may

not be given support and encouragement if it is assumed their disability will affect their ability to learn. In employment, people may be discriminated against because of the colour of their skin, age, gender or sexual preference.

Figure 3.1 How do you ensure you treat all people, including those from a different background equally?

Key terms

Direct discrimination occurs when a person is intentionally treated unfairly, for example when a person is discriminated against because of their gender or because of the colour of their skin.

Indirect discrimination occurs when rules or guidelines meant to apply to everyone unintentionally affect one person or a group of people more than others. For example, a workplace policy that requires all employees to work the night shift indirectly or inadvertently discriminates against those who find working the night shift difficult, such as single parents. in addition, a menu that fails to offer food that meets the needs of all cultures could indirectly discriminate against people with different dietary preferences or needs.

Case study

1.2 Discrimination

The head of St Ethel's care home is brushing up on appearances. She has brought in a new ruling that has banned both staff and service users from wearing anything on their heads and female staff and service users from wearing trousers. She states that any individual who fails to comply with the new ruling will be publicly challenged. What sort of discrimination is taking place here? Give reasons for your answer.

Evidence activity

1.2 Deliberate and inadvertent discrimination

Describe one way in which discrimination could deliberately occur in a health or social care setting.

Describe one way in which discrimination could accidentally occur in a health or social care setting.

AC 1.3 Explain how practices that support equality and inclusion reduce the likelihood of discrimination

Inclusive practice

Inclusive practice is about ensuring attitudes, approaches and strategies are adopted to ensure people are not excluded or isolated. It means supporting diversity by accepting and welcoming people's differences, and promoting equality by ensuring equal opportunities for all.

Inclusive practice is best practice. Health and social care workers demonstrate inclusive practice by working in ways that recognise, respect, value and make the most of all aspects of diversity. Having a sound awareness of and responding sensitively to an individual's diverse needs supports them in developing a sense of belonging, well-being and confidence in their identity and abilities. It also helps them to achieve their potential and take their rightful place in society.

In addition, inclusive practice involves having an understanding of the disastrous impact that discrimination, inequality and social exclusion can have on an individual's physical and mental health. Having such an understanding ensures appropriate, personalised care and support, thereby enabling an individual to develop self-respect and maintain a valued role in society.

Adapting ways of thinking

Because people who fail to support diversity or promote equality are usually entirely unaware of their attitudes and the impact of their behaviour, inclusive practice involves reflecting on and challenging your prejudices, behaviours and work practices. It also involves challenging those of colleagues and other service providers, with a view to adapting ways of thinking and working and to changing services to build on good practice and to better support diversity and promote equality.

Part of your role as a health and social care worker is about finding out about what makes each person individual. Inclusive working is based on promoting equal opportunities and therefore anti-discriminatory practices. This means that practices take into account the individual requirements of each person. Equality and inclusion involve focusing on ensuring that everyone has the opportunity to be engaged and involved in their community in a way that respects their individual needs. All health and social care workers should be aware of and should work to overcome barriers to inclusion – see Figure 3.2 on page 52.

Evidence activity

1.3 Good practice

Explain how practices that support equality and inclusion could reduce the likelihood of discrimination.

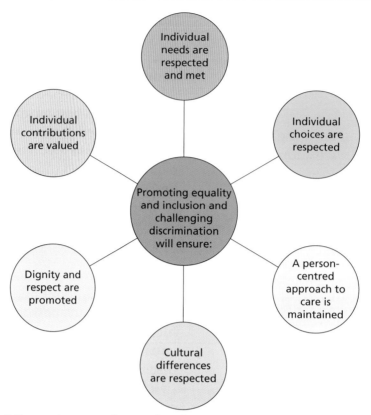

Figure 3.2 Promoting equality and inclusion and challenging discrimination

LO2 Be able to work in an inclusive way

AC 2.1 Identify which legislation and codes of practice relating to equality, diversity and discrimination apply to own role

Discrimination can have devastating effects. As we have mentioned, it is a denial of rights and can be focused on issues such as disability, age, gender or sexual orientation. Within the UK there are numerous pieces of **legislation** (laws) and codes of practice that are intended to put a stop to discrimination, promote diversity and ensure equality. In simple terms, they are in place in order to promote every person's right to fair and equal treatment, regardless of any differences they might have.

Key term

Legislation is defined as the laws and rules made by government.

Legislation relating to equality, diversity and discrimination includes:

- the Equality Act 2010
- the Human Rights Act 1998.

The Equality Act 2010

The Equality Act 2010 replaced previous anti-discrimination laws such as the Disability Discrimination Act, the Sex Discrimination Act and the Race Relations Act with a single act. This simplified the law, removing inconsistencies and making it easier for people to understand and comply with. It also strengthened the law in important ways, to help tackle discrimination and inequality.

The main aim of the Equality Act 2010 was to strengthen and streamline the law related to equality and to support wider work to promote equality. The Equality Act covers exactly the same groups of individuals that were protected by the previous legislation. However, the headings of age, disability, gender reassignment, race, religion or belief, sex, sexual orientation, marriage and civil partnership, and pregnancy and maternity are now known as '**protected characteristics**'.

The protected characteristics covered under this piece of legislation are shown in figure 3.4.

Key term

Protected characteristics describe different groups of people in our community.

Figure 3.3 The Equality Act 2010 aimed to tackle discrimination and inequality

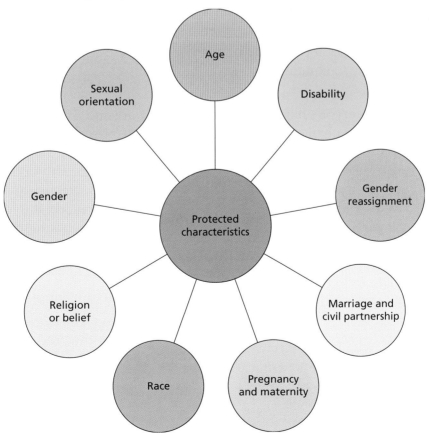

Figure 3.4 Protected characteristics

Another important aspect of the Equality Act 2010 is something known as the equality duty. The equality duty came into force on 5 April 2011. It replaces the three separate duties that previously existed in relation to race, gender and disability. There is now one single duty for the nine protected characteristics.

The equality duty requires public authorities to have due regard to the need to:

- eliminate discrimination, harassment, victimisation and other conduct prohibited under the Equality Act 2010
- advance equality of opportunity
- foster good relations, tackle prejudice and promote understanding.

The Equality Act 2010 applies to many organisations to protect people, for example:

- in the workplace
- in education
- as consumers
- when using public services.

The Human Rights Act 1998

The Human Rights Act 1998 Act is very broad, but the main parts that relate to equality, diversity and inclusion are:

- Article 2, Right to life – everyone has a right to life (except in the issue of execution following a conviction in court for a crime where the penalty is provided by law)
- Article 8, Right to respect for private and family life – everyone has the right to respect for their private and family life, and their home
- Article 14, Prohibition of discrimination – everyone has the right to freedom from discrimination on the grounds of gender, race, language, politics, etc.

Within any work setting, whether health, social care or children's and young person's settings, there should be **policies** and protocols that guide staff on acceptable behaviour. When starting employment

in these settings employees should be introduced to these policies and **procedures**.

It is up to every employee to ensure they understand them and that they keep themselves up to date with them. These policies and procedures will have been written in line with current legislation and good practice guidelines.

Skills for Care and Skills for Health have published a Code of Conduct for healthcare support workers and adult social care workers in England. The Code is based on the principles of protecting the public by promoting best practice. It describes the standards of conduct, behaviour and attitude that the public and people who use health and social care services should expect.

The Code of Conduct applies to:

- health care support workers who report to or work under the guidance of a registered nurse or midwife
- adult social care workers who work in an independent capacity (for example, as a personal assistant), for a residential care

provider or as a supported living, day support or domiciliary care worker.

Part Seven of the Code of Conduct requires health and social care workers to uphold and promote equality, diversity and inclusion. It states that in doing this, as a health or social care worker you must:

- respect the individuality and diversity of the people who use health and care services, their carers and your colleagues
- not discriminate or condone discrimination against people who use health and care services, their carers or your colleagues
- promote equal opportunities and inclusion for the people who use health and care services and their carers
- report any concerns regarding equality, diversity and inclusion to a senior member of staff as soon as possible.

You can access the Code of Conduct for Healthcare Support Workers and Adult Social Care Workers in England at **www. skillsforhealth.org.uk**

Research and investigate

2.1 The Children and Families Act 2014 and SEND Code of Practice

Find out more about the following pieces of legislation relating to equality, diversity and discrimination:

- The Children and Families Act 2014
- The Education, Health and Care (EHC) Plan
- The Special Educational Needs and Disabilities (SEND) Code of Practice 2014

Time to think

2.1 Code of practice

Take a look at the code of practice or the standard of conduct required for your work role.

What does the code state about your responsibilities relating to equality, diversity and inclusion?

Make a note of all the ways in which you apply the code to your work role.

Evidence activity

2.1 Legislation and codes of practice

Identify the legislation and codes of practice that relate to equality, diversity and discrimination and that apply to the role of a health or social care worker. Explain how one of these directly affects your role.

AC 2.2 Show interaction with individuals that respects their beliefs, culture, values and preferences

We develop our beliefs, values and **preferences** throughout our lives. As very small children we are dependent on close family and carers. It is their role to direct and shape our thoughts and behaviour and encourage and reward those that meet **cultural customs**, traditions and expectations with respect to manners, respect, what makes for right and wrong and so on.

As we grow and become increasingly exposed to society at large, our preferences, attitudes, values and beliefs develop as a result of new experiences and the influence of factors such as **role models**, **peer groups**, education, religious institutions and the media. The personal attributes we develop throughout our lives promote the development of our **identity** and the way we want others to see us. They make us the **individuals** we are. (See page 56 for definitions).

Beliefs

Beliefs are ideas or principles that we think are true. They may be religious, for example Christianity, Islam and Judaism; non-religious, for example humanism; or political, for example socialism, communism and feminism. Beliefs underpin the way we live – for example, beliefs concerning animals' rights mean that vegans will not consume meat or meat products of any description. The Human Rights Act 1998 protects our right to choose what to think and believe and to be free to express or act out our beliefs as we wish.

Key terms

Preferences refer to a strong liking for something.

Cultural customs are things that people have done for a long period of time. Usually the people come from the same country, culture or religion.

Role model is someone who serves as an example and whose behaviour is copied by others.

Peer group is a group of people of similar age and sharing the same social status.

Identity is the individual characteristics by which a person is recognised or known.

Individuality is the character of a person or features of their personality and character that distinguish them from others.

Moral code is a set of rules and guidelines that an organisation outlines to ensure that the standards of behaviour employees exhibit is correct.

Ethical code is a set of rules and guidelines that an organisation issues. These will focus on professional values that will ensure that their behaviour is appropriate and morally correct.

Code of conduct are rules and guidelines that an organisation outlines with regard to practice and the behaviour that employees must display. A code of conduct takes into account moral and ethical values of both the individual and the organisation.

Values

We give a value to something that we respect and admire or that we feel has worth. Tangible things like cars and jewellery have an economic worth. But health and happiness are qualities we appreciate, as are the family and friends we hold dear, even though we can't put a price on qualities and people. Other things we value, although to different degrees given that we are all different, are codes of behaviour, such as the following:

- **moral code**, which is to do with behaviour that is right and decent
- **ethical code**, which is to do with behaviour that is principled, fair and just
- **code of conduct**, which is to do with standards of behaviour.

The Human Rights Act 1998 protects our right to freedom of conscience, in other words, to decide for ourselves what to respect and value, and what is right, decent, fair and principled.

Culture

We use the term 'multi-cultural society' which acknowledges that as a nation we include people from different nationalities and cultural groups. Culture describes groups of people who are characterised by particular traditions values, preferences and beliefs. Values (discussed earlier) describe those things, ideas, beliefs and principles that we hold dear to us.

Preferences

Preferences are highly individual. They develop and change throughout our lives and having a preference enables us to make an informed choice. For example, a child might choose a cup of juice whereas an elderly person might prefer a cup of tea; people from different cultural backgrounds, for example Aboriginal and Inuit people, have entirely different preferences for dress, as do the Skinhead and Goth youth sub-cultures; someone who finds it increasingly difficult to swallow would choose to change to a liquid diet; and not until they have experienced the delights of chocolate might someone choose to eat it!

While a health or care worker might not agree with the beliefs and values of the people they work with, nor share their preferences, inclusive work practice involves respecting and promoting:

- the right to freedom of thought and religion, i.e. their beliefs
- the right to freedom to express their beliefs as they wish
- the right to freedom of conscience, i.e. to personal values and a sense of right and wrong
- respecting, promoting and responding to personal preferences.

Care work that does not demonstrate inclusive practice, for example denying someone the opportunity to worship in the way that their religion dictates or to choose what to eat or wear, is oppression. Oppressive behaviour denies people their freedoms and is a form of abuse.

It is important that health and social care workers always work in ways that recognise and respect the individual values, beliefs and preferences of all service users. If we are to truly embrace the principle of inclusion, it is important that we interact with service users in a manner that respects their individuality.

In order to interact with people in a way that respects their beliefs, culture, values and preferences it is important that health and social care workers ensure their work is inclusive and respectful of each individual's social identity. This can be achieved by:

- recognising that every person is an individual with their own social identity
- treating people fairly, recognising their differences and treating them appropriately
- respecting all individuals regardless of their social identity
- learning about different aspects of social identity
- avoiding stereotyping or making assumptions about individuals based on their social identity
- recognising that different opinions may impact on individuals in different ways
- avoiding the use of inappropriate and disrespectful language relating to social identity.

Time to think

2.2 Interaction

Think about the way in which you interact with the people you support and your colleagues.

Make a note of all the ways in which you respect their beliefs, culture, values and preferences.

Evidence activity

2.2 Beliefs, culture, values and preferences

Ask your manager to observe you communicating with service users and to give you written feedback on whether you interact with individuals in way that respects their beliefs, culture, values and preferences. Are there any ways which you can improve?

AC 2.3 Describe how to challenge discrimination in a way that encourages change

If you put into practice everything you have learned and understood so far about promoting equality, diversity and inclusion, you will be well on your way to demonstrating the competencies that this unit sets out. Your learning and understanding and your developing ability to reflect on ways of working should also have raised your awareness regarding the way that your colleagues, other professionals and the individuals you work with promote equality and rights.

Knowing what, when and how to **challenge discrimination** can be difficult. However, we know that some language and behaviour are never acceptable, for example language and actions that are racist, sexist, ageist or **homophobic**. Having looked at what discrimination is, we will now look at ways in which discrimination can be dealt with in order to encourage positive changes in behaviour.

Why does discrimination occur?

Discrimination generally happens due to misunderstandings and lack of knowledge and despite the presence of policies, discrimination may still happen. Many people who discriminate against others have no concept of the effects of discrimination. Very often discrimination occurs because of a lack of understanding and limited knowledge. People who discriminate usually do so for one or more of the following reasons:

Key terms

Challenging discrimination is about challenging people over their behaviour because it is potentially discriminatory.

A person who is **homophobic** demonstrates prejudice against gay or lesbian people.

- learned behaviour – people learn behaviours and attitudes from family and friends; this could lead to prejudice and behaviours where these people act on their long held opinions about certain groups of people
- lack of awareness – some people lack awareness of the differences between people
- lack of training – people who have not been properly trained may not be aware of the importance of ensuring their actions promote equality and diversity.

Why challenge discrimination?

If faced with discrimination, all health or social care workers have a duty of care to act upon it and challenge it so that inclusion can be promoted. It is therefore important that any discrimination that is identified is challenged in order to:

- promote an inclusive and positive culture that is free of discrimination and that values each person's differences
- reinforce workplace policies and procedures
- ensure the equalities legal framework is not breached.

How to challenge discrimination

Health and social care workers can challenge discrimination in a way that encourages change by:

- acting as a role model for positive behaviour and empowering service users to challenge discrimination themselves
- making it clear that discrimination is not acceptable
- reporting any episodes of discrimination to their line manager
- maintaining a calm and professional manner
- attending training and keeping their knowledge about equality, diversity and inclusion up to date.

Procedures for reporting discriminatory behaviour will vary from organisation to organisation and it is important that you follow your organisation's policy for reporting discriminatory practices. There are

laws against discrimination, which make it illegal. If you are in a position where you need to report discriminatory practices, you may need to seek advice and support from a more senior member of staff initially.

Primarily concerns about discrimination should be reported internally to your manager or supervisor at the earliest opportunity. If there are suspicions that your line manager is implicated in the discriminatory practice, you may have to follow your organisation's **whistle-blowing policy**.

Documenting discriminatory behaviour

When reporting an incident of discriminatory behaviour it is important to provide as much detail as possible about what has happened. The process of reporting is essential, and although it can be difficult and sometimes distressing, it is vital that all relevant information is reported. You may therefore be required to provide information in order that your manager can document all important information. Some of the facts that may be recorded include:

- the nature of the discriminatory practice
- where and when the incident took place

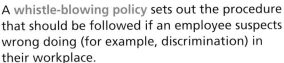

Key terms

A whistle-blowing policy sets out the procedure that should be followed if an employee suspects wrong doing (for example, discrimination) in their workplace.

If the discrimination is aimed at you, you may be able to get advice and support from a union representative or your organisation's human resources department.

Research and investigate

2.3 Challenging discrimination

Find out what you should do if you come across discrimination in your workplace. Where would you go to for support if you experienced discrimination in your workplace?

Case study

2.3 How should discrimination be challenged?

Mrs Singh is an 87-year-old lady. She is being cared for in a busy hospital ward after having a stroke. Because it is easier to get on and off, staff always dress her in a backless hospital gown. The stroke has affected her speech and also her mobility, so she spends most of her time in bed. Her religious and cultural beliefs mean that she must not eat meat, that she needs to shower every morning and that she needs to keep covered in order to retain her modesty. None of these needs is being met because she is unable to communicate them and because the staff on the ward are constantly under pressure to complete routine activities. To them she is simply 'the stroke in bed 7', not a person with her own individual set of needs. You notice that she is distressed by this.

Explain how this sort of discrimination should be challenged in a way that encourages change.

- what exactly happened
- who said/did what to whom
- the relationships/roles of the parties involved in the incident
- the names of those involved in the incident, including other possible witnesses
- relevant history between the parties.

This list is not complete. However, it should provide a good guide to the type of information that is needed for discriminatory practices to be assessed properly.

You should have a policy which details the steps you should take to report and escalate concerns relating to discriminatory behaviour. In general you should:

- discuss your concerns with your line manager
- record your concerns and if necessary take them to a more senior manager
- take your concerns to a director or chief executive
- share your concerns with the Care Quality Commission (CQC).

Time to think

2.3 Your behaviour

It is possible that you may have behaved in an unfair, discriminatory way at some time or other. It may not have been intentional.

Think about the reasons why you have treated – or maybe continue to treat – some people unfairly. If someone treated you in this way, how would you feel? How can you change your thinking so that you don't discriminate against them in the future?

Evidence activity

2.3 Challenging discrimination and change

Describe how discrimination can be challenged in a way that will promote change.

LO3 Know how to access information, advice and support about diversity, equality and inclusion

AC 3.1 Identify a range of sources of information, advice and support about diversity, equality and inclusion

There is a range of sources of information available about equality, diversity and inclusion. Consider the following examples of sources of information, advice and support about diversity, equality and inclusion:

- **Organisational policies** – a good starting point if you need to find out about diversity, equality and inclusion in your workplace is your organisation's policies. Your organisation should have a policy relating to equality, diversity and inclusion.
- **Your manager or supervisor** – should be able to provide advice and guidance about equality, diversity and inclusion. Your employer should also arrange for you to

Figure 3.5 There are many sources of information available to you

3.1 Sources of information

Identify four different sources of information, advice or support about diversity, equality and inclusion.

attend training relating to quality, diversity and inclusion, and the basics should be covered on induction.

- **Human resources** – should be able to deal with any concerns you may have. If your organisation has a human resources department you should be able to speak to them in confidence.
- **Equality and Human Rights Commission** – was created to challenge discrimination and promote equality and human rights. It is able to provide a range of resources about equality and human rights. It also produces guidance documents, particularly in relation to the Equality Act 2010. You can find information about the Equality and Human Rights Commission at **www.equalityhumanrights.com**.

AC 3.2 Describe how and when to access information, advice and support about diversity, equality and inclusion

It is important to know where to go to seek information and advice relating to equality,

Key terms

Continuing professional development (CPD) refers to the process of tracking and documenting the skills, knowledge and experience health and social care workers gain both formally and informally as they work, beyond any initial training.

A **trade union** is an organised association of workers in a trade, group of trades, or profession which is formed to protect and further their rights.

diversity and inclusion. There are many times when it may be important to access information, advice and support:

- **When first starting to work in the health or social care sector** – all staff should undertake a period of induction. There is so much to learn and it takes time to develop skills, experience and knowledge. New health or social care workers will therefore need to be supported to gather information, advice and support relating to equality, diversity and inclusion from their manager, colleagues and through attending training that is offered to them as a new employee.
- **When starting a new job with a new employer** – although every health or social care organisation is required to have a policy relating to equality and diversity, these policies may differ slightly depending on the nature of the organisation. Although people working in the health or social care sector may have a thorough understanding of equality, diversity and inclusion, they will be required to learn the systems that are in place when starting a new job with a new employer. Again, new members of staff should be given an induction and they should be able to approach their manager and colleagues for information, advice and support.
- **When keeping knowledge up to date** – all health and social care workers have a responsibility to ensure they keep their knowledge up to date. This is also known as **continuing professional development (CPD)**. It is therefore essential that staff

attend refresher training to ensure they continue to follow the most up-to-date rules, legislation, standards and good practice guidance. When undertaking CPD relating to equality, diversity and inclusion, staff should be able to seek support from their manager to ensure they are given the opportunity to continue to develop in this area.

● **When there is an issue relating to discrimination** – it is essential that staff understand the importance of seeking information, advice and support if any person in the workplace reports a problem relating to discrimination. In the first instance, staff should seek guidance from their line manager or a more experienced member of staff. In some instances, especially if discrimination is staff related, advice and support may be sought from a **trade union.**

● **When information is required** – for example, a service user or their representative may ask for information relating to equality, diversity and inclusion. It is important that any member of staff ensures their knowledge is up to date before giving advice to others. If in doubt, they could seek advice from their manager or a more experienced colleague.

Evidence activity

3.2 Accessing information

Describe four situations in which additional information, advice and support about diversity, equality and inclusion may be needed.

Legislation

The Equality Act 2010

The Human Rights Act 1998

Useful resources

Websites

Care Quality Commission

www.cqc.org.uk

Equality and Human Rights Commission

www.equalityhumanrights.com

Joseph Rowntree Foundation

www.jrf.org.uk

Skills for health

www.skillsforhealth.org.uk

Introduction to duty of care in health, social care or children's and young people's settings

This unit is worth 1 credit

What are you finding out?

This unit will introduce you to the concept of duty of care. Duty of care is not about making decisions for people, rather, it is about promoting the rights, of people to make decisions, take risks and participate in life. You will also learn about responding to complaints and ensuring that complaints are responded to appropriately.

By the end of the unit you will:

1 Understand the implications of duty of care
2 Understand support available for addressing dilemmas that may arise about duty of care
3 Know how to respond to complaints.

Links to Level 3 Certificate in Preparing to Work in Adult Social Care

Unit SHC 24 is one of the knowledge units included in the Level 2 Certificate in Preparing to Work in Adult Social Care. This unit is the same across both qualifications.

LO1 Understand the implications of duty of care

AC 1.1 Define the term 'duty of care'

The concept of 'duty of care' has an interesting origin which is known as the 'Paisley snail'. In 1932, a court in the UK considered a case that involved a snail that had found its way into a glass of ginger beer. The woman who drank the ginger beer suffered from a nervous shock as a result of seeing the snail in the bottom of her glass. The woman took action against the publican who had sold her the drink. She was able to establish that the publican owed her a 'duty of care' and that he had breached that duty of care by allowing the snail to get into her glass of ginger beer. The court upheld the woman's claim and the principle of 'duty of care' was established. This case was called the Paisley Snail because the incident took place in Paisley in Scotland.

Duty of care can be defined as a moral or legal obligation to ensure the safety or well-being of others.

Research and investigate

1.1 Paisley Snail

Research the Paisley Snail case. You can find out more about this at **http://paisleyonline.co.uk/html/paisley_snail.html**.

It is a legal obligation to:

- act in the best interests of service users and others
- always act in a way that protects people from harm
- act within your **competence** and not take on anything that you have not been trained to do.

It means that all people working in health or social care must always act in the best interests of the people they support. As a health or social care worker you owe a duty of care to service users, your colleagues, your employer, yourself and the public.

Duty of care applies to all staff regardless of their occupation or level. It applies to those who work as agency or in temporary roles, those who work part time or full time, or as students or volunteers.

Duty of care underpins all work that health and social care workers undertake. Duty of care is a legal requirement and can be tested in court should **negligence** or **malpractice** occur.

It is your responsibility to make sure you have the knowledge and skills that are required to undertake your work. If you know that you are not able to do a task, then you have a responsibility to speak up and say so.

Research and investigate

1.1 What does duty of care mean?

Different people that you work with might have their own ideas about what duty of care means. Take some time to speak with your colleagues about what they understand about duty of care and what it means. Make a note of their answers.

Are there any differences in people's responses?

AC 1.2 Describe how the duty of care affects own work role

Health and social care workers have a duty of care to ensure the safety and well-being of service users. People receiving health and social care services have a right to expect that they will not be exposed to any unnecessary risks and that staff are trained to ensure people are kept safe. It is therefore important that in exercising their duty of care, health and social care workers do what a reasonable person, with their background and training, can be expected to do.

Figure 4.1 Duty of care means you must always aim to supply the highest standard of care

Having a duty of care means that you must always aim to provide the highest standard of care, to the best of your ability, and that you must speak out if there are any reasons why you are unable to do so.

When you have a duty of care, this means that you must:

- only carrying out duties for which you have been trained and are competent to perform
- ensure your knowledge and skills are up to date
- only carry out duties that are outlined in your job description
- be **accountable** for your own decisions and actions
- follow standard procedures in all aspects of your work, including use of resources and equipment
- provide standards of care in line with your codes of practice
- maintain confidentiality
- report any concerns you have, using the whistle-blowing policy if necessary.

It is therefore important that duty of care is considered in any work you undertake within your role as a health or social care worker.

LO2 Understand support available for addressing dilemmas that may arise about duty of care

AC 2.1 Describe dilemmas that may arise between the duty of care and an individual's rights

A **dilemma** is a situation in which a difficult choice has to be made between two or more possibilities, neither of which is practically acceptable. During the course of their work, health and social care workers may find themselves in a position where an individual they are supporting does not agree with what is believed to be in their best interest. Sometimes, having a duty to act in a person's best interests and protecting them from harm can be difficult to balance against empowering people to take control of their own lives and this can lead to situations where dilemmas arise between duty of care and the rights of the individual.

Balancing decisions and rights

It is important to be aware of the fact that although duty of care is aimed at protecting people, it is not about preventing people from taking risks for fear that they may come to some harm. Although health and social care workers have a duty of care towards the people they support, we must always remember that people have the right to make their own choices and decisions about their care and the way they wish to be supported and live their lives. Examples may include decisions relating to:

- relationships
- choosing where to live and the level of support required
- maintaining independence in areas such as shopping and cooking
- self-management of medication.

Best interest decisions can only be made on behalf of individuals who do not have the capacity to make decisions for themselves at the time the particular decision needs to be taken.

Making decisions

The majority of people requiring the support of health or social care services will be in a position to make decisions about their everyday life. If the person has the capacity to make such a decision, health and social care workers do not have the right to over-rule that decision, even if they think it is an unwise one. In order to exercise their duty of care, health and social care professionals have a responsibility to ensure people understand the consequences and potential risks of what they are intending to do. It is therefore important that they have enough information about those risks and consequences, and that this information is presented in a format they can understand.

The following case studies are just a few examples of the types of dilemmas health and social workers might come across.

Case study

2.1 Your role

1 Mrs Barber is unable to move independently, and her moving and handling assessment states that she is to be hoisted at all times. Mrs Barber does not like to be hoisted and insists that staff physically lift her. Mrs Barber has the capacity to make decisions.

- What are the issues for staff supporting Mrs Barber?
- What should the health or social care worker do in these circumstances?
- What is the health or social care worker's duty of care in these circumstances?

2 Mr Sharma has decided that he does not want to take his medication any more. He states that he is having side effects that are making him feel uncomfortable.

- What are the issues for staff supporting Mr Sharma?
- What should the health or social care worker do in these circumstances?
- What is the health or social care worker's duty of care in these circumstances?

Evidence activity

2.1 Duty of care and an individual's rights

Describe a dilemma that might arise within your work place where you believe your duty of care conflicts with an individual's rights.

AC 2.2 Explain where to get additional support and advice about how to resolve such dilemmas

It is important that health and social care workers are aware of the limits of their role and that they realise the implications of acting outside the boundaries of their role. It is therefore essential that they realise the importance of requesting support as and when this is needed. If health and social care workers are faced with a dilemma rating to their duty of care and a person's rights it is essential that they know where to turn to for support.

Figure 4.2: Who do you speak to when you need additional support and advice about dilemmas you are facing?

In the first instance, if health and social care workers are unsure about how to respond to a dilemma relating to their duty of care and a person's rights, their first port of call should be their manager or supervisor, who should be able to advise on the best approach to take.

Whistle-blowing

If health and social care workers do not feel supported by their manager they may need to take their concerns further. Under the Public Disclosure Act 1998 all workers have a right to 'whistle-blow' if there is a **conflict of interest** with their duty of care and their ability to support service users. Every employer should have a whistle-blowing policy and procedure in place to facilitate the disclosure of this type of information.

People working in health and social care can get free, independent and confidential advice from the whistle-blowing helpline. This is a free-phone service for employees working within the **NHS** and social care sector. See useful resources for information on how you can contact them. Employees can also contact the Care Quality Commission (CQC) if they are concerned about the way in which people are being treated within their organisation.

See useful resources for more information on who you can go to about whistle-blowing.

Key terms

Conflict of interest is a situation where the interests of two different sides oppose one another. Or where one person might be compromised (put in a difficult situation which could affect their professionalism), for example, it is a conflict of interest for a care worker to make friends with a service user's family member-boundaries can become blurred.

NHS is the National Health Service which is a publicity funded organisation in the UK and offers a large number of free health care services.

Research and investigate

2.2 Dilemmas

Talk to your manager and identify your role in managing dilemmas within your place of work.

Make a list of what you can and cannot do and who you can call upon for advice if it is required.

Evidence activity

2.2 Additional support

Think about the dilemma you have described in evidence activity 2.1 and explain where you could get additional support to resolve the dilemma.

LO3 Know how to respond to complaints

AC 3.1 Describe how to respond to complaints

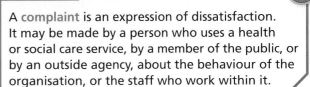

Key term

A **complaint** is an expression of dissatisfaction. It may be made by a person who uses a health or social care service, by a member of the public, or by an outside agency, about the behaviour of the organisation, or the staff who work within it.

A **complaint** can be described as an expression of dissatisfaction about a care services action or lack of action, or about the standard of service provided by or on behalf of the service. People who use care services, their carers, representatives and members of the public have a right to complain about the services they access.

Although many people have no problems when using health or social care services, sometimes things can sadly go wrong. For many, the thought of making a complaint can be daunting, but health and social care services should welcome the opportunity to respond to concerns and try to put things right. By law, all health and social care services must have agreed procedures for dealing efficiently with complaints.

Responding to complaints

Complaints may be received in person, by telephone, by email or by letter. Comments may also be received about the quality of care provided or suggestions may be put forward as to how things could be improved. Comments and complaints can help to improve services for people who require care and support.

Complaints should always be taken seriously and handled in a professional manner. Procedures for handling complaints should focus on the people who use or have an interest in care services.

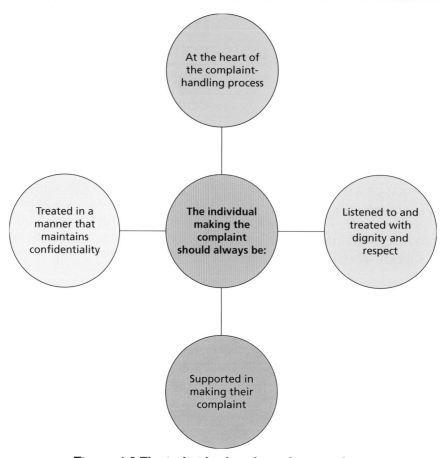

Figure 4.3 The individual making the complaint

It is important that health and social care workers offer support when a service user wishes to make a complaint about the service they receive and should offer information about how such support can be accessed.

Figure 4.4 How do you respond to complaints constructively?

It is important that complaints are viewed positively as a way to make improvements within the service. Complaints should be encouraged so that small problems can be dealt with at the earliest stage. The big advantage of a culture that encourages complaints is that lessons can be learned from mistakes, they can be rectified and formal complaints can be avoided in the future. If service users feel that people are listening to them and taking them seriously, there will not be such a need to complain because where possible issues can be resolved as soon as they arise. However, if there is a more serious issue, service users should always feel enabled to make a formal complaint.

Supporting people to make complaints

Part of your role as a health or social care worker may include supporting people to make complaints or you may receive complaints through your daily work. You may be required to support service users to follow the procedure for making a complaint or you may need to direct them by making them aware of your organisational policy for making complaints. Either way, if a complaint is made to you, it is important that you:

- follow your organisation's policy for handling complaints
- remain calm
- listen to the complainant and take the complaint seriously
- acknowledge the complainant's concerns
- be respectful of the individual and enable them to take their time
- record the complaint, ensuring that any documentation is accurate
- escalate the complaint to your supervisor or manager in a timely manner
- ensure the complainant can access your organisation's complaints policy and that they understand how to use it
- inform the complainant of what will happen next and when they can expect to receive a response
- use the complaint as a learning opportunity.

If a complaint is made to you, it is important that you don't:

- ignore the complainant
- attempt to solve the complaint yourself
- make excuses
- make promises about sorting out the complaint
- openly discuss the complaint with anyone other than your supervisor or manager.

The way in which complaints are approached can make all the difference between enabling people to feel satisfied and that they have been listened to or feeling frustrated that their complaint has not been taken seriously and that things will never change.

Case study

3.1 Responding to complaints

A daughter of a service user calls you over and tells you that she is not happy with the attitude of one of the members of staff. She states that the member of staff is very abrupt with service users and feels that the staff member sometimes dismisses service users' requests to use the toilet.

Explain the actions you would take to deal with this complaint.

Evidence activity

3.1 How to respond to complaints

What procedures or agreed ways of working are in place to raise and deal with complaints within your place of work? Make a list of the ways to respond to complaints.

AC 3.2 Identify the main points of agreed procedures for handling complaints

Agreed procedures for handling complaints are simply the policies and procedures for dealing with complaints within the care organisation you work for. By law, all health and social care organisations should have a **complaints policy**. The **complaints procedure** should be easily understood and made available to everyone. It should be well publicised and accessible to meet the needs of people using the service. For example, if necessary, the information should be available in different languages and in different formats such as easy to read leaflets or braille.

Key terms

The complaints policy sets out the course of action that should be followed if a complaint is received.

The complaints procedure details what has to be done to implement the policy.

The aim of any complaints procedure should be to:

- create a clear, efficient process for resolving complaints so that everyone involved knows where they stand
- ensure the complainant finds it easy to make a complaint regardless of their ability and that they feel they are being taken seriously
- ensure the complainant is kept well informed at all stages of the complaints process
- make every possible effort to secure a satisfactory outcome for the complainant
- ensure the complainant is informed of the appeals procedure if they are not satisfied with the outcome of their complaint.

The main points of any complaints procedure should include:

- the definition of a complaint
- who can make a complaint
- how to make a complaint
- timescales for complaints
- how the investigation will be carried out
- confidentiality
- consent for the sharing of information
- investigation and organisational response
- roles and responsibilities
- record keeping
- what will happen if a complaint is unresolved.

Research and investigate

3.2 Handling complaints

Locate a copy of your employer's complaints policy and answer the following questions:

- Where is the policy kept?
- How are service users informed about the policy?
- Who is responsible for dealing with complaints within your organisation?
- Over how many days must complaints be handled?
- Who should the person complaining write to if they are not satisfied with the outcome of their complaint?

Time to think

3.2 Complaints

Think of a time when a service user or their relative has complained to you about the service they have received. It does not have to be a serious complaint, but could be something minor that was handled informally. For example, a person may have complained because their meal was not warm enough.

Think of one thing you have learned from this complaint and, if possible, one thing you will do to ensure you improve your practice as a result. Make a note of the following:

- the complaint
- what you have learned as a result of this complaint
- the actions taken as a result of this complaint.

Evidence activity

3.2 Handling complaints

Locate your organisation's policy for handling complaints and make a note of the main points of the policy.

Legislation

Public Disclosure Act 1998

The Mental Capacity Act 2005

Useful resources

Websites

Care Quality Commission

www.cqc.org.uk

Social Care Institute for Excellence (SCIE)

www.scie.org.uk

The whistle-blowing helpline

www.wbhelpline.org.uk

Health and social care workers can whistle-blow to the whistle-blowing helpline by email at **enquiries@wbhelpline.org.uk** or by telephone on 08000 724 725. You can contact the CQC by email at **enquiries@cqc.org.uk** or by telephone at **03000 616161**. Check the website for the most up to date contact details.

Principles of safeguarding and protection in health and social care

This unit is worth 3 credits

What are you finding out?

We all have a responsibility to keep people who use health and social care services free from abuse and harm. These people may be vulnerable because of their age, health, mental, intellectual or physical ability and so may be more susceptible or prone to neglect, abuse, harm or **exploitation**. Providers of health and social care have a duty to comply with legislation and protect people using their services from harm, and health and social care workers have a duty to respond promptly and appropriately if they suspect abuse is taking place.

This unit will help you to develop and demonstrate your knowledge about the principles of safeguarding and protection in health and social care.

By the end of this unit you will:

1 Know how to recognise signs of abuse
2 Know how to respond to suspected or alleged abuse
3 Understand the national and local context of safeguarding and protection from abuse
4 Understand ways to reduce the likelihood of abuse
5 Know how to recognise and report unsafe practices.

Links to Level 2 Certificate in Preparing to Work in Adult Social Care

Unit HSC 024 is one of the knowledge units included in the Level 2 Certificate in Preparing to Work in Adult Social Care. This unit is the same across both qualifications.

LO1 Know how to recognise signs of abuse

AC 1.1 Define the following types of abuse:

- **Physical abuse**
- **Sexual abuse**
- **Emotional/psychological abuse**
- **Financial abuse**
- Institutional abuse
- Self-neglect
- Neglect by others.

The government paper '**No secrets**: Guidance on developing and implementing multiagency policies and procedures to protect **vulnerable people/adults** from abuse', published in 2000, defines abuse as 'a violation of an individual's human and civil rights by any other person or persons'.

Abuse can take place anywhere, including public places, hospital, places of worship, work, care homes, day centres and even the victim's own home.

Abuse can take many forms, some of which may not always be obvious. It can consist of a single act or repeated acts. We will now take a look at the forms of abuse a little more closely.

> **Time to think**
>
> **1.1** Abuse
> Write down the words that come into your mind when you think of the term 'abuse'.

> **Key terms**
>
> **Neglect** happens when no thought or care is given to a person or something.
>
> **Fraud** is where a person uses an act of deception to make a personal gain or to cause a loss to someone else.

> **Key terms**
>
> **Exploitation** is when one person treats another person unfairly in order to benefit from their work.
>
> **'No Secrets'** is a government paper which sets out a code of practice for the protection of vulnerable adults.
>
> A **vulnerable person/adult** is anyone aged 18 and over who needs Community Care Services because of mental or other disability, age or illness. They may be unable to take care of himself or herself. Or they may be unable to protect themselves against significant harm or exploitation from **perpetrators** or **abusers**.

> An **abuser** can be any person who takes advantage of a vulnerable person. Within a health or social care setting you might hear abusers being referred to as perpetrators. It is difficult to know what an abuser looks like because abuse could involve a wide range of people, including family members, friends, health and social care professionals, health and social care workers or volunteers.
>
> A **perpetrator** is a person who is a suspect until it has been proven that he or she carried out an offense.

Table 5.1 Types of abuse and definitions

Type of abuse	Definition
Physical abuse	Physical abuse happens when a person purposefully causes pain or injury to another person. It may involve hitting, slapping, punching, pushing, kicking or forcing people to take medication or eat against their will. It may also involve other actions such as restraint or inappropriate punishments such as enforced isolation or leaving people to sit in their own urine or faeces.
Sexual abuse	Sexual abuse happens when a person experiences sexual assault, sexual harassment or is forced to take part in a sexual activity to which they have not agreed. It may also include circumstances in which a person has been pressured into consenting to a sexual activity. It may involve actions such as inappropriate kissing or touching, unwanted advances, indecent exposure or rough washing or touching of the genital area.
Emotional/psychological abuse	Emotional or psychological abuse includes actions or behaviours that can have a harmful effect on a person's emotional health. Emotional or psychological abuse may include humiliation and intimidation, harassment, verbal abuse, isolation, threatening to harm a person, abandonment and threatening to withdraw services or supportive networks.
Financial abuse	Financial abuse may include theft, **fraud**, exploitation, pressure in connection with wills, property, inheritance or finances, or the misuse or misappropriation of property, possessions or benefits. Financial abuse may also include depriving a person of money for clothing, food or other essential items.
Institutional abuse	Institutional abuse occurs when the routines and regimes within care settings are organised in such a way that they deny people of their rights, choices and opportunities. Decisions are made for the benefit of the service rather than for the individuals receiving the service.
Self-neglect	Self-neglect happens when a person fails to care for themselves properly. This behaviour can pose a threat to a person's health and/or safety. Self-neglect could include living in unclean, hazardous conditions. The person may not eat properly and they may fail to maintain their personal hygiene. The person may also fail to recognise the need to seek help when they are ill and they may not take their prescribed medication.
Neglect by others	This is a passive form of abuse which can include ignoring medical or physical care needs, failure to provide access to appropriate health, social care or educational services, or the withholding of the necessities of life, such as clothing, medication, adequate nutrition and heating.

Evidence activity

1.1 Types of abuse

In your own words, give a definition of the following types of abuse:

- physical abuse
- sexual abuse
- emotional/psychological abuse
- financial abuse
- institutional abuse
- self-neglect
- neglect by others.

AC 1.2 Identify the signs and/or symptoms associated with each type of abuse

It is not always easy to spot the signs and symptoms of abuse. A person who is being abused may make excuses for their bruises, or why they don't want to talk to people or why they have no money. On the other hand, it is important not to jump to conclusions. It is however important to have some knowledge of the signs and symptoms of abuse so that you are able to act in a timely manner rather than doubting yourself.

Evidence activity

1.2 Signs and symptoms

Describe in your own words the signs and symptoms associated with the following types of abuse:

- physical abuse
- sexual abuse
- emotional/psychological abuse
- financial abuse
- institutional abuse
- self-neglect
- neglect by others.

Case study

1.2 Types of abuse

Explain the types of abuse that are being demonstrated in these case studies and why.

1 Elm View is a 30-bedded care home for elderly people, many of whom are living with dementia. Some of the service users are unable to speak out and are not enabled to make choices. The agency has telephoned you and asked you to do a night shift there. You agree and your shift starts at 9pm. You are due to finish your shift at 7am. You are working with another care assistant and a senior care assistant. At 4.30am, the senior care assistant asks you to help her to wash and dress a service user. The service user is asleep. The senior carer turns on the bedroom light and starts to fill a bowl with water. She then starts to wash the service user and get her dressed. She goes on to get another service user up and asks for your help. She has got five people up and out of bed by the time the day shift comes on at 7am. The day shift staff is pleased with her because it has taken some of the pressure off them.

2 Emily has a learning disability as well as a physical impairment. She recently went into hospital to have a simple operation on one of her legs. When she was discharged home the physiotherapist gave strict instructions that she needed to be assisted to walk as much as possible and she also needed assistance to maintain a range of exercises. Four months later she is going into a home for respite while her parents have a break. She arrives at the home in a wheelchair and is unable to stand. It becomes apparent that her parents have not been assisting her to walk and they have not supported her to maintain the exercises. The hospital has indicated that Emily will probably never walk again.

Table 5.2 Types of abuse and possible signs and symptoms

Type of abuse	Possible signs	Possible symptoms
Physical abuse	Unexplained cuts, scratches, bite marks, bruises, burn marks, scalds and blisters, pressure ulcers, fractures or broken bones.	Fear, anger, loss of self-confidence and self-esteem, pain due to injuries, withdrawal.
Sexual abuse	Injuries to the mouth, injuries or bruises around the genital or breast area, bloodstained underwear, urinary tract and sexually transmitted infections, pregnancy, inability to develop normal sexual relationships, overtly sexual behaviour.	Fear, shame, guilt, loss of dignity and self-respect, withdrawal, pain due to injuries and infection.
Emotional/ psychological abuse	Unusual behaviour such as rocking backwards and forwards, mood disturbances, flinching, self-harm, comfort eating, tearfulness, aggression.	Embarrassment, fear, humiliation, resignation, loss of self-confidence, self-esteem and sense of belonging, withdrawal.
Financial abuse	Unexplained loss of money and personal possessions, missing receipts, insufficient money for bills, buying products that don't match ability to pay, care workers and carers benefiting from 'buy one get one free' offers when doing the shopping, dependency on others, diminishing health status due to reduced quality of life.	Anxiety about financial affairs and fears for the future, loss of independence and control.
Institutional abuse	Loss of interest in the environment and loss of ability to make choices or to act independently, loss of ability to communicate, loss of clothing and personal possessions, aggression.	Loss of independence and control over own life, anger, frustration, depression, despair, hopelessness.
Neglect and self-neglect	Dirty, smelly, under/overweight, poor health, poor living conditions, inadequate clothing, loss of interest, withdrawal.	Symptoms associated with poor health status, such as pain due to pressure ulcers, hunger, cold, loneliness.

AC 1.3 Describe factors that may contribute to an individual being more vulnerable to abuse

While any person could be a victim of abuse or harm, some **individuals** are more vulnerable than others. The Health & Social Care Information Centre (**HSCIC**) defines a vulnerable adult as 'a person who is or may be in need of community care services by reason of mental or other disability, age or illness; and who is or may be unable to take care of him or herself' (**www.hscic.gov.uk**).

Some of the individuals who are more vulnerable to harm or abuse include people:

- with **sensory impairments** or those who have difficulty communicating
- who lack capacity to understand what is happening
- who are severely disabled
- who rely on others for care
- who are unconscious

- who do not have good support networks around them
- who lack self-esteem.

Other factors that can also contribute to an individual being more vulnerable to abuse are:

- The physical environment – for example, a person's home or room may not be safe or it may be inadequately equipped, making it difficult for them to avoid self-neglect, or neglect by others.
- The social environment – for example, the person may not have a good support network and may socialise with people who are more likely to take advantage of their situation. Equally, if the person is isolated, this can increase the chance that abuse will go undetected.
- People who have dementia – for example, a person with increasing confusion or who may be prone to displaying violent episodes can lead to an increased risk of harm to the individual or others.
- A lack of sufficiently trained staff on duty – if staff are not trained in safeguarding, or if supervision is not sufficient, the risk of individuals being harmed or abused will increase. In addition, staff will be less likely to notice or suspect abuse, meaning that abuse may go unreported.

Figure 5.1 How do you reassure an individual when they feel vulnerable or upset?

Key terms

Individual will usually mean the person supported by the learner but may include those for whom there is no formal duty of care.

HSCIC is a government body providing information and data (statistics) to the health and social care commissioner's (those officials who ensure that the most appropriate and cost effective services are provided) and clinicians which include for example, doctors, researchers or managers of services.

A **sensory impairment** is when one of your senses – sight, hearing, smell, touch, taste and spatial awareness – is no longer normal. For example, if a person wears glasses they are said to have a visual impairment. If a person finds it hard to hear or wears a hearing aid then they are said to have a hearing impairment.

Evidence activity

1.3 Factors

In your own words, describe the factors that could lead to an individual being more vulnerable to abuse.

LO2 Know how to respond to suspected or alleged abuse

AC 2.1 Explain the actions to take if there are suspicions that an individual is being abused

Safeguarding adults and children is everybody's business and if you work in a health or social care environment you must know what to do if you suspect abuse or are faced with allegations of abuse. Everyone working in a health or social care environment has a duty of care to react appropriately when faced with suspicions or allegations of abuse.

Suspicions or allegations of abuse should never be ignored. The procedures that should be followed if abuse is suspected or alleged should be explained within your organisation's **safeguarding policy**. It is important that all staff are familiar with

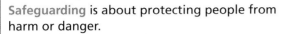

Key terms

Safeguarding is about protecting people from harm or danger.

Safeguarding policy sets out the steps that should be taken if abuse is suspected.

Evidence activity

2.1 Suspicions of abuse

It is important that you know what to do if you become suspicious that an individual might be being abused.

Access your workplace policy and read about the procedures you should follow if you suspect an individual is being abused. What are the actions you should take is there are suspicions that an individual is being abused?

Make a note of your findings.

the policy so that the correct procedure is followed if an individual is suspected as being at risk of abuse or harm. If you are unsure, you must check with your manager.

What to do if you suspect an individual is at risk of abuse

If you suspect an individual is at risk of abuse or harm, it is important that you do the following:

- Follow your organisation's adult safeguarding policy and procedures.
- Consider any immediate risks and actions that may be required to reduce or remove them.
- Report the facts immediately to an appropriate person – this may be your manager, or if you are the most senior person on duty, you may need to report the safeguarding concern directly to the local authority's adult safeguarding team. In some circumstances, you may also be required to contact the police.
- Maintain accurate records of your concerns and the actions that have been taken.
- Make a written account of the safeguarding alert.
- Make every effort to preserve any evidence of abuse.
- Request to be kept informed about whether the safeguarding alert has been substantiated and any actions that have been taken.

If your suspicions of abuse involve your manager or another member of staff in authority, you should talk things over with someone in a more senior position. You may need to take your concern to the Care Quality Commission (CQC). The CQC can be contacted anonymously at **www.cqc.org.uk**.

AC 2.2 Explain the actions to take if an individual alleges that they are being abused

Abuse may be alleged if the **victim** makes a **disclosure** that something has happened to them. It may also be alleged if a witness makes an accusation that abuse has taken place.

It takes a lot of courage for anyone to allege abuse because the person may fear reprisal, or they may worry that they may be blamed or that they will not be taken seriously. Your organisation will have a policy in place that should explain the procedure to be followed if an individual alleges they are being abused.

As a general rule, it is important that you:

- follow your organisation's safeguarding policy and procedures
- report the allegation to your manager or to your local safeguarding team
- listen to the individual and avoid making assumptions or judgements
- take the allegation seriously
- reassure the individual that they are right to disclose the information

Key terms

A **victim** is the person who has been abused.

A **disclosure** refers to when a person who has been abused tells somebody.

- never promise to keep things confidential – you have a duty of care to ensure the individual is not exposed to harm or abuse
- provide reassurance
- avoid asking lots of questions – resist the temptation to interview the person
- take steps to ensure the person's safety
- make every effort to preserve any evidence of abuse
- make notes and written reports about the facts that have been reported.

It does not matter whether the abuse is suspected or alleged – the forms, records and paperwork will be similar. Where your organisation's policies are stored depends on your organisation but typically they are stored on the company's intranet and are covered in your employee induction. These policies will detail the procedures that should be followed, but as a general rule you will usually be expected to complete the following documentation:

- an incident report form – this is a standard form to record what has happened, the date, time, location and who was involved
- a witness statement – this is the care worker's statement about what happened, what they saw, heard or were told.

Time to think

2.2 Your safeguarding policy

Access your organisation's safeguarding policy and make a note of the steps that should be taken if an individual is suspected of being abused or has alleged abuse has taken place.

Evidence activity

2.2 Actions to take

Explain in your own words the actions you should take if an individual tells you they are being abused.

AC 2.3 Identify ways to ensure that evidence of abuse is preserved

When abuse is suspected or alleged, it is vital that any potential evidence is preserved. This may be needed if an investigation takes place, and some evidence may be required in order to make a prosecution. The evidence may also be required in a court of law. Abuse is a crime, and evidence will be required in order to help secure convictions if the perpetrator is to be found guilty.

There are various types of evidence that may need to be preserved:

- **Direct evidence:** this is something that has been observed by a witness. It can be something they saw, heard, touched or physically felt – for example, a witness may be able to give a statement relating to what they saw; or the victim may give evidence about what the perpetrator did to them.
- **Forensic evidence:** this is evidence based on something that has been left at the scene where the abuse has taken place – for example, blood, hair, saliva or semen.
- **Primary evidence:** this is original, concrete evidence – for example, closed circuit television (CCTV) footage.
- **Secondary evidence:** this could be copies of original documentation – for example, copies of witness statements or incident reports.
- **Circumstantial evidence:** this is evidence that indicates a person might have committed the offence – for example, fingerprints at a scene or cash deposits made into a bank account that cannot be explained.

It is important that evidence is not tampered with and as much evidence is preserved as possible. This is especially important if sexual abuse is suspected. In order to preserve evidence it may be necessary to:

- advise the victim to avoid washing themselves or any clothing as there may be body fluids or hair that could be used as forensic evidence
- close the door and prevent people from waking through the area as this will help

to stop contamination of the area and will make it easier for the investigation team to collect and analyse forensic evidence

- refrain from cleaning the area
- prevent anyone other than the police from removing anything from the scene
- make available any documentation or CCTV footage
- ask any witnesses to wait to be interviewed by the police.

Figure 5.2 Evidence should be kept secure

Evidence activity

2.3 Evidence

Identify ways in which you would preserve evidence of abuse.

LO3 Understand the national and local context of safeguarding and protection from abuse

AC 3.1 Identify national policies and local systems that relate to safeguarding and protection from abuse

National policies set out the standards and procedures for the safeguarding and protection of adults in the UK.

Every Child Matters

Following the report into the death of Victoria Climbié, who was tortured and eventually killed by her great aunt and her partner, the government published the Green Paper 'Every Child Matters' (2003). This paper prompted wide consultation about services for children, young people and families. As a result, the government passed the Children Act in 2004, which provides the legislation for ensuring the safety and protection of children, young people and families.

'Every Child Matters' made it clear that professionals must work together to provide children's care. It is based on five outcomes, which local authorities use to put together their 'Children and Young People's Plans'. These plans describe how services are to be developed and delivered, and are used to measure success. One of these outcomes is that children 'stay safe', in other words, that they have security, stability and are cared for.

Key term

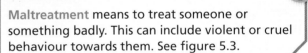

Maltreatment means to treat someone or something badly. This can include violent or cruel behaviour towards them. See figure 5.3.

Research and investigate

3.1 Policy and procedure

Locate your organisation's safeguarding policy, read it and make a note of the procedures that must be followed to ensure individuals are safeguarded and protected from abuse. Think about how this local policy fits in with national policies such as No Secrets and Every Child Matters.

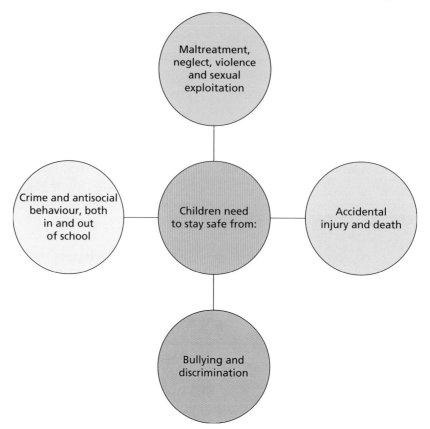

Figure 5.3 Safeguarding children

Working together to safeguard children

In March 2010, the government published the guidance document 'Working Together to Safeguard Children'. This document describes the roles of the different agencies that are involved in safeguarding and **protecting** children and young people, including:

- **public sector organisations** such as health care providers, police, probation services, youth offending teams, schools, early years services, Children and Family Court Advisory and Support Service (Cafcass) and the UK Border Agency (UKBA)
- **voluntary sector organisations**, such as the NSPCC and Barnardo's
- parents, carers and faith communities.

Key terms

Protecting means to keep someone or something safe from harm, abuse or injury.

Public sector organisations are supported financially and controlled by the government or local government. These can include the NHS and Local Authorities for example and aim to offer public services.

Voluntary sector organisations are not for profit organisations that are not run by the government and aim to provide services not necessarily for money. These can also include charities and charitable organisations.

Children's Trusts consist of all the agencies working to safeguard and protect children within a locality. Children's Trust Boards oversee the multi-agency working agreements made between the different agencies.

Local Safeguarding Children Boards (LSCBs) have a legal responsibility to agree how agencies will work together in implementing the local 'Children and Young People's Plans' in practice.

No Secrets

The prevention of abuse of adults has not always been high on the adult safeguarding agenda. The publication of 'No Secrets: Guidance on developing and implementing **multi-agency** policies and procedures to protect vulnerable adults from abuse' in 2000 was a landmark in setting up a framework for adult safeguarding. It emphasised the importance of multi-agency working and established that local authorities should lead adult safeguarding. Its agenda was set largely by the incidents of serious abuse revealed over the previous decade, resulting in a focus on ensuring that agencies be alert to the signs of abuse taking place and that they respond appropriately.

Statement of Government Policy on Adult Safeguarding

Another document known as the 'Statement of Government Policy on Adult Safeguarding' was produced by the Department of Health in May 2011. It provides information about principles that are used by government agencies, including local authorities, housing departments, health agencies and the police force. It sets out the government's policy objective to prevent abuse and reduce the risk of significant harm to vulnerable adults from abuse and other types of exploitation. It supports individuals in maintaining control over their lives and making informed choices.

Adult Safeguarding Boards

The safeguarding and protection of vulnerable adults is part of the safeguarding adults agenda at both a national and a local level. Local authorities now have Adult Safeguarding Boards and these boards are responsible for delivering a multi-agency approach to safeguarding adults and ensuring all partner agencies are recognising and acting on safeguarding issues both at a strategic level and on an individual level. This means that local authorities, the police and NHS agencies involved with adults who might be at risk of abuse have a responsibility to ensure they have systems in place that encourage the reporting of suspected abuse, and they also take action to stop the abuse.

The systems aimed at protecting individuals from abuse work in a variety of ways – for example through:

- screening people who work with children and vulnerable adults
- raising awareness and providing education on safeguarding and prevention of harm
- reviewing and developing policies to improve safeguarding and protection
- regulating health and social care providers, monitoring standards of care and undertaking inspections.

Disclosing and Barring Service (DBS)

Every person working in health or social care must complete a criminal record check by the Disclosure and Barring Service. The DBS helps employers to make safer recruitment decisions and prevent unsuitable people from working with vulnerable adults and children.

The DBS conducts searches through police records and, in relevant cases, barred list information, then issues a DBS certificate to the applicant and their potential employer to ensure a suitable recruitment decision is made.

Safeguarding Vulnerable Adults Policy

The Office of the Public Guardian (OPG) issued this national policy in 2008. It deals with multi-agency arrangements to prevent, identify and deal with abuse. The main responsibility for safeguarding rests with local authorities, and this policy gives national guidelines and standards for them to follow. The OPG national policy sets out guidelines about, for example, the meaning of abuse, who may be an abuser, the role of the Public Guardian and how to involve external agencies.

Key term

Multi-agency working is when organisations cooperate or work together to provide services or support through multi-agency protection (which can include social care, the police, NHS, and trading standards).

Local systems

At a local level, the main responsibility for safeguarding and protecting vulnerable adults will always rest with local authorities. There are various agencies, departments and organisations that are involved with safeguarding at a local level, and they work together to protect vulnerable adults. Each local authority must have an Adult Safeguarding Board for the protection of vulnerable adults. The Board is responsible for setting out and implementing policies and procedures, identifying and protecting those at risk, and ensuring each appropriate responses to abuse are maintained. We will look at the role of the Adult Safeguarding Board in the next section.

Evidence activity

3.1 National and local policies

Identify the national and the local policies that influence safeguarding in your area of work.

AC 3.2 Explain the roles of different agencies in safeguarding and protecting individuals from abuse

At a national level, there are many government departments and agencies, charities, companies and other organisations that are concerned with the safeguarding and protection of vulnerable adults. These include:

- local authorities – county, city or borough councils
- the Department of Health (DoH)
- the Care Quality Commission (CQC)
- Office of the Public Guardian (OPG)
- Action on Elder Abuse (AEA)
- Equal Human Rights Commission (EHRC)
- Disclosure and Barring Service (DBS)
- National Health Service (NHS).

Here are a few more details about some of the organisations mentioned.

Local authorities

The welfare and protection of vulnerable adults is primarily the responsibility of each and every local authority working in partnership with other public agencies, the voluntary sector, service users and contracted services. Throughout the UK, councils have social services departments. They are the main agencies involved in safeguarding and protecting individuals from abuse. Some councils have special departments for adult safeguarding.

Local councils co-ordinate and promote safeguarding by working with their own social care team and other agencies in the local area. This information should be available on the website of each local council. Names of agencies, organisations, government initiatives, reports and policies change quite often, but it should be possible to access up-to-date procedures.

Safeguarding Adults Boards bring together all individuals and representatives from various local agencies to work in partnership and develop best practice to safeguard vulnerable adults. Although the main responsibility rests with local authorities, there are many agencies involved with safeguarding and protecting individuals from abuse.

Department of Health

The Department of Health is the UK government department that deals with all aspects of health and social care. It works with other agencies and bodies, such as the CQC, to develop and enforce legislation and policies.

For more information go to **www.dh.gov.uk**

Care Quality Commission

The CQC is the governing body that regulates all health and social care services in England, including services provided by the NHS, local authorities, private companies and voluntary organisations. These include hospitals, hospices, nursing homes, care homes, home care services, dentists and other specialist health and social care services.

As part of its regulatory activities the CQC monitors and acts upon safeguarding concerns that are reported to it. It also raises safeguarding alerts to the relevant local authority if it unveils safeguarding concerns through its intelligent monitoring or regulation of services.

For more information go to **www.cqc.org.uk**

Police

Adult protection investigators and all police officers are responsible for protecting life and preventing crime. The police could, for example, respond to alerts about abuse, oversee investigations and work in partnership with other agencies.

Office of the Public Guardian (OPG)

The OPG deals with vulnerable adults who are covered by the Court of Protection. This court of protection deals with the affairs of people who cannot longer make their own decisions. Some people set up a power of attorney so that they can nominate someone to look after their affairs if they become unable to make decisions in the future. The Court of Protection registers and monitors powers of attorney and can also appoint a deputy to look after a vulnerable person's affairs.

Action on Elder Abuse (AEA)

This is a charity that works to protect older vulnerable adults across all of the UK. The members of this charity are service providers, regulators, policy makers, academics and members of the public. AEA works to raise awareness, promote education, and share research and information.

For more information go to **www.elderabuse.org.uk**

AC 3.3 Identify reports into serious failures to protect individuals from abuse

Abuse may be perpetrated by carers, care workers, including professional staff and personal assistants, people who deliberately exploit vulnerable people, friends, neighbours and strangers. Abuse can take place anywhere and in any context.

Unfortunately, safeguarding systems do not always protect vulnerable adults and children. Many incidents of abuse are not acknowledged, recognised or reported and will never be known. Sometimes, allegations and suspicions of abuse come out years afterwards, making it difficult to investigate and take action against the perpetrators.

In cases where suspected abuse or neglect has resulted in death, or abuse or neglect is known or suspected to be a factor in the death (including death by suspected suicide), or for cases of serious and significant harm, a **Serious Case Review (SCR)** will be undertaken.

Failure to protect vulnerable people from abuse is frequently reported in the media. You may have heard of some cases being reported by the press, such as the failings:

- at Staffordshire hospital
- at Winterbourne View
- that led to the death of Daniel Pelka.

> ### Key term
>
> A Serious Case Review (SCR) is a process for all partner agencies to identify the lessons that can be learned from potentially serious or complex safeguarding cases.

> ### Research and investigate
>
> **3.3** Serious failures
>
> Using any resources available to you, find out about an area where there have been serious failings in care. Make a note of what the failings were.
>
> What types of abuse were uncovered?
>
> What actions were taken and did people respond the way they should have done?

> ### Evidence activity
>
> **3.3** Serious failures
>
> Undertake a piece of research using any resources that are available to you.
>
> Identify one report into a serious failure to protect people from abuse within the sector you work. This could be child care, adult social care, health care or primary medical services such as a doctors' surgery or dental care.

AC 3.4 Identify sources of information and advice about own role in safeguarding and protecting individuals from abuse

As mentioned previously, safeguarding is everyone's responsibility. It is therefore everyone's responsibility to keep service users safe from abuse and harm. You must never assume that somebody else will recognise and report what you have seen or heard.

Abuse can result in serious physical and mental health problems, and in some cases it can even lead to death. It is therefore essential that you are aware of how you can access information and advice about your own role in safeguarding and protecting individuals from abuse. The following is not a complete list, but it will give you an idea of some of the sources of information that are available to you:

- your organisation's policies and procedures
- your job description and work contract
- supervisors and managers
- work colleagues, including designated safeguarding officers
- the CQC
- professional body codes of practice
- training resources
- specialist books and journals
- **Skills for Care**
- Health and Care Professions Council (HCPC)
- national telephone helplines and websites
- specialist books and journals
- service users
- legislation
- guidance documents
- leaflets.

> ### Key term
>
>
>
> Skills for Care is an independent registered charity working with adult social care employers to set the standards and qualifications. This is to ensure social care workers have the skills and knowledge needed to deliver high standards of care to people who use services and their carers.

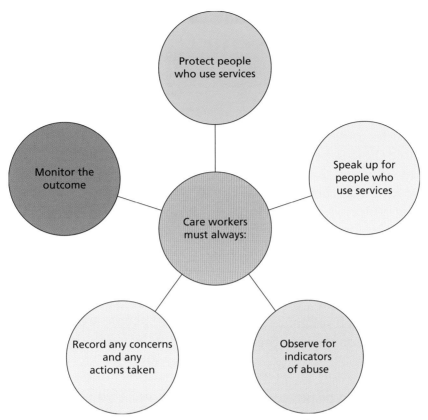

Figure 5.4 Your role in safeguarding

Evidence activity

3.4 Sources of information and advice

Identify all of the sources you could use within your area of work to help you find out what you should do to protect people from abuse.

Key terms

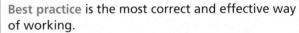

Best practice is the most correct and effective way of working.

Standards of care are the most accepted and correct ways of providing care in a health or social care environment.

LO4 Understand ways to reduce the likelihood of abuse

AC 4.1 Explain how the likelihood of abuse may be reduced by:

- working with person-centred values
- encouraging active participation
- promoting choice and rights

There are a number of ways in which the likelihood of abuse can be reduced. **Best practice** and **standards of care** are focused on addressing individual service users' needs, wishes and preferences, supporting their rights and promoting their well-being and independence. We will now consider how these approaches to care can help to safeguard individuals and to reduce the likelihood of harm and abuse occurring.

Person-centred values

Person-centred care is based on the understanding that each person is an individual with a unique history, and with their own needs, wishes and preferences. Having a strong working relationship with the individuals we are supporting can help us to understand and focus on these person-centred values and reduce the likelihood of abuse. (See unit HSC 026 for more information). For example, we can use person-centred values to promote:

- individuality – to help each person feel positive about being different and individual; to feel confident about themselves and their own preferences
- rights and choice – by understanding their rights and possible choices, people have a framework for making decisions
- privacy – by knowing that each person's privacy should be protected, the individual can assert their right to privacy if they feel uncomfortable; they can also appreciate other people's need for privacy
- independence – by gaining confidence from doing things on their own, an individual can be more self-reliant and not depend on others so much, making them less vulnerable
- dignity and respect – by being aware that dignity and respect should be protected, an individual can insist that they are given respect by others, and preserve their own dignity whenever possible
- partnership – by seeing themselves as an active partner, the individual can feel more confident if a situation arises that makes them feel undermined by someone.

Active participation

Active participation is a way of working that recognises an individual's right to participate in the activities and relationships of everyday life as independently as possible; the individual is regarded as an active partner in their own care or support, rather than a **passive recipient**. This can support safeguarding from abuse when:

- participating in activities and relationships in everyday life – by increasing the individual's self-confidence and belief that they can do things for themselves and have normal relationships where possible
- being as independent as possible – by doing more for themselves, people are less likely to think of themselves as dependent victims and passive receivers of care

- by engaging in active participation – the chances of being abused reduce because the individual feels more engaged socially, mentally and physically. This improves self-belief and creates a sense of achievement, determination and confidence in their own decisions and preferences, making them more likely to resist something that makes them feel uncomfortable, or to speak up about it.

Promoting choice and rights

By ensuring that each individual's rights and choices are protected and promoted, the care team can help reduce the chances of abuse occurring.

Where people are able to make decisions, they should be supported to do so. If an individual lacks the capacity to promote their own rights and choices, care staff must ensure the individual's choices and rights are protected. Vulnerable adults with physical or mental impairments and disabilities may need more support and intervention to protect their rights and choices. Identifying the individuals who are more at risk is crucial so that appropriate support can be provided.

Key term

A **passive recipient** is someone who receives treatment without an active response.

Figure 5.5 How do you encourage active participation in physical well-being?

Time to think

4.1 Your conduct

Think about the way you conduct yourself at work. Make a note of the actions you personally take to:

- work with person-centred values
- encourage active participation
- promote choice and rights.

Evidence activity

4.1 Reducing likelihood of abuse

Explain using your own words how the likelihood of abuse may be reduced by:

- working with person-centred values
- encouraging active participation
- promoting a person's choices and rights.

AC 4.2 Explain the importance of an accessible complaints procedure for reducing the likelihood of abuse

Because abuse is a violation of **civil** and **human rights**, it must be taken very seriously in order that individuals can be protected. An accessible complaints procedure is an essential part of providing a framework to safeguard and protect adults who are vulnerable to abuse.

Key terms

Civil rights are the rights that all people in a country have.

Human rights are the rights that all human beings are entitled to.

Evidence activity

4.2 Accessible complaints procedure

Explain how an accessible complaints procedure can reduce the likelihood of abuse occurring.

Complaints procedures will be laid down in your employer's policies and procedures. Complaints procedures must also be accessible to service users, their friends, family and informal carers.

This means that they must:

- be publicised and easy to access
- be clear and understandable
- be published in a range of different formats and languages, taking into account the person's age, understanding, ability and communication needs
- ensure confidentiality
- ensure that complaints will be listened to and taken seriously
- ensure that complainants will be treated with fairness, honesty and respect
- reassure complainants that they will receive appropriate support while their complaint is being investigated.

LO5 Know how to recognise and report unsafe practices

AC 5.1 Describe unsafe practices that may affect the well-being of individuals

It is important within your role as a health or social care worker that you are able to recognise and report unsafe working practices that could impact on the well-being of service users. Unsafe practices can even lead to institutional abuse, or other types of abuse such as physical or emotional abuse.

Unsafe, abusive working practices that could affect the well-being of service users include:

- poor working practices
- resource difficulties
- operational difficulties.

Poor working practices may affect the well-being of individuals. **It is therefore essential that health or social care staff should NOT:**

- ignore abuse by believing that poor practices are acceptable
- intentionally or unintentionally ignore the organisation's policies and procedures
- use unsafe moving and handling techniques when supporting service users
- use poor hygiene practices, for example not washing hands between tasks leading to an increased risk of spreading infections
- misuse medication, for example by hiding medication in food or giving medication to control or sedate a person
- ignore the health and social needs of service users
- deprive service users of sufficient/adequate food or drink, or not assist a person to eat and drink when this help is required
- deprive a person of using the toilet when they need to go, or leave them in wet or soiled clothing or bedding
- use inappropriate restraint, such as tying a person to a chair or bed
- dismiss service user's right to be treated with dignity and respect, for example not promoting privacy when a person is washing and dressing or using the toilet force people to do things they do not want to do, for example eating or going to bed when they are not ready
- control people and not enable them to make decisions
- abandon people or isolate them
- use crude or unacceptably explicit language.

Resource difficulties that may affect the well-being of individuals include things such as:

- not having enough staff on shift to provide safe and adequate care
- staff not being trained appropriately
- too many inexperienced staff – who may not realise that abuse can occur unintentionally in certain situations
- individuals being isolated too often – at home or in a residential setting

- staff rushing through care tasks due to lack of time
- **inadequate equipment/resources** – such as moving and handling equipment (see page 89 for definition).
- lack of facilities and activities – leading to insufficient mental stimulation, or buildings or facilities that are not fit for purpose – making it harder to provide a high standard of care and support.

Operational difficulties that may affect the well-being of individuals include issues such as:

- staff absences – meaning that tasks need to be covered by colleagues or unfamiliar agency workers
- inadequate policies and procedures in place
- inadequate monitoring and training of staff
- inadequate systems for multi-agency communication
- poor documentation and inadequate records, so that patterns of potential abuse are harder to spot
- inadequate systems for preventative action and dealing with complaints
- financial issues affecting policies, staffing levels, etc.

If unsafe practices have been identified, it is essential that prompt action is taken. It might be 'the tip of the iceberg' and if it is left unreported, and the practice is allowed to continue, it could eventually affect the overall physical and mental well-being of service users. Some unsafe practices may not be intentional, but these practices amount to neglect and neglect is also a form of abuse, so prompt action is an important part of your role.

Evidence activity

5.1 Unsafe practices

Describe any unsafe practices that could impact on a person's well-being.

AC 5.2 Explain the actions to take if unsafe practices have been identified

Health and social care providers have a duty of care to ensure that their employees use safe practices and help them to improve their performance. They must also have systems in place to enable staff to report unsafe practices, inadequate resources or operational difficulties that could impact on the delivery of safe and effective care.

Early action is important. When unsafe practices have been identified, staff can, for example:

● report the matter to the person in charge, manager or supervisor as soon as possible
● report unsafe practices to others in the organisation in accordance with the organisation's policies and procedures
● ensure that their own skills and knowledge are up to date and that they are following principles of best practice
● ensure that they are following policies and procedures correctly.

Key terms

Inadequate equipment/resources relates to not enough or insufficient staff or physical resources within the workplace.

Operational difficulties relate to the difficulties within the organisation such as lack of policies.

Evidence activity

5.2 Actions to take

Explain to another person the procedure you should follow if you witness any unsafe practices within your area of work.

AC 5.3 Describe the action to take if suspected abuse or unsafe practices have been reported but nothing has been done in response

If suspected abuse or unsafe practices have been reported but no action has been taken,

it is important that the concerns are escalated to the next level within the organisation. For example, if the original complaint was made to a supervisor and no action has been taken, the next stage would be to report the matter to the manager. Depending on the level at which the concern has been reported, the next level could also include reporting to:

● social workers or other health professionals who are involved with the care and support of the individual
● the CQC
● the police.

Reporting or disclosing abusive or negligent behaviour in the interest of the individuals you work with is known as 'whistle-blowing'. The Public Interest Disclosure Act 1998 protects workers who 'blow the whistle' from victimisation by their manager or employer, providing they follow the correct procedures. Therefore, you are protected as a whistle-blower if you:

● are a 'worker'
● believe that malpractice is happening at work, has happened in the past or will happen in the future
● disclose information of the right type
● disclose to the right person and in the right way (making a **'protected disclosure'**).

It is acceptable to 'whistle-blow' if action is needed. For example, stopping the abuse at the Winterbourne View care home needed people to persist in their complaints when the initial reports were not believed.

Key term

The aim of **protected disclosure** is to encourage people to report bad practice in the workplace.

Evidence activity

5.3 Action to take

Think about and explain the action you should take if you have reported unsafe practices to your manager but nothing has been done.

Legislation

Health and Social Care Act 2008

Safeguarding Vulnerable Groups Act 2006

Mental Capacity Act 2005

The Equality Act 2010

The Public Interest Disclosure Act 1998

The Children Act 2004

Useful resources

Websites

Social Care Institute for Excellence
www.scie.org.uk

Care Quality Commission
www.cqc.org.uk

Action on Elder Abuse
www.elderabuse.org.uk

National Dignity Council
www.dignityincare.org.uk

The Health and Social Care Information
Centre (HSCIC)
www.hscic.gov.uk

Statement of Government Policy on Adult
Safeguarding
www.gov.uk/government/publications/adult-safeguarding-statement-of-government-policy

Unit HSC 025

The role of the health and social care worker

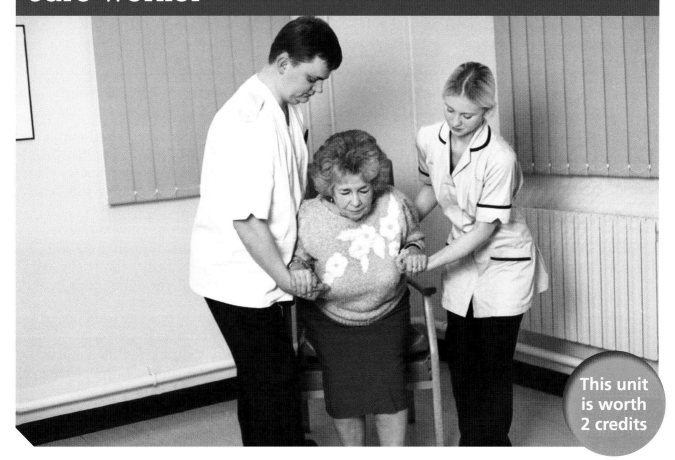

This unit is worth 2 credits

What are you finding out?

As a health or social care worker you will have a range of responsibilities, and the way in which you undertake your role can have an impact on the well-being of service users. It is therefore important that you work in professional ways that are expected by your employer. It is also important to be aware of the responsibilities of working in partnership with other agencies and recognise the boundaries of your role when providing support for people using services. This unit will help you to develop and

demonstrate your knowledge about the professional role of the health and social care worker.

By the end of this unit you will:

1 Understand working relationships in health and social care
2 Be able to work in ways that are agreed with the employer
3 Be able to work in partnership with others.

Links to Level 2 Certificate in Preparing to Work in Adult Social Care

HSC 025 Assessment Criteria	Unit PWCS25
AC1.1	AC1.1
AC1.2	AC1.2
AC2.1	AC2.1
AC3.1	AC3.1
AC3.3	AC3.3

LO1 Understand working relationships in health and social care

AC 1.1 Explain how a working relationship is different from a personal relationship

Many people have differing relationships with different people who mean different things to them in their life. Relationships can range from family relationships to professional relationships. Every relationship we have is important and is essential to contributing to our well-being. However, different relationships have different boundaries. We will look at these relationships in a little more detail here.

Personal relationships

Relationships are probably the most involved and emotionally charged area of our lives. From the moment we are born we form relationships, each one requiring something different from us and giving us something different in return. We learn to identify people we like and don't like. We learn that we need to relate differently to different people; that some relationships are satisfying and rewarding while others are not. However, relationships are a basic human need and something that the majority of us strive to develop and maintain throughout our lives.

All relationships involve some level of **interdependence**. People in **personal relationships**, for example family members, friends, sexual and business partners, tend to influence each other, share personal and sometimes intimate thoughts and feelings, engage in activities together, and give and take emotional, physical and financial support. Because of this interdependence, things that impact on one member of the relationship will also impact on the other.

According to psychologist George Levinger, the natural development of a personal relationship follows four or five stages:

Time to think

1.1 Different relationships

Think about the different sorts of relationships you have in your life and make a note of them.

Now make a note of the differences between the relationships.

Key terms

Interdependence means dependence between two or more people.

Personal relationships refer to close connections between people, formed by emotional bonds and interactions.

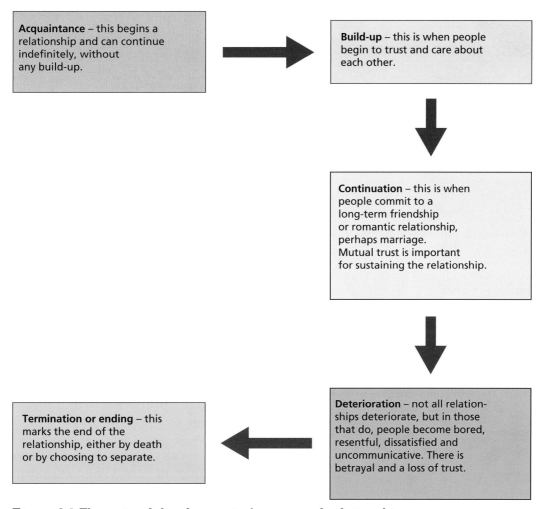

Figure 6.1 The natural development of a personal relationship

Working relationships

When a personal relationship ends for whatever reason, we say it has lost its **integrity**. Similarly, because it is unthinkable that users of health and social care services should lose their trust in and feel betrayed by workers on whom they depend, best practice in a health and social care setting is built on the integrity of **working relationships** (see page 94 for definition).

Figure 6.2 It is important to create meaningful relationships

Key terms

Integrity is the quality of being honest, credible and trusting.

Working relationships are ones that are formed with a colleague or an employee.

Professionalism is built on values, attitudes and behaviours that underpin best practice and help shape positive outcomes for service users.

Working relationships in health and social care settings are built on **professionalism**. Professionalism is built on a set of values, attitudes and behaviours that underpin best practice and help shape positive outcomes for the service users you support and the individuals you work with.

Meaningful relationships

While it is not appropriate to make personal disclosures in a professional working relationship, some individuals you support may need to relax in your company, especially if you help them with personal care needs. Letting work relationships become more personal does not mean you need to disclose personal things about yourself or ask personal questions. However, mentioning holiday plans, remembering birthdays and asking after grandchildren, for example, can create a more meaningful relationship, which helps you get to know each other better. This makes working together easier and more person-centred. It also shows that you are approachable and that you are human.

Effective work relationships are based on principles of care. When supporting individuals you should:

- show respect for their beliefs, opinions, life experiences and social, cultural and ethnic backgrounds
- shape the way you work around their wishes, expectations and preferences
- support their rights to dignity, choice, privacy, independence, equality and fair treatment, risk taking, protection from harm, confidentiality, communication using a method of their choice, and care that meets their specific needs.

You have a professional duty of care to the individuals you support that is different to the relationships you have with your friends and family. Your role is to guide and support individuals and to help them to live as independently as possible. You should listen to them carefully and never put pressure on them.

These are some of the ways that you can maintain professional boundaries:

- Be reliable and dependable.
- Do not form inappropriate intimate or personal relationships with individuals.
- Promote individuals' independence and protect them as far as possible from harm.
- Do not accept expensive gifts or money from individuals or their family members.
- Be honest and trustworthy.
- Comply with policies and procedures or agreed ways of working stated by your employer.
- Co-operate with colleagues and treat them with respect.
- Do not discriminate against people.
- Maintain clear and accurate records.
- Continue to improve your knowledge and skills.
- Respect confidential information and know when it is appropriate to share.
- Report any concerns you may have to your manager or a more senior colleague.

The difference between a working relationship and a personal relationship

So we can see there are significant differences between working relationships and personal relationships. A working relationship is different because of:

- professional codes of conduct
- boundaries
- policies and procedures
- the nature of the relationship.

In a working relationship there are clear reasons why that relationship exists, for example a person may need support for their health or social care requirements. The way in which service users are supported will be determined by their support or care plan and you will be required to work within the boundaries of your code of practice and policies and procedures within your organisation. You will also have a working relationship with colleagues and other health care professionals.

Professional relationships have clear boundaries that must never be crossed. For example, health and social care workers should never invite a person they support to their home, nor should they visit them in a social capacity. They should not accept personal gifts or give personal gifts to people using their services. However, the team as a whole may choose to give gifts to service users, for example on birthdays. If you are unsure about giving or receiving gifts within your place of work you should seek guidance from a senior member of staff or your manager.

We have to work within codes of conduct and standards set out by regulators such as the **Care Quality Commission** (see page 96 for definition). These spell out the way in which working and professional relationships should be conducted.

In contrast, there is no written code of conduct for personal relationships such as friendships and family relationships. We each have our own standards and moral codes, but within our personal relationships these are not monitored or inspected by a regulator, nor are they a requirement for maintaining a professional position.

In general, professional or working relationships are one way, in which we do not expect anything back from the people we support. The benefits come in job satisfaction and not in personal friendship or support as well as being paid for the care they provide as a health and social care worker.

Evidence activity

1.1 **Relationships**

Use the following table to compare aspects of the relationships you have with a friend and someone you support and care for at work.

Behaviours	My friend	The person I support at work	Reasons for the differences in my behaviour
How I communicate with this person:			
How I show respect for this person:			
What I tell this person about me:			
What I ask this person about:			
What this person and I do together:			

Key term

The Care Quality Commission regulate all health and social care services in England.

AC 1.2 Describe different working relationships in health and social care settings

Everything we do as health or social care workers involves joint working or partnership working with individuals within the workplace and with people from other agencies. This is also known as **inter-agency** working. As a result, every person who works in health or social care is required to develop working relationships with:

- service users
- the carers, family, friends and advocates of service users
- colleagues, managers and other members of the multidisciplinary team
- professionals from other agencies such as doctors, nurses and social workers
- voluntary organisations including faith groups, and voluntary workers including members of support groups
- regulators, manufacturers and suppliers of equipment, and maintenance and repair personnel.

Key term

Inter-agency working is a term used to explain the joined-up working of different health and social care professionals.

So we can see, within any health or social care setting there will be a requirement to build relationships with many different people. Teams of workers take time to bond and work well. Some teams work better than others. Team members come and go and all of this can have a positive or a negative effect on team work. Not all team members will have the same views on how care should be delivered, and the success of the team work you experience will depend on the direction that is given by management.

Each of these relationships will have different requirements of you, but in general you will need to be:

- a clear verbal and written communicator
- courteous, reliable, trustworthy, responsible, co-operative, well organised and a good time-keeper
- able to get on with others, use your initiative and work under pressure
- able to take, follow and give instructions
- willing to learn new skills and develop your understanding.

It is worth mentioning here that the general public is very much dependent on professional working relationships for their own and their loved ones' support and care. Health and social care workers are therefore perceived to be in a working relationship with the public. Unfortunately, events continue to undermine public trust in health and social care services. You therefore have a responsibility to behave, both at work and outside, in such a way as to develop and maintain public trust and confidence in the profession.

LO2 Be able to work in ways that are agreed with the employer

AC 2.1 Describe why it is important to adhere to the agreed scope of the job role

Understanding the importance of working within the boundaries of your job role is vital. There are many different roles within health and social care, so it is important that you have a **job description** that clearly spells out the boundaries of your role. Your manager should be able to guide you as to where you can access your job description.

The scope of your job role is made up from the different tasks or activities that you need to carry out to get your job done and this should be explained within your job description. This job description will form part of your contract and should explain to you:

- the responsibilities of your job role
- where you will undertake your role
- who you will report to
- any staff that will report to you
- your rate of pay
- the hours you will work.

Recognising boundaries

Your job description (the scope of your job role) should also clarify what you must not do. This could include activities for which you have yet to be trained; activities that you are not capable of doing. These could be due to your health status or lack of seniority or experience; or activities that your age, gender and understanding

> **Evidence activity**
>
> **1.2 Different working relationships**
> Think about all the working relationships in which you are involved, identify the people you work with and describe the personal qualities and skills expected of you in your role as a partner.

> **Key term**
>
> A **job description** generally includes information about the duties, purpose, responsibilities, scope and working conditions of a job, as well as the name and designation of the person to whom an employee reports to.

Research and Investigate

2.1 Scope of the job role

Think about your current job role. Make a note of any tasks that you are not permitted to undertake within this role.

prevent you from carrying out, such as helping someone of the opposite gender with personal care needs. If you step outside of the boundaries that have been set by your job description, you could run the risk of putting the health, safety and emotional well-being of service users, yourself and/or your colleagues at risk.

Performance management

Your personal objectives will be used to measure your performance, so it is important that you are consulted by your line manager about what is expected of you. Informal supervision, such as **observation**, enables your supervisor to identify your strengths any opportunities for further development and to chat with you about your performance. Formal supervision, such as appraisals and one to one meetings, give you an opportunity to resolve any areas for improvement. This is done by discussing any concerns and suggestions you have regarding:

- your understanding and performance
- improving your learning and performance
- adapting activities to make them more successful
- situations you find difficult to handle
- personal, resource and operational difficulties that impact on your performance.

The main purpose of appraisal is to give the worker whose appraisal it is, the opportunity to reflect on their work and learning needs in order to improve their

performance. A one-to-one meeting is a supportive meeting that takes place between an employee and their line manager.

The aim of supervision is to reach a **mutual agreement** about the scope of your job role. You should come away with a clear understanding of what you can and cannot do, an improved understanding of your work activities and how you can improve your performance, and an updated **continuous professional development (CPD)** plan that describes your learning and performance needs and how and when they will be met.

Figure 6.3 Your appraisal should reflect your learning needs

Key terms

Observations mean when you watch or view someone at work, and these usually take place to assess and give feedback on practical skills.

A **mutual agreement** is an agreement that is reached and agreed by all parties.

Continuing professional development or **CPD** refers to the process of tracking and documenting the skills, knowledge and experience an employee gains through their work, beyond any initial training.

2.1 Agreed scope of the job

- Make a list of all the activities where you have a responsibility.
- Make a note of the purpose of each activity.
- Explain what could happen if you failed to carry out these activities as required.
- Make a note of any activities that you are not allowed to undertake.
- Explain why you are not allowed to undertake these activities.
- Explain what could happen if you carried out these activities.

AC 2.2 Access full and up-to-date details of agreed ways of working

Your job description sets out what is required of you in your work role, but the way in which you are to undertake certain aspects of your job is set out in your organisation's policies and procedures. Workplace policies set out the arrangements that a workplace has for complying with legislation. For example, in order to comply with the Health and Safety (First Aid) Regulations 1981, every workplace should have a policy that describes how it manages first aid.

You will also come across procedures within your place of work. Procedures describe the ways of working that need to be followed for policies to be applied. The procedures set out the finer details of how to carry out the day-to-day activities. They record who does what, when and how in order to maintain health, safety and well-being at all times. For example, first aid procedures describe the roles of **first aiders**, the people responsible for maintaining first aid equipment and facilities, when and how to call the **emergency services**, and when and how to complete an **accident report form**.

Key terms

First aiders are people who have been trained to provide first aid.

Emergency services include police, ambulance and fire services.

Accident report form is a form on which accidents are recorded.

All workplaces have procedures and agreed ways of working in place to ensure that work practice conforms to a vast array of legislation. Because health and social care settings vary in the type of work they do, their procedures and agreed ways of working will also vary. However, in general, health and social care settings have procedures and agreed ways of working that address:

- safeguarding and protection
- equal opportunities
- confidentiality
- record keeping
- medicines administration
- first aid
- concerns and complaints
- missing persons
- emergency evacuation.

It is a legal requirement that you follow procedures and agreed ways of working. They promote and maintain safe work practice and failure to follow them could put people at risk of avoidable harm. Failure to follow procedures could also put the organisation's reputation at risk; you could also lose your job.

Workplace procedures and agreed ways of working are usually stored centrally on the company's computer system, where they can be easily accessed by any employee who needs to look at them.

Policies and procedures must be reviewed regularly and updated where necessary, for example because of changes in legislation.

2.2 Agreed ways of working

This activity requires you to access full and up-to-date details of agreed ways of working. In order to demonstrate that you can do this, answer the following questions:

- Where does your organisation store policies, procedures and agreed ways of working?
- Identify three activities that you carry out on a regular basis. For each activity you have identified, access the procedure or agreed way of working documents used in your place of work and make a note of the main points. Does this reflect the way in which you carry out the procedure? What could be a consequence of not following this procedure?
- Explain how you would know if the procedure or agreed way of working was up to date.

Updates to agreed ways of working are also made in response to changes in the condition and needs of the individuals you support. This ensures that care needs continue to be met appropriately.

AC 2.3 Implement agreed ways of working

Policies and procedures set out the agreed ways of working and how your employer requires you to work. They should be written to incorporate various pieces of legislation and should also be written in line with best practice guidelines. They are there to benefit and protect every person within your workplace, including employees, service users and the employer. They provide the basis for staff to provide a good quality of service within a legal framework and also to keep everyone in the workplace safe from harm. It is therefore essential that all health or social care workers implement these agreed ways of working within the workplace.

Here are **ten top tips** for implementing procedures and agreed ways of working.

1 Carry out a procedure or agreed way of working only if it is included in the scope of your job role and you have had the relevant training.
2 Make sure you know and understand what you have to do before you start working. If there is anything you don't understand, ask for help.
3 If you identify operational problems, such as being short staffed, or problems with resources, such as faulty equipment, tell the appropriate person and do not proceed until you are confident that the problem has been solved.
4 Constantly monitor the activity for hazards. If anything happens that could put health, safety and well-being at risk, stop working and get help.
5 If the activity provides care and support to an individual, give them clear and accurate information about what you have to do and encourage them to work with you.
6 If the activity involves team work, accept and follow the team leader's instructions. If you are the team leader, give clear, authoritative instructions.
7 Take responsibility for your own actions and those of the people to whom you give directions.
8 Accept responsibility for and learn from your mistakes so that you don't repeat them.
9 Accept and use feedback from others to enable you to improve your understanding and performance.
10 Report and record any problems with the activity and be prepared to suggest how the activity could be improved.

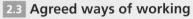

Time to think

2.3 Agreed ways of working

Look at the list of 'Ten top tips for implementing procedures and agreed ways of working'. Can you honestly say you bear each of them in mind when carrying out your activities?

Are there any top tips you would add to the list?

Evidence activity

2.3 Implement agreed ways of working

Ask for supervision as you carry out your activities and for feedback regarding how well you perform.

Keep a diary to show how you are developing professionally. The entries you make will be useful for appraisals and for completing your CPD plan – the document in which you record your learning and performance needs and how and when they will be met.

LO3 Be able to work in partnership with others

AC 3.1 Explain why it is important to work in partnership with others

Partnership working in health and social care is the coming together of agencies that have a shared interest in supporting people who have care needs. These may include:

- the person you are supporting
- internal colleagues
- external colleagues
- carers and informal support network
- regulatory bodies such as the Care Quality Commission.

Effective partnership working

Effective partnership working is based on good team work.

Evidence activity

3.1 Working in partnership

Make a list of all the people you work with, both individually and in a team.

- Explain why it is important to work with each of these people.
- Explain what each of these people brings to the team.
- Explain what the consequences would be if these people were not part of the team.

Partnership working is central to delivering good quality health and social care services. There are so many aspects to supporting people using health and social care services that no one person or organisation can deliver them alone.

AC 3.2 Demonstrate ways of working that can help improve partnership working

Partnership working is spread right across the public, private and voluntary sectors. The partners or '**stakeholders**' that you work with will include the individuals you support, their carers, family and friends; your colleagues and team members; other professionals; and people who are important to the individuals you support, such as **advocates** and members of faith and support groups. (See page 102 for definitions).

You can help encourage and improve partnership working by promoting the three key principles: shared values, agreed goals or outcomes for the individuals you support, and regular communication.

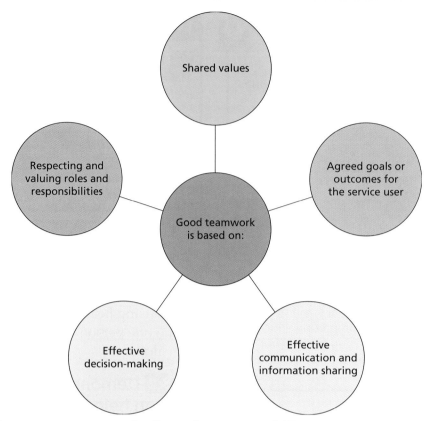

Figure 6.4 How do you ensure you work effectively as a team? Which of these key principles do you apply?

Shared values

- Have a genuine desire, commitment and enthusiasm for working with other people.
- Be open, trustworthy, honest and professional in order to gain the confidence of everyone concerned.
- Always have the interests of the individuals you support at the heart of your work.
- Be prepared to learn new things and adapt the way you work.

Agreed goals or outcomes

- Understand what goals or outcomes the partnership is trying to achieve, and by when. If you don't understand, ask.
- Understand exactly what is expected of you in achieving goals or outcomes, but remember not to act beyond your job scope or competence. If you have any concerns about what is expected of you, talk to your manager.
- Understand exactly what is expected of everyone else. If you're not sure, ask.
- Keep people informed about what you have been doing. The more you inform them, the more satisfied people will be.

Regular communication

- Make sure you attend all meetings and appointments; be punctual and well presented.

- Use **jargon**-free communication. The individuals you support, their carers, family and friends, volunteers and people working in other agencies may not understand the language of your workplace, so using it would put them at a disadvantage.
- Listen actively to others and show that you value their contribution.
- Be sensitive to and supportive of each other's well-being, and acknowledge and

respect other people's perceptions and points of view.
- Ensure confidentiality.
- Remain positive if communication becomes tense and conflicts develop.

Key term

Jargon is the specialist or technical language of a trade or profession.

Evidence activity

3.2 Improving partnership working

The most important people in any partnerships in a health or social care environment are the individuals using the service and those who are important to them.

- Ask service users and those important to them how they feel about your efforts to secure and deliver care that meets wishes and needs. Do they have any suggestions as to how you could improve their situation?
- Partnership working requires co-ordination – there is usually a person with overall responsibility for co-ordinating the required

support. This will depend on the environment in which the service user is being supported. In a hospital this may be the person's named nurse, within a social care environment this may be a social worker or a care co-ordinator. Make an appointment to talk to the person responsible for co-ordinating partnership working within your place of work. Find out how they think you perform within the partnership, whether you demonstrate shared values and goals, and whether your communication skills promote partnership working. Do they have any suggestions as to how you could improve your ways of working?

AC 3.3 Identify skills and approaches needed for resolving conflicts

Because partnership working requires individual people and agencies to set aside their own agendas and work towards a common goal, there is always a risk of conflict. Conflict is not necessarily a bad thing. If it is dealt with effectively, we can learn from it and develop personally and professionally. However, if it is not resolved effectively, the results can be damaging. Conflicting goals can rapidly turn into personal dislikes; team work breaks down; talent is wasted as people remove themselves from the partnership; and in a health or social care environment,

this may lead to disjointed care for people using the service. This can happen because communication breaks down and people are reluctant/do not want to share information. Morale may suffer which can also affect the quality of care a person receives.

The guiding principles behind successful conflict resolution are:

- mutual respect
- effective communication
- an open mind and a desire to understand different points of view
- an enthusiasm to work co-operatively with others
- a willingness to consult, negotiate and compromise.

Figure 6.5 Partnership working

Five steps to conflict resolution

Step 1: Effective communication

Effective communication is essential for resolving conflict. People who are involved in a conflict must be given an opportunity to express their perception of the problem, and active listening ensures that they are heard and understood. It is therefore important that you:

- show that you are interested in what the other person is saying, for example by maintaining eye contact
- show that you are trying to understand their point of view, for example by mirroring their facial expressions and tone of voice, by using appropriate body movements, such as head nods, and by making affirmative noises such as 'mmm' and 'yes'
- check your understanding by asking questions, **paraphrasing** what they tell you

> **Key term**
>
> **Paraphrasing** is rephrasing in your own words what someone else has said.

and summarising what you understand them to have said

- maintain a calm, courteous and assertive manner rather than being confrontational and aggressive.

Step 2: Gather information

Everyone has their own interests, requirements and concerns. Conflict may arise if an individual feels they are being ignored or their contributions are not taken into account. It is therefore important to understand how the partnership's way of doing things can impact on members of the team – for example, is it affecting their work performance,

Case study

3.3 Mr Sheldon

Mr Sheldon is an 89 year old man. He has recently been admitted to hospital following a fall. The falls are becoming more frequent and up until now he has been lucky as he hasn't seriously injured himself. His daughter has suggested that he goes into a care home because he keeps falling and needs someone to keep an eye on him. Mr Sheldon does not want to go into a care home and insists he is fine in his own home. His daughter is worried because when he falls he automatically relies on her to be there regardless of the time. She feels she can't cope any more.

Identify the skills and approaches that might be needed to resolve this conflict between the wishes of Mr Sheldon and his daughter.

disrupting team work, hampering decision-making? Or is it affecting the way an individual feels cared for or supported? It is important to be objective and focus on work issues. While personalities can conflict, it is important to set personalities aside.

Step 3: Identify the problem

Everyone needs to have a clear understanding of the problem. As you read above, different people have different needs, interests and concerns, and as a result they perceive problems differently. It is therefore essential to reach an agreement about what the problem is before seeking a mutually acceptable solution.

Step 4: Negotiate a win–win solution

It is important that everyone feels comfortable with the way a problem is solved. It is therefore important to involve relevant people in identifying possible solutions. If agreement cannot be reached, it is important to consider a compromise.

Step 5: Problem-solving

This involves actioning the agreed or compromise solution and monitoring it to ensure that it does resolve the problem. Be prepared to try out any of the other proposed solutions to see whether they might prove more effective.

AC 3.4 Demonstrate how and when to access support and advice about:

- **partnership working**
- **resolving conflicts.**

Partnership working

As we have discovered, working in partnership with other people can lead to conflicts. For example, there may be a personality clash or you may be asked to carry out an activity that:

- is outside the scope of your job role
- is within the scope of your job role but for which you have yet to be trained or, because of inexperience, you are not confident to do competently
- is not written into an individual's care plan
- would compromise your integrity, for example if you were asked to disclose confidential information
- would compromise the professional boundaries between you and an individual you support, for example if you were asked to use your position to exploit them in some way.

Resolving conflicts

If you experience conflict it is important to seek advice and support. In the first instance it is important to speak with your manager or supervisor. Most organisations have procedures in place to deal with disputes and conflicts and it is important that these are followed. They may require you to speak with someone in human resources, a union representative or an outside source, such as a **mediator** or the **Advisory, Conciliation and Arbitration Service (ACAS, www.acas. org.uk).**

If you want to complain about being a victim of a dispute or conflict, keep a record of what happened, when and where as well as anything else you think might be relevant, such as emails, texts, notes and letters. If it gets as far as a hearing, you will need these as evidence.

Disputes and unresolved conflicts affect people professionally and personally, so should never be ignored.

Key terms

A mediator is an intermediary third party, who is neutral and helps negotiate agreed outcomes.

The Advisory, Conciliation and Arbitration Service (ACAS) provides confidential and impartial advice to assist workers in resolving issues in the workplace.

Evidence activity

3.4 Accessing support

Explain how and when to access support and advice about partnership working and resolving conflicts within your place of work. Your manager should be able to give you some guidance with this activity. They should observe you demonstrating this and give you feedback on your performance.

Legislation

The Health and Social Care Act 2008 (Regulated Activities) Regulations 2010.

The Equality Act 2010

The Health and Social Care Act 2012

The Human Rights Act 1998

Useful resources

Websites

Care Quality Commission (CQC)

www.cqc.org.uk

Advisory, Conciliation and Arbitration Service

www.acas.org.uk

Skills for Care

www.skillsforcare.org.uk

Skills for Health

www.skillsforhealth.co.uk

Social Care Institute for Excellence

www.scie.org.uk

Implement person-centred approaches in health and social care

This unit is worth 5 credits

What are you finding out?

In this unit you are exploring the nature of 'person-centred care' and how we ensure, through our everyday working practice, that we keep the person at the centre of the support we offer. You will examine your own values and how these may impact on your work, and how you must adopt a non-judgemental attitude. You will explore the concepts of consent, choice, positive risk taking and sense of identity, and look at how they influence person-centred approaches in health and social care.

By the end of this unit, you will:

1 Understand person-centred approaches for care and support
2 Be able to work in a person-centred way
3 Be able to establish consent when providing care or support
4 Be able to encourage active participation
5 Be able to support the individual's right to make choices
6 Be able to promote individuals' well-being.

Links to Level 2 Certificate in Preparing to Work in Adult Social Care

HSC 026 Assessment Criteria	Unit PWCS26
AC1.1	AC1.1
AC1.2	AC1.2
AC3.3	AC3.4
AC4.1	AC4.2
AC5.3	AC5.4
AC5.4	AC5.5

LO1 Understand person-centred approaches for care and support

AC 1.1 Define person-centred values

Promoting individuality

We are all individuals. We continue to need things, feel fear, have ambitions and worries. This is what makes us **individuals** – because we all experience these things in different ways and at different times in our lives.

Some people think that being an individual means not following the crowd, but it is possible for us to express our views, thoughts and emotions and still be part of a group. Human society is made up of different people, all individuals but united in common purpose or culture or belief. Equally, those individuals who use health and social care services are a part of society with the same need, hopes and fears of unique individuals. We should regard them as individuals regardless of, for example, their gender, age disability or social circumstances. To group individuals together based on a particular attribute like age or disability is to 'stereotype' them. See AC 6.4 for more information on stereotyping.

> **Key terms**
>
> **Person-centred values** means we recognise that the individual is in charge of their own care and so we adopt an approach which places them at the centre, rather than imposing our own ideas and beliefs.
>
> **Individual** in the context of this chapter, this will refer to a person requiring care or support, often a person supported by the learner.

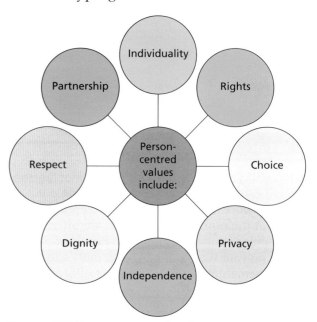

Figure 7.1 Person-centred values

Accessing rights

Rights are part of the rules of a society or civilisation. They can be seen as the 'building blocks' that ensure that people are protected as individuals – from abuse, exploitation, etc. They also give people the freedom to choose, and are supported by the laws in society. This also means that we do not exclude individuals from services or organisations because of for example their age or disability. They should be respected as citizens and given access to the right to participate or contribute.

Making Choices

Choice can be expressed in many ways and can range from something quite trivial like 'Which bar of chocolate do I want to buy?' to something major like 'Which house do I want to live in?'. However, choice – and the ability to make choices on any level – is one of the things that make us individuals.

Think about the person living with a disability, or an older vulnerable person, or a child. How important do you think choice is for these individuals? Is it any different for them? Think about an older person or a person with learning disabilities who may be living in a care setting. What kind of choices can they make, who supports them to do so and how important is it for them to be able to exercise choice?

When we are able to choose we are **empowered**, and this in turn helps our **self-esteem** – the way we can have positive thoughts about ourselves.

Privacy, dignity and respect

People usually like to socialise – we are 'social' beings – we join clubs and work together in teams and we seek support

Key terms

Empowered means to give someone the right or power to do something.

Self-esteem means to have a sense of value about yourself, to feel valued by others, and so feel 'good' about yourself.

Privacy means to provide the individual with the time, space and opportunity to be alone, or not have confidential affairs aired in public.

Dignity means to always treat the individual with respect, observing their need for privacy and independence and to value their feelings, wishes, rights and opinions.

from others. However, we also like to have our own space and the opportunity to be left to enjoy our own company.

For a person with a disability, or who is older, frail and who depends on others for care and support, maintaining privacy can be a challenging issue. For example, the individual may need to discuss a confidential matter or may want to grieve in private. This may be challenging if they live in a group situation or heavily rely on others for support.

As care workers we should uphold two fundamental (important and key) principles – **privacy** and **dignity**. These two standards go hand in hand. However, although it sounds easy to say 'we maintain a person's privacy and dignity', the key thing is to demonstrate or show that in your daily practice – minute by minute, hour by hour. It is, in fact, not something you can turn on or off. Maintaining a person's dignity and privacy is very much part of person-centred care – it influences or guides our actions and attitudes.

1.1 Dignity and privacy
- The 'Dignity in Care' campaign
- Essence of Care 2010
- CQC standards of quality and safety

These are all policies that guide us in our working practice.

Use your search engine to look at these policies and think about how they apply to your work.

Produce an information leaflet explaining the standards of dignity and privacy.

We can uphold dignity and privacy by respecting:

- **confidentiality** – and gaining access to personal information
- relationships – understanding and respecting people's needs for relationships
- personal space when going into people's homes or bedrooms
- conversations about people and keeping them private – sharing information on a 'need-to-know' basis only.

Promoting and supporting independence
We all value our independence. This can be a relative thing and means different things to different people. Independence can vary depending on the age, abilities or circumstances of the individual.

- Consider a child growing up and developing. We do not let a small child cross the road independently or on their own, but we do teach them road safety so that as they develop more skills, they reach the point where they can cross unsupervised and be independent.
- Consider the older person who may be unable to move about easily because they have severe arthritis. They are an adult and are able to understand road safety, but physically, they cannot cross the road without help. They can tell you they need to cross to go to the post office and so can display independence by telling you what they need to do.
- Consider the person living with dementia. They struggle to understand risk and have poor **spatial awareness**. They are at risk of injury if they cross the road without supervision.

Working in partnership
With individuals
As care workers, we must understand and respect the different levels of independence that the different people we support can achieve. We can do this by working in partnership with them. For example, three people could cross the road but their levels of independence will vary. Supporting individuals to be independent means giving

Key terms

Confidentiality is a set of rules or an agreement that places restrictions on certain types of information. For example, it means that only certain people may be allowed to see the information. It means that information should only be shared 'on a need to know' basis.

Supporting independence is about enabling individuals to do as much as possible for themselves as well as giving them the support to manage their own risks within their own level of independence.

Spatial awareness is to be aware of yourself and your own movements within the space around you in order to manage those movements.

Showing respect means to take into account the feelings, values and opinions of others irrespective of their age, gender, disability, social circumstance etc. For example, you can show respect to the individual when supporting them with activities of daily living. You can do this in a practical way by ensuring you include them in the day-to-day decisions and choices they make about what to wear or eat.

them choice and encouraging them to take an active role in decision making. Individuals may, for example, share joint responsibility for their care budgets.

With others

Working in partnership can include working with other colleagues as well as with the individual and their families and friends. This may mean a care plan is written co-operatively or that a service is delivered jointly. Also, a charity might have an agreement with a local authority to provide a tailor-made service for younger people living with dementia, for example.

AC 1.2 Explain why it is important to work in a way that embeds person-centred values

We have already thought about person-centred values. See AC 1.1 for what person-centred values mean. To work in a person-centred way, we must embed these values in our

support. Ignoring them can have a very negative effect on the person.

We should ensure we respect person-centred values and apply them in our everyday work. They are not 'optional' – something to be switched on and off. Rather they are a way of approaching our work by always remembering the uniqueness of each individual we support, **showing respect** (see page 110 for definition), and ensuring that they retain control while we support them.

If we do not respect these values we can affect:

● Confidence – people begin to lose confidence in themselves and you. They begin to realise they are not being listened to and can lose interest in trying to communicate.
● Independence – people lose the skills they already have if we do not help them to maintain them. Their level of independence becomes less, and they may become more dependent on others which can result in a loss of self-esteem, increased frustration and possibly anger.

Promoting person-centred values in practical ways

You can promote person-centred values in practical ways. For example, we can think about:

● Where the person lives – this could involve the social worker and/or an **advocate** who can help the person decide the best place to live.

- The food the person eats – think about religious requirements, or whether the person is a vegetarian.
- The clothes the person wears – encourage people to dress independently and express their individuality in the clothes they choose to wear.
- The family and friends they wish to see – provide opportunities for the person to socialise and maintain their social network.

AC 1.3 Explain why risk taking can be part of a person-centred approach

Risk taking and maintaining independence go hand in hand. There are risks in everyday situations like crossing the road or choosing to go on a rollercoaster ride! We make choices that involve risk – we may choose to smoke or not wear a seat belt. By doing so we are taking some control over our lives. We are also expressing our individuality – it may be unwise to smoke or not wear a seat belt but the person may do so because they have personal views about this and are expressing their individuality.

Some risks are negative, such as not wearing a seat belt, because they ignore our safety; others are positive and give us pleasure, like rock climbing using all the correct equipment and having the proper training.

Risks can be large or small and help us to keep our independence as well a sense of what our own limitations might be. Managing and taking positive risks is an essential part of person-centred care planning, because we express our need for independence partly through the risks we wish to take. We must support the individual to take appropriate risks that are manageable within their level of ability and confidence. At the same time, we should ensure that we are not putting them in danger/or that they are exposing themselves to a dangerous situation.

If we ignore our right to take 'positive' risks and 'wrap people up in cotton wool', we take away a right. When we support people we should ensure that we do the appropriate risk assessments, ensure that the risk is managed but make sure that we focus on the needs, rights and choices of the person and ensure that risk management does not stop individuals from living their lives. We may need to balance the risk and the right to independence and find a compromise. For example, we may often choose not to wear a seat belt but we wear it because that is the law, and it means that we are safer and still able to travel in a car.

Evidence activity

1.3 Risk-taking

Think about an individual you support. What risks are they currently able to take? Do you think they could, with encouragement, take more positive risks? How could you discuss this with them and who else would you need to involve? Why can risk taking be part of a person-centred approach?

AC 1.4 Explain how using an individual's care plan contributes to working in a person-centred way

What is a care plan?

A care plan might also be called a support plan, or an individual plan. It is used to record the day to day needs and preferences for the care and support of the individual.

The care plan should be a 'living 'document and should therefore be changed when the person's needs, preferences, etc. change.

A care plan is helpful only if it helps care support workers to support the person in a way that really meets their needs.

A care plan can be written only when the individual has been assessed. Care plans can be written for the general support of personal care needs, or can be more specific – for example, people who live with a condition like diabetes may have a care plan that is specially designed to help them manage their condition.

Section 47 of the NHS and Community Care Act 1990

Local authorities have a duty to carry out an assessment of need for community care services with people who appear to them to need such services. Local authority care plans record how the person's eligible needs will be met. A care plan cannot be withdrawn without a reassessment.

There is a process when we develop a care plan:

- Assess the person – this is usually done by a qualified colleague like a nurse, social worker or therapist, depending on the needs of the person. The assessment process is aimed at finding out the abilities, needs, wishes and problems the person is experiencing and looking at the outcomes they wish to achieve.
- Develop the care plan in partnership with the person, their friends and family, ensuring you focus on what the individual can do for themselves and the service(s) that they need. A care plan also needs the authorisation of the manager in some circumstances, for example, when it involves a budget to spend on services.
- Ensure that the care support workers who are delivering the care plan understand how to implement it (carry it out).
- Review the care plan on an agreed regular basis.
- Adapt the care plan as the needs of the person are reassessed.

Care plans and person centred planning

The individual is included at the centre of each stage and thus we can adjust their care plan to meet their needs in a person-centred way. We know that the individual should always be the focus and at the centre of the care plan by building support around their needs and preferences, and thinking about what they can do for themselves. It is important (with permission of the individual) that their care plan includes input from family and friends and acknowledges the role they play in the individual's life. Most care plans are written by qualified staff and the care support staff carry out the plan. The family can contribute to the plan but do not usually have responsibility for writing it.

Case study

1.4 Walter

Walter lives alone. He has learning disabilities and after assessment it was agreed with him that because he struggled to go out alone and found it difficult to manage his money, his care plan would include the help of a care support worker to accompany him to the supermarket each week. Some time later, Walter falls and breaks his leg. He is unable to leave the house.

- What do you think Walter's new needs may be?
- How might his care plan be changed to reflect this, bearing in mind a person-centred approach?
- How should his care plan be changed to address these new needs?

Evidence activity

1.4 Care plan

Look back at the Mrs Singh case study. Write a care plan that helps the worker to support Mrs Singh in a person-centred way.

LO2 Be able to work in a person-centred way

AC 2.1 Find out the history, preferences, wishes and needs of the individual

Working in a person-centred way means that we do not make assumptions about the individual. For example, do you assume that a person with a physical disability cannot do sport? In fact, we know that is not the case – think about the Paralympics.

Think about a person who is in hospital. They immediately become a 'patient' and the care they receive is designed around their needs as a patient. It does not necessarily take into account all their needs as a person.

Person-centred approach

To be truly person-centred, we must remember that all people are individuals, made up of many components, and remember that their wishes should be at the centre of that support. In order to work with individuals in a person-centred way, you will need to find out as much as possible about them. You can do this in a number of ways. Talking to them about their lives, their history and **preferences** (see page 115 for definition) will enable you to find out more about them as a person and also to find out what they would like from their care and support. This will then mean that you can know them better as a person, see them more than just an individual who requires care, and provide support that is appropriate and right for them. In some circumstances the individual may not be able to easily communicate their needs and preferences. If this is the case talk to family and friends and use their knowledge; look at the individual's life history – what does this tell you about them? Finally, remember that there are different methods of communication – you should consider sign language, and picture cards, for example.

In order to learn about the individual, you will need to find out the following:

History	Our history is our unique life story which has shaped who we are and how we and others see us.
Preferences	We prefer or choose particular things. This also defines us – for example 'I prefer the country to the town'.
Wishes	We all have hopes and fears. If these are not understood we may become withdrawn or frustrated.
Needs of the individual	We have many needs – physical, emotional and spiritual. If these needs are not met, we cannot thrive as individuals.

Encourage individuals to tell you about them

You should make sure that you encourage individuals to tell you about their preferences, wishes and needs, and also what they would like to achieve from their care. You may for example discuss topics such as nutritional needs and personal care, information that will help you to cater for their needs. Always try to use open questions rather than questions that only require a yes or no answer, for example, 'tell me about your usual routine when you get up – what kind of things are you managing and how do you think some support might help you?'

Developing a care plan with the individual will also help you to find out more about the individual and what they would like to achieve from their care and support. Your setting may also have assessments that they use. See AC 1.4 for more information on the process for developing a care plan. See unit SHC 21 for more information on communication. This is called a '**holistic** approach.'

When we are supporting the person in their own environment, in their own home or supported living or a care home, we must take a more **holistic** view.

Figure 7.2 One person, many roles

Time to think

2.1 **History, preferences, wishes and needs**

Think about your history, needs, wishes and preferences.

Discuss with a colleague how you would expect them to respect these if they were supporting you.

Research on how people who receive support see person-centred care found that people need to live their lives on as equal terms as possible with non-service users, and person-centred support should not be based on procedures, it should be based on the following values:
- putting the person at the centre, rather than fitting them into services
- treating service users as individuals
- ensuring choice and control for service users
- setting goals with them for support
- emphasising the importance of the relationship between service users and practitioners
- listening to service users and acting on what they say
- providing up-to-date, accessible information about appropriate services
- flexibility and a positive approach, which highlights what service users might be able to do, not what they cannot do.

Source 'Supporting people: Towards a person-centred approach' by Peter Beresford, Jennie Fleming, Michael Glynn, Catherine Bewley, Suzy Croft, Fran Branfield and Karen Postle, Joseph Rowntree Trust.

Evidence activity

2.1 **History, preferences, wishes and needs**

Think about a person you have supported. How did you find out more about them? How could you find out more? What kind of questions could you ask, bearing in mind their right to privacy? How would you ensure you do not intrude into areas they do not wish to discuss?

AC 2.2 **Apply person-centred values in day-to-day work taking into account the history, preferences, wishes and needs of the individual**

We have briefly described looking at the individual in a holistic way.

This means that we need to consider the individual as a whole, and:

- Their health – has this changed – either improved or got worse? How does this affect the individual? Do they require more practical or emotional support to manage this?
- Education – the education an individual receives can impact on their ability to access services. We should also bear in mind their level of literacy and numeracy – do we need to offer additional support and ensure they they are not disadvantaged?
- Employment or occupation – is the individual able to engage in a meaningful activity? How can they access opportunities to engage in activities which help them feel fulfilled and valued?
- Social needs – how can they maintain or even improve relationships with family and friends? How can we support the person to be included in social activities (social inclusion) and how can we help them access social

Table 7.1 History, preferences, wishes and needs of the individual

	What does this mean?	Example of how to apply this in your day-to-day role
History	Our history is our unique life story, which has shaped who we are and how we and others see us.	Individuality is shaped by our history, and when you are finding out more about the individual to help shape their care plan, use their personal history to help this.
Preferences	We prefer or choose particular things. This also defines us – for example, 'I prefer the country to the town'.	Take into account the rights of the individual and the choices they wish to make. Partnership working – you should not adopt a one-sided approach but remember that you are working in an equal partnership with the individual. This helps us to respect the rights and choices of the individual.
Wishes	We all have hopes and fears. If these are not understood we may become withdrawn or frustrated.	Respect – we must respect and have empathy (understand) the emotions of the individual in order to help them fulfil their wishes.
Needs of the individual	We have many needs – physical, emotional and spiritual. If these needs are not met, we cannot thrive as individuals.	As support workers we should enable the individual to maintain: - their privacy - their independence - their dignity.

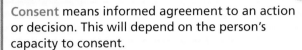

Key term

Person-centred values means recognising that the individual is in charge of their own care and so we adopt an approach which places them at the centre rather than imposing our own ideas and beliefs.

Key terms

Consent means informed agreement to an action or decision. This will depend on the person's capacity to consent.

Informed means having enough information and knowledge in order to make a decision.

Evidence activity

2.2 History, preferences, wishes

Look at the table on the previous page. Choose a care plan for one of your service users. Has the care plan been written using person-centred values?

How might you be able to improve the care plan?

Discuss these issues with your manager.

If you do not have access to a care plan, write a care plan for a family member, using the table as a prompt. Think about the different areas of holistic care we have described.

support through housing, social clubs, neighbourhood schemes etc.?

- Religious and cultural needs – we must bear this in mind when working with the individual because they may have particular preferences in food, dress or worship that should be taken into account.

LO3 Be able to establish consent when providing care or support

AC 3.1 Explain the importance of establishing consent when providing care or support

We have talked about supporting the individual using the value of partnership working. Person-centred care plans are usually made with the **consent** of the person and in collaboration with them. This means that they have understood what is in the care plan, how it will affect them and what the outcomes might be.

Informed consent is a legal requirement under the Mental Capacity Act 2005 and if the person is assessed as being unable to agree to something because they are unable to understand what this means, this assessment should be carefully recorded and a responsible person like an advocate or a close family member may be required to make particular decisions on their behalf.

Importance of establishing consent

In order to respect the wishes and preferences of the individual we must establish their consent. Initially we must gain their consent and agreement to be referred to services, then that they agree to an assessment and finally that they are involved in and agree to their care plan. They should agree to planned activities, and it is important to ensure consent for all activities every time you perform them, in case the individual has changed their mind. It is important to ask them questions about this, and also to make sure that they feel comfortable asking questions and giving their views rather than simply accepting your views as the worker. For example, you may want to check that the individual would still prefer to have a shower at a particular time, or that they prefer to be given some privacy when managing an aspect of their personal care.

It is also important to support families and carers in this. Well-meaning families can be so worried that they may want to make a referral to health or social care on their loved ones' behalf.

It is important to make sure that the individual has given their consent first – imagine how you would feel if things were done without your knowledge or permission.

- unable to understand the information provided
- unable to weigh up the information as part of the decision-making process.

Usually, the individual who has capacity agrees to care, treatment or support. They indicate that by signing their assessment and care or treatment plan.

It is important, however, not to assume that just because they have done so, they have not changed their mind, or would prefer not to have a part of their care plan carried out on a particular day. For example, the individual may have a shower at a particular time, but may need that changing if they are going out, or are unwell. Although routine is important to all of us, sometimes we need to change our routine to suit our circumstances. This should be acknowledged in the care plan. If this change is ongoing, it would be helpful at that point to reassess the situation in order to respect the individual's needs and wishes.

Informed consent

This means that the individual has the right information, given to them in the correct way to help them understand and be able to agree or disagree with a decision, understanding what giving or not giving their consent means. This should include both the positive and negative effects and risks, so that they can make an informed decision.

Implied consent

When the individual is able to indicate by other means that they are agreeing to something – this may be, for example, that they co-operate happily (you can, for example judge this by their body language).

Figure 7.3 It is important to listen to people and ensure they feel comfortable challenging your opinions

AC 3.2 Establish consent for an activity or action

Mental Capacity

Mental Capacity Act 2005 (enacted 2007)

For the purposes of your work in health or social care it is important that you are aware of the individual's agreement to your support or care.

When the individual is being asked for their consent, the law says:

Every adult must be presumed to have the mental **capacity** to consent or refuse treatment, unless they are:

- unable to take in or retain information provided about their treatment or care

Evidence activity

3.2 **Consent**

Read the NHS Choices 'Consent to treatment' online. Design an information leaflet explaining the different types of consent and how to ensure that the individual is protected by this.

Written consent

This may be a signature on a care plan agreeing to its content. It is important to check again that the individual understands before they sign any agreement. This could be asked for in clinical settings, and may also be needed for financial matters. Again, you will need to explain the risks and consequences before the individual signs anything.

Verbal consent

When the individual agrees with a decision by saying so – this might be in a formal review setting or during an assessment. It is important to ensure verbal consent is also recorded in written records.

AC 3.3 Explain what steps to take if consent cannot be readily established

When an individual cannot readily (easily) give consent it may be for a variety of reasons. We must not immediately assume it is because they do not understand or that they 'lack capacity'.

The **Mental Capacity Act 2007** says that when the term 'a person who lacks capacity' is used, it means a person who lacks capacity to make a particular decision or take a particular action for themselves at the time the decision or action needs to be taken.

This means that we must check the person's ability to make individual decisions or to give consent for particular things. They may be able to agree to wearing a particular dress but

do not have the capacity to make a decision to agree to live in a particular place.

This means that capacity is 'decision-specific'.

If you are not sure whether the person can or cannot give consent, they may need a mental capacity assessment. It is very important that you seek advice and do not go ahead. The person may not be able to easily give consent because of:

- sensory problems – they cannot read the consent form or care plan, or cannot easily hear your explanation
- mental health issues – they may have difficulty understanding or retaining (keeping in their memory) the information.

As care support workers we have a responsibility to ensure we have used ways of communicating with the individual that best meet their needs – not being able to hear does not mean the person cannot understand.

There are circumstances when the well-being of the person takes over and consent might not be gained immediately – this is the case in life-saving situations, when the person is unconscious, for example.

However, the person may have made an 'advanced wish' about the kind of care or

Figure 7.4 Lines of communication must be kept open

treatment they would prefer if they were ever in a situation when they could not give full consent. It is important to talk to next of kin – the people closest to the individual – to find out if they have made such arrangements.

Different professional organisations give advice and guidance on gaining consent and action to take if consent cannot be easily established.

In the first instance, you must gain the individual's consent. However, if it already established that they lack capacity and the consent required was, for example, to have support with personal care, this should be recorded on their care plan. The person may have dementia and if it has been assessed that they no longer have insight, in these circumstances it is not necessary to go through the process of gaining consent each time you support the individual. Instead, you should use your person-centred skills to the full and support them to be involved in the process as much as possible. If they say no, or have changed their mind, stop the procedure or what you are doing and consider how to approach the situation in a different way.

- You should ensure that the individual understands the risks and consequences and give them the opportunity to discuss this and express any concerns they may have.
- You should not put any pressure on the individual.
- If the individual disagrees or does not want to or, in your judgement, is unable to give consent, then you must record this and inform your supervisor or line manager.

You may then need to assess the individual further and decide with other professionals and where appropriate, family and friends, whether acting in the individual's best interests means you should do the procedure/go ahead without gaining consent. The Mental Capacity Act offers guidelines about 'best-interest decisions' – how these should be arrived at and how they should be recorded and reviewed.

LO4 Be able to encourage active participation

AC 4.1 Describe how active participation benefits an individual

Benefits of active participation
As individuals with free will we all like to be able to take part or contribute to something – this includes within society as a whole (for example voting) or our own neighbourhood (for example by joining a local committee) or our own family (by organising or attending family events). All this helps us remain part of a group, gives us a sense of 'ownership' and helps us feel valued and listened to.

Active participation can also apply to activities of daily living (ADL) – if we encourage the individual to contribute

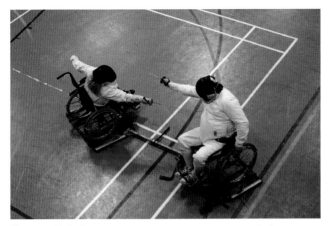

Figure 7.5 Active participation is essential

or participate in their own care we can increase their self-esteem and their sense of achievement, which in turn will add to their well-being.

The **Human Rights Act 2004** says that people have the right to:

- freedom of association
- take part in public life
- have the opportunity to take part in the conduct of public affairs, directly or through freely-chosen representatives.

Individuals as social beings

This means that we all have the right to friendships and relationships as well as the right to take part in social activities.

Although there are times when we prefer our own company, people are naturally social creatures. We live, work and socialise in groups. There are many advantages to being part of a social group.

Time to think

4.1 Social groups

Think about social groups – for example, scouts or a day centre for older people or a night class.

The people in these groups have a common bond. What benefits do you think they gain from belonging to such groups?

Key term

Discrimination is action that prevents people being able to participate in society based on a particular 'category' they are seen to 'belong' to. For example, travellers may be prevented from settling in an area of a town because they are viewed as outsiders.

Evidence activity

4.1 Benefits of active participation

How does active participation benefit an individual? Think about the ways in which you have encouraged active participation in your setting.

People naturally gather in groups to:

- share experiences and knowledge
- comfort one another
- entertain each other
- protect the group
- form action plans to change or improve things in society.

People are also identified by the groups they are associated with. There is a sense of pride and belonging, and common purpose.

Illness, disability or ageing should not prevent the individual from participating in social activities. It is a fundamental part of personhood and a support plan should recognise the importance of maintaining relationships and social activities. We should not **discriminate** against people by either preventing them from continuing with their social and personal life or by not supporting them in doing so.

AC 4.2 Identify possible barriers to active participation

There are many **barriers** that can prevent individuals from actively participating, and they can be both **internal** and **external**.

Internal barriers

- Illness or disability: due to illness or disability or mental health issues, the individual may experience a barrier to active participation.

- They may struggle to attend a group due to poor mobility, or find difficulty socialising in the pub because they are living with dementia and their communication skills are affected.
- Emotional barriers: people may feel insecure or a lack confidence because of their circumstances. They may struggle to join in conversations or mix in groups because of anxiety.

External barriers

- Communication issues: for example, lack of information or in suitable formats.
- **Risk**: sometimes there is also the issue of risk – the activity may be assessed as too risky for the person to participate in, or family and friends may feel it is too risky for the person. It is very important that we are objective in these situations – that we assess the risk and work together to find a solution.
- **Lack of support** and understanding from other people: individuals who need support may rely on their care worker, friends or family to enable them to participate. There is a danger that they may 'take over'.
- **Lack of time staff**: support workers may feel under pressure to complete a task and there can be a danger that interaction with an individual is merely seen as a task rather than an encounter with another person. This may be because of limited time and lack of staff, so the task becomes the priority.
- There may be more **physical barriers**: access to buildings and public areas can be a problem. There may be limited access to ramps or other people may be unco-operative in offering support. There might be inadequate signage or information about what is available.

The care plan

The care plan should reflect the individual's need to participate. However, this might depend on the time available or the skills of the care worker in supporting the person in particular activities.

Other factors

There are also other factors – the individual may have unrealistic expectations of what they are still able to do and in those circumstances it will be important to work in **partnership** with them to find a compromise.

Key terms

A **barrier** is an obstacle.

Internal barriers are elements specific to the individual and their own circumstances.

External barriers are elements outside the individual which may be out of their control, like the lack of access to a building or the attitude of others.

Case study

4.2 George

George went to the pub every Friday to spend time with a group of friends. He has been diagnosed with dementia. He decides he does not want to go to the pub any more because he cannot remember his friends' names.

You are George's support worker. You would like to help him get back into his social routine.

- What effect do you think not socialising is having on George?
- Can you think of some strategies to support him?

Evidence activity

4.2 Barriers to active participation

In your place of work discuss with colleagues the barriers the individuals you work with encounter. Discuss options for an action plan of how you can work with individuals to reduce some of these barriers. You may want to develop some group work to support people or work on individual outcomes. Discuss these ideas with your supervisor or line manager before introducing them as ideas to the individuals concerned.

AC 4.3 Demonstrate ways to reduce the barriers and encourage active participation

Good person-centred care takes into account the possible barriers to active participation. Through finding out about the lives and histories of individuals, it is possible to understand their preferences and the activities they have always enjoyed. There should also be a clear understanding of the importance of particular relationships for the individual.

We have explored some of the potential barriers to active participation in AC 4.2. Here we look at examples of how we can reduce these barriers and encourage active participation.

Internal

Illness or disability

We can reduce barriers by ensuring that others understand the needs of the individual. Sometimes people put up barriers because they do not understand how to communicate or interact with an individual.

Emotional issues

We can encourage the individual to think about what they can rather than what they cannot do. We should always acknowledge emotional issues and support the individual to talk about their concerns and ensure they receive the appropriate help.

External

Communication issues

The individual may experience problems communicating, for example with seeing or hearing. We can ensure that appropriate equipment is provided and that hearing aids and spectacles are in good working order. Buildings can provide helpful signs to enable the individual to navigate their way to particular areas. These should be at eye level so people can read them easily, in plain English and other languages if necessary. Symbols are also very helpful.

Lack of information or in suitable formats

We tend to rely on leaflets or the internet to inform the general public, or people who use our services. However, it is important to recognise that information should be given in a variety of ways to meet the needs of the individual. People need to be well informed, but may not always be able to cope with a lot of information at once. It is not good enough to give them a pile of leaflets or a web link and expect them to understand or manage the information without support.

You should discuss the use of information with your manager and consider the most appropriate way of giving information to the individual, carer or members of the public.

Risk

It is not enough to assume that a particular activity may be too risky for the individual to participate in. A risk assessment should be done, the preferences and wishes of the individual listened to, and the benefits of the activity weighed against the risk. Protective factors should be looked at – for example, can specialist equipment be used? Are adaptations available? Most recent developments include '**Assistive technology**' like telemedicine or telecare. Telecare, for example, includes fall alarms, flood alerts and 'wander alerts'. These alarms are connected to a central control which alerts a responder that the individual has fallen, or has flooded a room by leaving a tap on or has left their home. The responder can then respond to this.

> **Key term**
>
> **Assistive technologies** are electronic and physical items, devices or systems that enable individuals to maintain and develop their independence and skills for everyday life.

Lack of time

It is true that care support workers may not always have the time to spend with an individual in a particular activity. Personalisation is a method by which people are awarded their own budgets to buy the type of support they require. This might include support to participate in social or family events. Dementia Friends are being recruited to support people living with dementia in continuing their favourite pastimes – to share a game of golf or go to the theatre, for example.

Lack of support and understanding from others

Some individuals, because of their illness or disability or situation, are not able to clearly explain what they want and they need the help of not just family and friends. Advocates can represent their views and make sure they are taken into account. Advocates are 'impartial' or unbiased, which means that they may be required to act on behalf of the individual to make sure it is their views alone that are represented. Remember that when family and friends are involved, it is important that they do not 'take over'.

Lack of opportunities or access to buildings

This relates to physical disabilities. The Equality Act 2010 ensures that people with a disability should have equal access to buildings, facilities, public transport, etc. Some practical ways of improving access include parking badges for people with a disability, specially designed toilets, and the use of ramps. It is also common now to see the pavement edge of a pedestrian crossing marked out with a raised 'pebble like' design so that people with visual impairments can feel the change in the texture of the pavement and know they are at the kerbside.

Evidence activity

4.3 Reduce barriers and encourage active participation

Consider some of your local resources – the library, local pub, etc. Do they present barriers?

How could you improve access for people through adjustments to the building?

How might the staff be able to support the individual?

LO5 Be able to support the individual's right to make choices

AC 5.1 Support an individual to make informed choices

A choice is a personal decision a person makes about how to live and behave, according to their attitudes, tastes, and values.

A care support worker acts in the best interests of the individual when they remain objective. It is easy to try to influence or persuade someone because we have our own views. However, the person must be at the centre of the process and the support worker's role is to ensure they are well informed and understand all the choices available.

The Mental Capacity Act 2007 describes 'unwise choices'. Individuals have the right to make unwise choices and as long as they have the capacity to do so, we may have to respect their wishes.

Key term

Informed choice is having the correct and full information that the individual can understand and use to weigh up decisions and choices, while understanding advantages and disadvantages. An example of this is 'Helping people make informed choices about health and social care', from the Department of Health (2013).

Individuals who receive health and social care services have to make informed choices – for example, about their GP, the hospital they wish to be treated at or the type of care they need to receive. The Care Act 2014 is aimed at local authorities developing more choice.

How to support individuals to make informed choices

Consider the type of information an individual may need to make an informed choice. Traditional leaflets and brochures may not always be appropriate. Information can also be provided verbally, using the internet, or by going on visits to service providers.

The type of information they might require includes:

- The aims of the service
- Where it is based
- Who is responsible for the service
- What the costs are
- How and where do they provide support?
- Do they have a complaints and comments process?
- Are they registered with CQC?

Individuals may need help and support to make/achieve choices, and these will vary from day-to-day choices like what to wear or eat, to more significant choices like where they want to live. In each situation it is important that we try to ensure the person is at the centre of this decision-making process, and if they have been assessed as lacking capacity, we should ensure we work in their best interests. The Mental Capacity Act states that capacity is decision-specific so, for example, the individual may not have the capacity to decide where they live but do have the capacity to choose what to wear. Refer to SCH 21 for information on effective communication.

Direct payments and individual budgets are practical ways to empower individuals by giving them more choice. They are based on outcome care planning and help the individual to choose the best way for them to meet their assessed needs.

Also think about all the things we have discussed in this unit, such as the use of advocates, giving individuals information so that they are able to make informed decisions, the relevant information that they will need, and ensuring that a person-centred approach is at the heart of what you do.

AC 5.2 Use agreed risk assessment processes to support the right to make choices

Why do we risk assess?

We have already thought about risk being a normal part of everyday life. Risks can be high or low depending on the person's level of frailty or ability to cope with risk. This means that risk is relative and very personal to the individual.

Most health and social care organisations use risk assessments. Assessments should help people to live fulfilled lives safely, and not be used simply for restricting independence. They should not stop people from choosing to take part, but are there to protect individuals and workers, reduce risks, and still enable them to participate in the activity safely.

Using agreed risk assessment processes

We can use specific risk assessments or techniques, for example:

- Falls assessments
- Moving and handling
- Kitchen assessments
- We can observe people carrying out activities and gradually withdraw support and supervision as they gain in confidence
- We can devise prompts and lists for people – this can be effective for people living with dementia, for example.

Risk assessment and choice

Being 'risk averse' is not helpful to the individual. As health or social care workers, we can worry that if the individual makes a particular choice, things could go wrong, and therefore we may not want to support some choices.

As a society, our attitude to disability is changing. People with disabilities and older people are being encouraged to increase their independence in their daily activities and in the decisions about the services they receive.

We now focus on what people **can** do rather than what they **cannot** do.

Using agreed risk assessments for particular situations can support people to make choices. The risk assessment should:

- describe the risk
- how likely it is to happen
- how severe the risk is
- what measures can be taken to reduce the risk
- what the consequences might be if the risks are not addressed.

Case study

5.2 Ella

Ella lives alone and after a fall is losing her confidence. She is reluctant to carry out any **activities of daily living** and thinks she may need to go into a care home. The **Occupational Therapist** has been asked to complete an assessment.

What type of risks might the occupational therapist assess? How could you support Ella in minimising her risks? Why is this assessment an important part of helping Ella to make choices about her future?

Key terms

Risk averse means not wanting to participate in or being negative about taking risks or not enabling other people in taking risks.

Activities of daily living are tasks that we associate with our everyday life, such as washing, dressing, cooking, cleaning.

Occupational Therapists help people overcome difficulties caused by physical or mental illness, an accident, or the ageing process. They work with clients to help them lead as full and independent lives as possible.

Evidence activity

5.2 Risk assessment processes

How do you use agreed risk assessment processes to support the right to make choices?

AC 5.3 Explain why a worker's personal views should not influence an individual's choices

The role of the care worker and professional boundaries

It is very important to reflect on or think about what the role of a care support worker is when they are working with individuals who are making choices. A person who works in any care or health setting must comply with (obey the rules of) professional standards.

This means that although we support the individual, have a friendly approach and work with **empathy**, we are *not* a friend. We must remain objective.

Vulnerable people sometimes have difficulty coming to terms with this and would prefer the care support worker to be seen as a friend. However, when our professional boundaries are blurred and we do not work within the standards expected of professional staff, we can run into difficulties. Care support workers have close contact with people who rely on them to provide support in many ways. This dependence can affect the relationship – to some extent the support worker has power or influence over the vulnerable person and this can be abused.

Why your personal views should not influence the individual's choices

We all have views which in our personal life we can express. However, in our professional life we must put these aside because they may not be the views of the person we work with, and our views should not influence their choices. We may not agree on a personal or professional level with the choice of the individual, but we must remember that they have the right as we all do, to make choices of their own. Ensure that the individual is making a choice based on all the facts available to them, and if they do ask your opinion, be very clear that this is your personal opinion and not meant to influence them. If necessary, record that you were asked for your opinion, and if possible, ask the individual what they think first so that you are not influencing them.

Key term

Empathy means the ability to understand and share the feelings of others – 'to be able to walk in their shoes'.

Case study

5.3 Ella

You are Ella's care support worker and you are talking to her about future options.

These are your personal views:

- 'I don't like that care home because it is too far away.'
- 'I think that day centre is too noisy.'
- 'That supermarket doesn't have all the things you need – I would rather go to the bigger one.'

Then think about working professionally in the role of the support worker talking to Ella:

- 'If you are considering going into a care home, you may want to think about different options, such as how close it is to your family and friends.'
- 'One idea you could think about is whether you would like to attend a day service. There are different types – some are luncheon clubs where you can go for a meal and a chat, others have more activities and are busier.'
- 'We can try a couple of supermarkets – one is bigger than the other.'

How does the second approach enable Ella to make her own choices rather than be influenced by you?

Evidence activity

5.3 Personal views and individual choices

Explain the different reasons why the care worker's personal views should not influence those of the individual. Think about how you might respond if you are asked for your opinion.

AC 5.4 Describe how to support an individual to question or challenge decisions concerning them that are made by others

Reasons why individuals may not question or challenge decisions

We all have the right to question decisions – the right to say 'no' or ask 'why?' There are times and circumstances when we feel confident enough to do this, but for some people, being **assertive** is very difficult.

The individual may find it difficult to question or challenge decisions for many reasons:

- low self-esteem or lack of confidence
- they may feel intimidated by the worker or feel that they do not have the right to challenge decisions
- they want to 'please' the care support worker – think about the 'power' relationship, they might think the worker 'knows best' because they are the 'expert' (they may think this because of the worker's body language, or the fact that they may wear a uniform)
- communication issues – the person may have difficulty expressing themselves or may not be given enough time to weigh up the options
- pressure from family and friends
- lack of advocacy – they do not have access to an independent person who can help them express their views
- they have not been given enough information to help them challenge decisions/may not know how to challenge them
- they may have had a bad experience of challenging decisions in the past or it was not successful and so do not challenge.

Always remember that as a care worker you are seen by the individual to be in a position of control or authority. The individual may see you in a uniform and view you as an important person who has control over their life. They may not feel in a position to challenge or

Figure 7.6 Uniforms may mean individuals do not feel they can challenge you because a uniform is associated with authority or power

disagree with you. It is your responsibility to work with them in equal partnership, to make sure they can express themselves. You can do this by responding in a non-judgemental way.

How to ensure these situations do not arise and how to support individuals to challenge

- Low self-esteem or lack of confidence – we should work with the individual to build their confidence. Encourage them to start with small decisions – what to wear, what to eat. Give a lot of **positive reinforcement** such as 'I really thought you made a good decision about that' or 'That is a great idea!' Remember positive feedback can be simple and effective.

Key terms

Assertive means having the confidence to explain your views, particularly in an argument or discussion.

Positive reinforcement is to 'reward' a person for a positive behaviour. So if you are encouraging the individual to make a decision, once the decision is made you might say 'that's a lovely idea', or 'that seems like a sensible choice'.

- They may feel intimidated by the worker or feel that they do not have the right to challenge decisions
- They want to 'please' the care support worker – we should maintain professional boundaries and not give the impression that the choices affect us personally. To be truly person-centred we should always keep the discussion and decision-making process focused on the individual.
- Communication issues – ensure you are using methods of communication that suit the person. Go at their pace and check that they understand the decision making process. You can find more information on communicating effectively and appropriately in unit SHC 21.
- Pressure from family and friends – it is important to support the family and friends. Often they are trying to influence decision-making because they are concerned for the safety and welfare of the person. Do not 'take sides'. Try to acknowledge and recognise their concerns, yet emphasise that the individual has the right to make their own choices.
- Lack of advocacy – advocacy services have their own information and you must ensure that the individual has access to these if necessary. Advocacy should be used when there is a **conflict of interest**, or when families are not working in the best interests of the individual, or where there is a disagreement about the decisions to be made about future care arrangements
- They have not been given enough information to help them challenge decisions/may not know how to challenge them – it is very difficult to challenge other people if you

> **Key term**
>
> **Conflict of interest** is when there are multiple interests which may go against the main objective or duty of care for the individual.

> **Evidence activity**
>
> **5.4 Questioning and challenging decisions**
> Think about a situation where you felt that you could not challenge other people's decisions made for you.
>
> - How did it make you feel?
> - How did it affect your life?
>
> Think about how you can use this experience to help you improve your practice with individuals.
>
> Keeping in mind your own experiences, how would you support an individual to question or challenge decisions concerning them that are made by others?

do not have all the relevant information, so make sure information is given in a way that the person understands – leaflets, brochures, audio tape, braille, etc.

- They may have had a bad experience of challenging decisions in the past or it was not successful and so do not challenge – in these circumstances it is important that the individual is made aware of the organisation's policy, which should be not to discriminate against people who have challenged or complained in the past. The individual should have access to staff who are independent of the decision and who can deal with the situation objectively.

LO6 Be able to promote individuals' well-being

AC 6.1 Explain how individual identity and self-esteem are linked with well-being

Identity, self-esteem and well-being
Identity is our own idea of ourselves and how we are seen by others and society. Our identity can also be defined by our role in the family or our career, gender, race etc. Identity is therefore complicated – we are many things and have many roles!

Self-esteem describes how we give value to ourselves. We might show this by how confident we are or how comfortable we feel with ourselves. If we are sure and confident about our identity and feel good about ourselves, it is likely that we are physically healthier and emotionally stronger. To have self-esteem means that you feel valued by others. Self-esteem can be affected in a negative way by the criticism of others or the loss of a person who supported you. Self-esteem is affected in a positive way by praise, affection and by being given responsibilities.

Well-being describes the aspects of the person that help them feel well, mentally, physically and spiritually. There is a recognition now of the strong link between mental health and physical health. As individuals we are made up of many parts and a strong personal sense of identity and high self-esteem contribute to both mental and physical well-being.

Maslow talks about people needing a series of things to make them 'human'. These things start with the basic needs that keep us alive, such as food and air, and end with a feeling of 'self' and truly understanding who we are as people – this is our sense of identity.

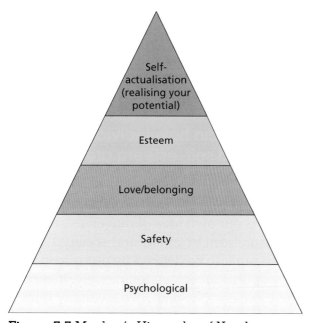

Figure 7.7 Maslow's Hierarchy of Needs

Research and investigate

6.1 Maslow's hierarchy of needs
Research Maslow's hierarchy of needs on the internet. How can you apply this to the needs of individuals in your setting?

Evidence activity

6.1 Identity, self-esteem and well-being
Think about a person you support and how their sense of self and self-esteem affects their well-being.

Is there anything you can do to support them to improve their situation?

Well-being may include aspects that are:

- Spiritual and religious – a person's religious belief can be very important to them and can contribute to a sense of identity and well-being. This also includes spirituality.
- Emotional well-being – helps keep us physically well – we are more likely to look after ourselves and maintain our self-esteem in a positive way.
- Cultural – we all belong to a culture or social group and this adds to our sense of identity.
- Social and political – this defines where we see ourselves in society and adds to our identity. Our status in a society can be linked to our self-esteem because we may be respected and valued by others.

AC 6.2 Describe attitudes and approaches that are likely to promote an individual's well-being

We have already discussed the importance of not influencing the individual with our own beliefs and opinions. However, we can make sure we adopt the correct attitude towards people and approach them in a person-centred way.

Society's attitudes

Think about the **attitudes** some members of society have towards particular groups of people and the effects that this may have on these groups. For example.

- asylum seekers or immigrants
- people who receive benefits
- people who are gay, lesbian or bisexual
- people with religious beliefs
- people with a disability.

Wider society may have different attitudes and **approaches** towards different groups: **intolerant**, discriminatory, **judgemental**, impatient or **dismissive**. Can you imagine how the person you support would feel if they experienced any of these attitudes?

For example, intolerant attitudes may mean that groups may feel rejected, or feelings of being 'odd' because they are different.

Discrimination can isolate people or make them feel they are not allowed to join in.

Judgemental attitudes can lead to the person feeling angry and marginalised, not important, or misunderstood.

Impatient or dismissive attitudes, or feeling patronised, may take away feelings of self-worth.

Attitudes and approaches that promote well-being

To promote well-being, it is important to ensure that individuals feel valued and respected. This helps to build their self-esteem and ensures that they are the centre of the service you are providing. This starts when you begin your assessment and think about your care plan. Care workers should ensure that they ask individuals about their requirements and needs or that there is an advocate who can do this. You will need to understand and think of them as an individual with their own history, experiences and preferences, and find out about them so that they feel valued, all of which we have discussed in this unit.

AC 6.3 Support an individual in a way that promotes a sense of identity and self-esteem

We rely on the people we interact with to help us identify and understand ourselves and to give us self-esteem. For example, in a reference, a manager may say that you are a very experienced and professional worker or that you are inexperienced and not competent (good at your job). Consider both versions and the difference between the ways they make you feel about yourself.

The way we offer support can make big differences to the way the individual feels. We must remember that we are concentrating on what the person **can** do and not on what they **cannot** do.

- **Safe/observe**. We must behave in a way that is safe for the individual. This might include being discreet and observing the person to ensure that they are not putting themselves at risk. However, we must respect their rights and adopt a positive risk-taking attitude.
- **Partnership**. The care support worker and the individual are partners – the person is not a 'task', they should not have things 'done to them'. Supporting a person to wash or dress or eat should be approached in a way that supports dignity and respects the choices of the person.
- **Trust**. There should be feelings of trust. The individual is putting their faith in the care support worker and this should be acknowledged and treated with respect.
- **Empathy**. We should 'walk in other people's shoes' and try to understand their world and how things must feel for them. By doing so we are able to support them as individuals and not make assumptions or judgements.
- **Approval/encouragement**. We show approval or encourage the individual to help their confidence and boost their self-worth or self-esteem. However, we must be aware that this can sound patronising if we do not use language well, so avoid phrases like 'good girl!'
- **Appropriate communication methods, use of language, tone of voice**. A good approach is also demonstrated by how we communicate, not just what we communicate. See SHC 21 for more information.
- Overall, your role is to ensure that individuals feel valued and respected in

order to promote their sense of identity and the way they feel about themselves.

AC 6.4 Demonstrate ways to contribute to an environment that promotes well-being

Contributing to an environment that promotes well-being

This means that the environment is meaningful to the individual and that it is a comfortable place to be in because:

- they can find their way around (good signage)
- it meets their needs (ramps, effective lighting)
- the staff are helpful and welcoming
- it provides a safe and stimulating space
- it also means an environment that takes into account the beliefs, values and culture of individuals.

Case study

6.4 Environments

Our environments send messages that affect our well-being and self-worth.

Think about this:

A new team is about to be formed. They are moving into an empty office. The manager checks the room and finds that it is dirty, undecorated and untidy. She decides that the room must be sorted out and tidied up before the team can move in.

Why do you think the manager considers this important? What kind of a 'message' would it give to you as a member of the new team if you were expected to work in a dirty, untidy environment?

Environments in hospitals, care homes, education facilities, clinics, etc. are vital to well-being.

There has been a lot of research, for example, about the best environments in care homes for people living with dementia.

Research and investigate

6.4 Environments

Look at the Stirling University model by going to: **dementia.stir.ac.uk/design/virtual-environments:**

Environments should have a 'therapeutic' element – they should add value for the person. This 'value' might include:

- Familiarity
- Sensory stimulation (interesting things to look at or hear or smell)
- Information
- Entertainment
- Comfort
- Safety.

Legislation

Mental Capacity Act 2007

Human Rights Act 2004

The Equality Act 2010

The Care Act 2014

Useful resources

Websites

Stirling University Dementia Services Development Centre

dementia.stir.ac.uk

Royal College of Nursing

www.rcn.org.uk

www.rcn.org.uk/development/ personcentredcareplanning

British Institute of Human Rights

www.bihr.org.uk
The Health Foundation

www.health.org.uk/person-centredcare

Skills for Care

www.skillsforcare.org.uk

Evidence activity

6.4 Environments that promote well-being

Figure 7.8 A functional space for dining

Look at this photograph of a dining room in a care home.

How could this environment be improved?

How could you ensure it is an environment that promotes well-being?

List or discuss with your manager ways that you could improve your setting so that it promotes the well-being of the individual.

Unit HSC 027

Contribute to health and safety in health and social care

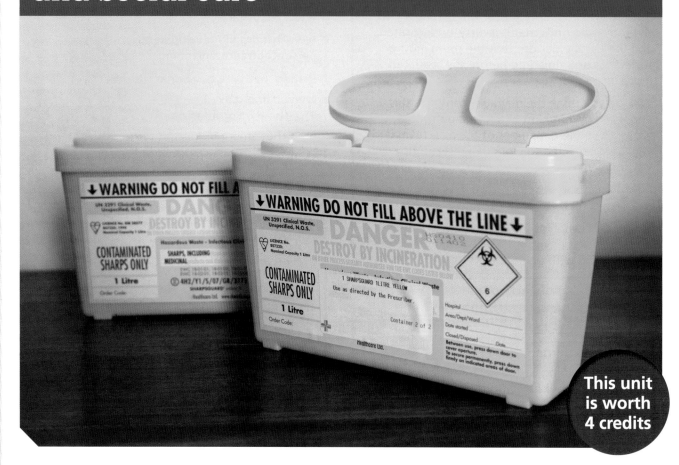

This unit is worth 4 credits

What are you finding out?

All health and social care organisations and settings are governed by laws, policies and guidelines that help and support the individual, the employee and employer to work in a safe and healthy manner. Laws and policies ensure that risks are managed, people are kept as safe as possible and workers are given appropriate training to carry out their work in a safe way.

By the end of this unit you will:

1 Understand own responsibilities, and the responsibilities of others, relating to health and safety in the work setting
2 Understand the use of risk assessments in relation to health and safety

3 Understand procedures for responding to accidents and sudden illness
4 Be able to reduce the spread of infection
5 Be able to move and handle equipment and other objects safely
6 Know how to handle hazardous substances and materials
7 Understand how to promote fire safety in the work setting
8 Be able to implement security measures in the work setting
9 Know how to manage own stress.

Links to Level 2 Certificate in Preparing to Work in Adult Social Care

HSC 027 Assessment Criteria	Unit PWCS27
AC1.1	AC1.1
AC1.2	AC1.2
AC1.3	AC1.3 (social care worker, employer/manager)
AC1.4	AC1.4
AC2.2	AC2.3
AC3.1	AC3.1
AC3.2	AC3.2
AC5.1	AC5.1
AC6.1	AC7.1(hazardous substances)
AC6.2	AC7.2(hazardous substances)
AC7.2	AC8.2 (fire)
AC9.1	AC9.1
AC9.2	AC9.2
AC9.3	AC9.3

LO1 Understand own responsibilities, and the responsibilities of others, relating to health and safety in the work setting

AC 1.1 Identify legislation relating to general health and safety in a health or social care work setting

Legislation

The main piece of legislation that will cover your setting is the Health and Safety at Work Act 1974. This includes many regulations which you need to know about as they will affect your day-to-day role.

The table on the next page shows the different legislation that come under this Act and the purpose of each one.

Health and Safety Executive (HSE)

The Health and Safety Executive (HSE) enforces and regulates health and safety at work legislation. It also gathers the statistics on to work-related injuries, illness and death.

The Health and Safety Executive reports that the most popular regulations people seek guidance on are those relating to:

- asbestos
- COSHH

Table 8.1 Purpose of legislation

Legislation	Purpose of the legislation
Health and Safety at Work Act (HASAWA) 1974	The legal framework guiding all employers and employees. This Act gives responsibilities to both the employer and employee to work as safely as possible.
Management of Health and Safety at Work Regulations 1999	Employers and managers are required to assess and manage risks.
Manual Handling Operations Regulations amended 2002	Minimise risks when moving and handling people.
Provision and Use of Work Equipment Regulations 1998	Minimise risks when using equipment such as hoists.
Personal Protective Equipment at Work Regulations 1992	Minimise risk when using protective clothing such as disposable gloves and aprons.
Reporting of Injuries, Diseases and Dangerous Occurrences Regulations (RIDDOR) 1995	Employers are required to report certain work-related injuries, diseases and work-related accidents.
Control of Substances Hazardous to Health Regulations (COSHH) 2002	Minimise risk related to hazardous substances like bleach.
Regulatory Reform (Fire Safety) Order 2005	A duty to manage risks associated with fire – for example, supporting those service users who choose to smoke to do so safely. There are well known health risks associated with smoking and if possible we should discourage the individual from smoking. However, this must be done bearing in mind their right to choose and in consultation with others like your line manager, the GP etc. (people who choose to stop smoking may need appropriate medical support from smoking cessation practitioners). Never impose your own views and values about smoking because although it is a harmful activity it should be seen in the context of their history, life style and mental well-being.
Health and Safety (First Aid) Regulations 1981	To ensure everyone can receive immediate attention if they are injured or ill at work.
Food Safety Act 1990 and the Food Hygiene (England) Regulations 2006	To minimise risks to health and safety associated with food handling. This includes understanding how to handle cooked and raw meat, for example.

- reporting RIDDOR incidents
- risk assessments
- manual handling and lifting
- stress
- skin conditions.

The following statistics remind us that health and safety at work is a very serious subject and affects all of us. As employees we have a responsibility to keep ourselves safe at work, report any risks or accidents and comply with regulations and procedures which are there to keep us safe. All these procedures are underpinned by legislation (the law).

Employers have a responsibility to maintain health and safety at work.

The numbers

- 133 employees were killed at work, 2013/14.
- 78,000 other injuries to employees were reported under RIDDOR (Reporting of Injuries, Diseases and Dangerous Occurrences Regulations), 2012/13.
- There were 175,000 absence injuries lasting more than seven days, 2012/13.
- million working people were suffering from a work-related illness, 2011/12.

- 27 million working days were lost due to work-related illness and workplace injury, 2011/12.
- Workplace injuries and ill health (excluding cancer) cost society approximately £13.8 billion, 2010/11.

Source: Health and Safety Executive, www.hsc.gov.uk.

AC 1.2 Describe the main points of the health and safety policies and procedures agreed with the employer

All workplaces must have a health and safety workbook, and it is usual that as part of your induction as a new member of staff you familiarise yourself with those policies (rules) and procedures.

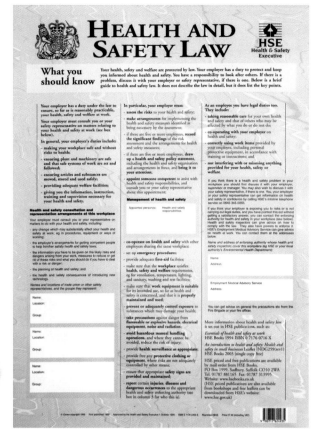
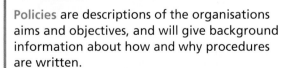

Figure 8.1 A health and safety at work poster

Policies for example, may include a policy about health and safety, explaining what the organisation expects of its employees in terms of their behaviour and ways of working.

Some of the more common procedures include:

- kitchen food handling – maintain food hygiene to protect individuals
- clinical waste disposal – ensure any hazardous waste is safely disposed of and individuals are not exposed to it
- display screen equipment – people working with computers for prolonged periods must

have an assessment to ensure that they do not have any ill effects from sitting looking at a screen for long periods

- first aid at work – all workplaces should have a nominated trained first aider
- lone working – some staff work alone in the community or in offices. it is important that the risks of working alone are assessed and dealt with
- manual handling – ensuring that staff lifting or moving objects and people are properly trained
- new and expectant mothers have risk assessments to ensure that they are able to carry out their role in a safe manner throughout their pregnancy and do not put themselves, the baby or others at risk.

AC 1.3 Outline the main health and safety responsibilities of:

- self
- the employer or manager
- others in the work setting.

Self and others

The Health and Safety Executive (www.hsc.gov.uk) states that:

- Workers have a duty to take care of their own health and safety and that of others who may be affected by your actions at work. Workers must co-operate with employers and co-workers to help everyone meet their legal requirements.
- Workers must follow the policies and procedures.
- Workers must follow safety procedures. This might include tying long hair, or

headscarf back or not wearing jewellery in certain environments. It may also include avoiding loose clothing that could for example get caught in equipment.

- Workers must use all appliances, equipment, etc. correctly in accordance with training and instructions.
- Workers must report any faults or hazards.
- Workers must deal with spillages, trip hazards as soon as possible – do not leave them to the next person!
- As a worker, if you have specific queries or concerns relating to health and safety in your workplace, you should talk to your employer, manager/supervisor or a health and safety representative.
- You should take care of your own health and safety and that of people who may be affected by what you do (or do not do) – for example, it may be appropriate to inform your manager or employer if you are taking medication that could affect your safety or the safety of others when carrying out your job. This might mean you should not operate machinery or drive.
- You should co-operate with others on health and safety, and do not interfere with, or misuse, anything provided for your health, safety or welfare.
- You should follow the training you have received when using any work items your employer has given you.
- You should follow and keep up to date with changes to training and procedures.
- You should ensure visitors, families, etc. comply with safety regulations.
- It may be appropriate to inform your manager or employer about injuries strains or illnesses as a result of your job. This might mean you should not operate machinery or drive. You should also let your manager know about other condition such as illness or pregnancy. They have legal responsibilities to look after their staff.

Workers must, for example wear protective clothing or attend particular Health and

Safety training if it is a requirement of the job. If they do not comply (obey) with these requirements they could, for example expose others to unsafe practice. This might lead to infections or injury.

The employer or manager

The Health and Safety Executive states that:

● It is an employer's duty to protect the health, safety and welfare of their employees and other people who might be affected by their business. This means making sure that workers and others are protected from anything that may cause harm, effectively controlling any **risks** to injury or health that could arise in the workplace by providing risk assessments.
● Education and training should include the responsibilities of the employer and employee, specific training required for the job, for example, food hygiene or moving and handling. They must also provide training on what to do in an emergency like a fire.
● Employers must give you information about the risks in your workplace and how you are protected, and instruct and train you on how to deal with the risks by providing education and development.
● Employers must consult employees on health and safety issues. **Consultation** must be either direct or through a safety representative who is either elected by the workforce or appointed by a trade union.
● Employers have a legal duty to display the approved poster in a prominent position in each workplace or to provide each worker with a copy of the approved leaflet 'Health and safety law: What you need to know'.
● Employers should provide an up-to-date health and safety policy.
● Employers must provide the right workplace facilities.

Employers must also display a health and safety policy. They have a responsibility to provide supervision, training and education, adequate access to first aid, emergency plans, protective clothing and must give appropriate advice about hazards including noise, radiation, flammable and explosive **hazards** and substances as well as ways to prevent exposure to them. Employees have a responsibility to report any accident, infectious disease, injury, dangerous or potentially dangerous occurrence to their employer.

Key terms

Risk means the likelihood of a causing harm.

Consultation means talking to workers and taking their views into account.

A **hazard** is something that could cause harm.

Evidence activity

1.3 Health and safety responsibilities

You observe a colleague moving a service user in a way you consider unsafe.

What responsibility do you, your colleague and your employer have in terms of health and safety?

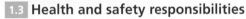

AC 1.4 Identify tasks relating to health and safety that should not be carried out without special training

We all have different roles in health and social care and training should be given to fit with the particular role. It is your responsibility to attend all training and to ask for training if you are unfamiliar or uncomfortable with an aspect of your job.

When you start a job you should have an induction session, which should include training to equip you to work safely and competently. You should never attempt to undertake a task if you do not have the skills to do it.

Training can be described as 'statutory' and 'mandatory':

- Statutory training is required by law as part of the Health and Safety at Work Act.
- Mandatory training is also required by your own organisation to ensure you are able to do your job without putting yourself and others at risk.

There may also be training that is only required for your particular role – for example, a nurse must train to administer (give) medication safely.

Tasks that the care worker should not carry out without special training may include those relating to:

- **Use of equipment** – without training the worker might use equipment incorrectly or for the wrong purpose- so putting themselves and the individual t risk
- **First aid** – all workers should have some basic first aid training so they can look after their own safety more effectively and are aware of the need to respond to and report any injuries or accidents. There is specialist training for "designated" first aiders
- **Medication** – NO health or social care worker should give out medication without training. If you are asked to do so explain that you have not had training and bring it to the attention of your supervisor or manager.
- **Health care procedures** – these are usually carried out by qualified staff- as with medication NEVER carry out a task (for example, emptying a catheter bag) without training as you need to be aware of the health and safety issues as well as the approved techniques (ways) of carrying out the task
- **Food handling and preparation** – remember, you are preparing food in another environment and poor hygiene and incorrect preparation of food could lead to food poisoning.
- **Moving and handling** – this is a very skilled activity- poor or no training means that you do not have the right skills and knowledge to hold and move an individual safely.
- **Managing violence and aggression** – you should receive training in this to protect

yourself an others. Depending on your role, the level of training may include de-escalation (calming down a situation) to "breakaway- safe methods of getting away from an individual who may have grabbed you by the wrist or hair.

- **Supporting people to eat and drink** – this is because some people have difficulty chewing and swallowing and may be at risk of choking. It is therefore important that you have training in how to support the individual safely in eating and drinking and have the skills to deal with possible choking.

Diets can vary from soft diets, thickened fluids or liquidised food and you must have an understanding of each diet and how they have to be prepared and offered to the individual. This is because the individual can choke or aspirate (food going into the lungs).

AC 1.5 Explain how to access additional support and information relating to health and safety

Health and safety affects both our working and our home lives. Look at most environments – a restaurant, a school, or a shop, for example, and you will see posters or leaflets related to health and safety. This is because it is a legal requirement to inform the public about the responsibilities of the organisation.

Health and safety is an important issue and it is important to find out where you can learn more about it if you are unsure about anything. For example, you may need more information about moving and handling or food hygiene. This is particularly important if you change your work setting and are expected to perform new tasks. There are a number of ways you can access additional support and information relating to health and safety.

Workplace and colleagues

Your line manager should be the first person you approach if you have any questions or queries relating to health and social care. Colleagues may also be able to help, although you must be confident that their advice is accurate. If you are unsure, ask your manager or supervisor.

Your workplace might also provide a health and safety work book or manual – ensure you familiarise yourself with it.

The internet

The most obvious way to find information on health and safety is through a search engine on the internet. Some helpful websites are listed in the useful resources section at the end of the unit.

Organisations

Organisations that can help and offer information include:

- Citizens Advice Bureau
- libraries
- health centres
- community centres
- hospitals
- trade unions
- professional organisations like the Health and Care Professions Council.

Manufacturers

Manufacturers also provide leaflets to advise on the use of the equipment; all medication has a written explanation of the use of the medication and its side effects.

LO2 Understand the use of risk assessments in relation to health and safety

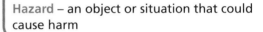

AC 2.1 Explain why it is important to assess health and safety hazards posed by the work setting or by particular activities

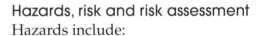

Key term

Hazard – an object or situation that could cause harm

Hazards, risk and risk assessment

Hazards include:

- use of chemicals, e.g. bleach, medication
- equipment that is not maintained and is broken or faulty
- fire exits obstructed
- excess noise or dust or heat or cold
- poor storage
- obstructions in public areas
- poor lighting
- poor hygiene, e.g. not washing your hands when handling food or after supporting an individual with personal care
- not using universal precautions when dealing with bodily fluids, i.e. not using disposable apron and gloves
- poor security in buildings.

It is important that we recognise any risks in the workplace and then decide how likely that risk is to occur. This is a risk assessment – we describe the risk and then measure how likely it is to occur and consider how serious the impact would be. Settings are required to do this by law and you should refer to AC 1.1 for all the legislation they need to follow.

An example of a risk assessment might be supporting an individual to use a kettle. The risk is the hot water or the kettle boiling dry, the likelihood would depend on who was using the kettle and why, if they were physically able to hold a kettle safely. The severity of the risk would be the impact boiling water would have if spilt. This type of risk assessment would be used when carrying out care planning for the individual, particularly if they were working towards being more independent with their activities of daily living.

Why is it important to assess health and safety hazards posed by the work setting?
Duty of care
It is important that we carry out these assessments and reduce risks as much as possible because we have a duty of care to protect our service users, families, friends and any visitors to an establishment.

Process for assessing health and safety hazards
Remember, the purpose of the assessment is to help to reduce any unnecessary risks to the individual. Risk assessments can be carried out by qualified or trained staff. These include Occupational Therapists, nurses, physiotherapists and trained care workers. Risks should be assessed when a new service is introduced or the individual's circumstances change, or a new piece of equipment is introduced, for example.

The process:

1 Describe the hazard.
2 Who might be affected?
3 Measure the risk – how often, how serious is the risk?
4 Plan how to reduce or eliminate (get rid of) the risk.
5 Review the risk assessment.

Working with individuals in their own home
When we work with individuals in their own home we must still be aware of potential risks and carry out risk assessments. This is because we have a duty of care. We may need to work with the individual and their family to try to reduce some of the risks. For example, there may be a risk of falls in the home and the Occupational Therapist might recommend that a rug which is a trip hazard is removed.

Regulations
Regulations are the rules that professional bodies use to ensure staff work in a safe and consistent way.

See AC 2.3 for more information on risk assessment.

Consequences
The consequences of not assessing the risks could affect you, the service user and your organisation. There could be issues of negligence (not following the correct procedures and laws), which carry financial penalties as well.

Evidence activity

2.1 Assessing health and safety hazards
Choose three of the potential hazards listed above. Have a look in your work setting. Are there any risk assessments for these hazards?

If not, discuss this with your supervisor or line manager.

With their support, write a risk assessment.

If there are risk assessments, are they visible? Are your colleagues aware of them?

Could they be improved? If so, make an action plan with your manager/supervisor.

AC 2.2 Explain how and when to report potential health and safety risks that have been identified

Health and social care workers will come across hazards every day and it is important to understand how to:

2.2 Reporting

Jim is a health care worker. He is walking down a corridor in another part of the building when he sees a pool of water on the floor. As this is not his usual work area he decides to leave it and ring 'someone' when he gets back to the ward.

You are asked to explain the correct procedure to Jim and explain the possible consequences of his actions and his role in maintaining health and safety.

Write a brief report with the main points.

- recognise the hazard
- assess any risk
- immediately minimise the danger/risk
- report it to the appropriate person in the appropriate way. This is your responsibility under the HASAWA.
- follow up your action.

You have a responsibility to report hazards, and you share the health and safety responsibility with the employer. Some hazards will need to be reported officially. You should refer to RIDDOR which will help you to work out risks and causes of incidents, accidents and diseases.

The employer has a duty to report incidents that are harmful or dangerous or might be harmful or dangerous. These include major injuries, deaths, and some diseases. Any accident in the workplace which means the injured worker has to take more than three days off work must also be reported.

AC 2.3 Explain how risk assessment can help address dilemmas between rights and health and safety concerns

Life is risky! Boiling a kettle, crossing the road, supporting a service user with challenging needs. We all have the right to take risks, and risks vary greatly in their impact on the individual. For example, the majority of us take a positive risk to cross a road every day and the impact of taking this risk is usually low. However, for someone with poor mobility or visual impairment the risk might be higher and the impact of making the decision to take that risk is greater, because they are more vulnerable crossing the road.

When we support service users we have a duty of care to enable them and encourage their independence as well as ensure they are not exposed to unnecessary risks.

The individual may not have capacity to understand the risks involved in an activity and care organisations have a legal responsibility to carry out risk assessments and to balance the risk to the individual against their right to maintain their independence. This is the dilemma.

It would be easier to take a **paternalistic** view – to make decisions on behalf of the individual to ensure we do not have to manage their risks. However, risk taking contributes to our quality of life and all individuals have the right to a quality of life that helps their well-being – just imagine being told you could not go swimming, or take a bus, or go for a walk because there were risks involved.

Risk assessments have several functions:

- They identify the risk.
- They quantify the risk (how likely, frequent and intense is the risk?).
- They give solutions to manage the risk and how to respond to the risk.
- They help us to avoid accidents.
- They ensure that we work within the law and the internal procedures in the organisation.

Key term

Paternalistic means taking charge and assuming the right to act as a parent by making decisions on behalf of the individual.

2.3 Risk assessment

Discuss with your manager or supervisor how in your organisation you manage the dilemma between the rights of the individual and health and safety concerns.

How are disputes between the individual and the care provider dealt with?

Rights and health and safety concerns

As a health or care support worker you may have to balance the rights of the individual against any specific concerns for their safety. On the one hand you are working with them to promote their independence, but equally, you have a duty of care to ensure they do not take risks that might seriously impact on their physical or mental well-being.

Once we understand the risks and how to deal with them, we can manage the balance between the risk to the individual and their rights. For example, a service user who is visually impaired may wish to go for walks, but the identified risk is crossing the road. In order to manage both the risk and the individual's right, the risk assessment identifies that to minimise the risk, the person could be accompanied on walks.

This activity can also be part of the care planning process to help all concerned understand the situation and work together co-operatively.

LO3 Understand procedures for responding to accidents and sudden illness

AC 3.1 Describe different types of accidents and sudden illness that may occur in own work setting

Work settings are within an establishment like a hospital, day centre or care home, but also in an individual's own home. The type of accidents and illness can be the same, but the way you deal with them may be different because of the circumstances.

Accidents and injuries

Accidents can be defined as an incident that has not been anticipated and that can result in the individual being hurt.

The Health and Safety Executive reports that in 2012/13 half of fatal injuries to workers were of three kinds:

- falls from height
- contact with moving machinery
- being struck by a vehicle.

Falls, trips and slips made up more than half of all reported major injuries. Approximately 3 million working days were lost due to handling injuries and slips and trips.

Other accidents and injuries are caused by the following:

- **Assault**. This was the third highest reported injury kind in health and social care. Some of the reasons service users may assault care workers are because they are confused, angry, frustrated or dealing with substance misuse. All assaults should be reported and, if necessary, the worker should receive appropriate support to deal with the physical and emotional effects of the assault. In some areas of health and social care there is an expectation that there will be some incidences of assault – in accident and emergency departments, or in mental health services, for example. This does not mean that this is acceptable, but risk assessments and appropriate training for staff should be in place. Staff should be trained in **de-escalation** and **breakaway** techniques, for example.
- **Needle stick injury**. There are strict procedures to follow when this injury occurs and all nurses and doctors are trained to deal with such an injury. Needle stick injuries can expose people to infectious diseases, like hepatitis B, or HIV.

Exposure to harmful substances

This includes both bodily fluids and chemicals such as bleach. We can be exposed to harmful substances when carrying out personal care tasks or cleaning equipment. A risk assessment should take place to ensure that you are taking the right precautions. There are specific guidelines regarding cleaning up spillages of harmful substances like blood or vomit. Your organisation should provide guidance on the products you should use, how and when to use them.

Illness

The Health and Safety Executive reports that some of the most commonly reported illnesses include:

- **Muscular skeletal disorder**. Back problems are common and can often be attributed to

poor techniques when moving and handling people and objects. There are also issues associated with sitting at computers. If you sit at a computer for any length of time, you should ask for a 'work station assessment' to ensure you are sitting in the right position and have the appropriate chair, etc.

- **Skin problems**. These may be caused by exposure to soaps, etc. Ensure you are supplied with and use the correct protective gloves. Some service users are uncomfortable because their care worker has to wear protective clothing, but it is important to work in partnership and explain it is as much to protect them as you. This should be discussed with your manager or supervisor in the first instance to ensure the right approach is established.

- **Stress, depression or anxiety**. Living with these conditions is very difficult, particularly when you are acting in a supportive way in your working life. It is important to seek professional help to ensure these feelings are dealt with as soon as possible, and that coping strategies and professional advice and support are given.

- **Infectious diseases**. These should be reported to your manager or supervisor immediately and the correct procedure observed. It is likely that you will not be able to return to work within a specified period.

Sudden illness might occur as a result of a medical problem like diabetes or heart disease. It is important that you are made aware of the symptoms of these conditions if you know either a colleague or a service user who lives with a particular condition.

AC 3.2 Outline the procedures to be followed if an accident or sudden illness should occur

There are two aspects to these procedures:

- reporting your own accident or illness
- dealing with the accident or sudden illness of a service user.

You must report an accident or illness as soon as you are aware of it. It is therefore important to familiarise yourself with the procedure for reporting and recording these occurrences. You will also be expected to record the facts of the situation, including details of what you saw, what action you took and the timing of each stage of the incident. You should therefore familiarise yourself with workplace procedures and find out where the accident forms are kept and who is responsible for recording these.

Own accident or illness

Your workplace must have procedures in place which comply with the law. If you are unwell or have an accident at work you must inform your manager/supervisor as soon as possible and most certainly on the same day. It may be reportable under RIDDOR.

You have a responsibility to keep yourself as safe as possible. This means not undertaking tasks you are not trained to do, or becoming involved in unsafe activities. You should also read all relevant risk assessments.

Dealing with the accident or sudden illness of a service user

Dealing with accidents or emergency situations involving individuals can be distressing and that is why it is important to understand your role. If you are not a trained first aider you must summon help straight away by finding a qualified first aider or calling an ambulance.

You may be asked to help the person who is dealing with the situation. Listen carefully to any instructions and never carry out a task if you do not feel confident or safe.

- Never put yourself in danger – we do not want another casualty.
- Be observant – you will be required to help with a report about the incident (who, what happened, when, what happened afterwards).
- Listen carefully to instructions if you are helping in the situation.
- Do not undertake anything without understanding what is expected of you or you have not been trained to do.
- Offer emotional support to family, friends, etc. if required.
- Ensure that all the relevant people have been informed.

First aid

There are basic first aid techniques that you can use. However, it is important that you discuss using these techniques with your manager and ensure that you have attended a basic first aid course.

Basic first aid uses the 'ABC' approach:

A Airway – checking it is clear.
B Breathing – look for chest movements which would mean the person is breathing.
C Circulation – this is compressing (pushing down) on the person's chest in a regular way; you should not do this unless you have been shown how to do it properly first.

Accidents, signs and symptoms and actions to take

Table 8.1 Accidents, signs and symptoms, and key actions to take (the information offered in these tables is advice only and you should consult your manager/supervisor for further guidance).

Type of accident	Signs and symptoms	Key actions to take
Fracture	Swelling Oddly positioned limbs Pain around the fractured area	• Do not move the injured person. • Support the injured limb. • Reassure the injured person. • Call and ensure that the fracture is diagnosed correctly at a hospital – you should not try to bandage this yourself. • Do not give the injured person anything to eat or drink.
Cut	Large or small amounts of blood	• Apply pressure to a cut that is bleeding. • Use a dressing if one is available. • Call for help.
Bleeding	Large or small amounts of blood	• Apply pressure to a bleeding wound. • If there is an object in the wound, do not remove the object, but do apply pressure either side of the wound. • Protect yourself from coming into contact with the blood. • Raise the injured body part if possible and ensure the casualty is comfortable. • Call for help.
Burn/scalds caused by heat/flames/hot liquids/chemicals/ electrical currents	Swollen or blistered skin The person may be in severe pain or shock	• Call for medical help immediately. • Cool the burn with cold water (keep it underwater for 10 minutes for burns, 20 minutes for chemical burns. Ensure that you safely dispose of water used to cool chemical burns. • Remove if possible any clothing or jewellery that is not stuck to the skin.
Poisoning caused by chemicals, plants or substances like drugs and alcohol	The person may be unconscious The person may be in severe pain Swollen or blistered skin around the mouths and lips	• If the person is unconscious, place them in the recovery position and call for medical help. • Try to find out either from the person or from objects left in the area what the poison may have been and how much has been taken.
Electrical injuries caused by high voltages (e.g. railway lines) or low voltages (e.g. electrical appliances such as a kettle or heater)	The person may have burns The person may have had a cardiac arrest	• Do not touch the person until the electricity supply has been cut off. For low voltage currents switch the electric off at the mains if you can; if you can't then try to move the casualty using something dry and not made of metal, e.g. a wooden broom. • Call for medical help immediately. • When safe to do so, treat the injured person (i.e. for burns) and if the person is unconscious place them in the recovery position.

Source: Maria Ferreiro Peteiro, *Level 3 Health & Social Care Diploma*, Hodder Education 2015

Table 8.2 Types of sudden illness, signs and symptoms, and key actions to take (the information offered in these tables is advice only and you should consult your manager/supervisor for further guidance).

Type of sudden illness	Signs and symptoms	Key actions to take
Cardiac arrest is caused by a heart attack, shock or electric shock	The person has no pulse The person is not breathing	• Reassure the person. • Call for help. • Carry out cardio-pulmonary resuscitation (CPR) only if you have been fully trained to do so.
Stroke is caused by blood clots that block the flow of blood to the brain	The person may have an uneven face The person may not be able to raise and hold both arms up The person's speech may be confused	• Call for help. • Reassure the person.
Epileptic seizure is caused by changes in the brain's activity	Involuntary contraction of muscles	• Make the immediate area safe. • Do not attempt to move or restrict the person; make sure the person's clothes are loose. • Once the seizure has ended, place the person in the recovery position. • Reassure the person, ensure they are comfortable, and be particularly careful to prevent any head injury. • Call for help.
Choking and difficulty with breathing can be caused by food becoming stuck in the throat	Coughing Difficulty breathing (gasping) Difficulty speaking	• Encourage the person to cough and remove their dentures if possible from their mouth. • If this fails, use the heel of the hand to give five blows between the shoulder blades while person is bent forwards. • If this fails use abdominal thrusts (the Heimlich manoeuvre), but only if you have been trained to do so. • Call for help.
Shock is caused when blood is not flowing round the body effectively	Cold, clammy and/or pale skin Fast pulse Fast breathing May feel sick	• Call for help. • Lay the person on the floor and raise their feet off the ground if possible. • Monitor and reassure the person, ensure they are warm, that their clothing is not too tight, and regularly check on their breathing and pulse. • Do not give the casualty anything to eat or drink and do not leave them alone.
Loss of consciousness is caused by fainting or a serious illness	Not being responsive: either partial or total unresponsiveness	• Check if the person is breathing and has a clear airway. • Reassure the person. • Look for reasons why they may be unconscious. • Place the casualty in the recovery position to maintain their safety, but only if they do not have any injuries to their back or neck or any fractured limbs, in which case the casualty should not be moved. • Call for help.

Source: Maria Ferreiro Peteiro, *Level 3 Health & Social Care Diploma*, Hodder Education 2015

You will be expected to make a record of incidents. You may have internal incident report forms to complete, or you may be asked to make an entry in the individual's notes. This should include:

- the date of the incident
- the time of the incident and if possible the time help arrived, how the situation was dealt with and what happened next
- what happened leading up to the accident or illness
- who summoned help and what they did
- details of the injury/accident/illness
- what was the consequence for the individual
- your signature and date of the entry
- names and designations (job role) of people who witnessed it
- their condition after the accident (if known).

LO4 Be able to reduce the spread of infection

AC 4.1 Demonstrate the recommended method for hand-washing

In the course of your work you will be in contact with many people, either supporting them with personal care or eating and drinking. You will be writing records and handling documents. All these activities have the potential to spread germs or bacteria from one person to another. This is why it is crucial that you pay attention to thorough hand-washing, and take steps to control the spread of infection.

Public Health England supported the World Health Organisation's Clean Your Hands Campaign in 2014.

It states that our hands touch hundreds, possibly thousands of surfaces every day and hands help to spread bacteria and viruses.

There is a certain technique for effective hand-washing that prevents the spread of bacteria (germs) and infection, and it is important that you learn this technique. In many work areas there are illustrations in toilets and bathrooms that give a step-by-step guide to hand-washing.

Washing your hands is one of the most effective ways of preventing the spread of bacteria. But you must follow certain rules:

- Wash your hands **before** dealing with food or an individual.
- Wash your hands **after** dealing with food or an individual.
- Wash your hands after going to the toilet, sneezing, smoking, touching your hair or body.
- Wash your hands if you know you have come into contact with dirty or potentially dirty surfaces.
- After dealing with soiled linen, dressings, etc. (You may also need to wear gloves, but you should still wash your hands afterwards.)

1 Wet hands with water

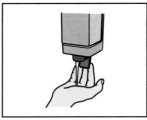
2 Apply enough soap to cover all hand surfaces

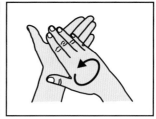
3 Rub hands palm to palm

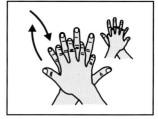
4 Right palm over back of left hand with interlaced fingers and vice versa

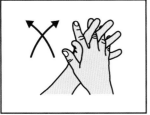
5 Palm to palm with fingers interlaced

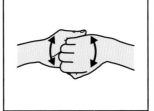
6 Backs of fingers to opposing palms with fingers interlocked

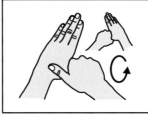
7 Rotational rubbing of left thumb clasped in right palm and vice versa

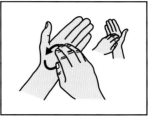
8 Rotational rubbing, backwards and forwards with clasped fingers of right hand in left palm and vice versa

9 Rinse hands with water

10 Dry hands thoroughly with a single-use towel

11 Use towel to turn off tap

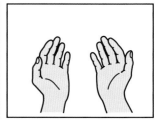
12 Your hands are now safe

Figure 8.2 The hand-washing process

There may also be an expectation, depending on your work role, for you to:

- be 'bare below the elbow' – this means rolling up your sleeves and not wearing a watch or bracelets
- keep your fingernails short
- remove nail polish and jewellery except a plain wedding band.

You must cover all cuts and abrasions with a waterproof dressing. If you work in a food preparation area you should use blue plasters.

Alcohol rubs

Although you can use alcohol rubs or gels they are not recommended as a substitute for hand-washing. They can also dry out the hands, which can cause cracks in the skin and this can trap bacteria, so it is recommended that you use hand cream to moisturise the skin. Alcohol gels are useful if you work in the community and do not have ready access to soap and running water, but you should always try to find proper washing facilities.

Evidence activity

4.1 Hand-washing

Go to:

www.gov.uk/government/news/the-invisible-bugs-that-lurk-on-your-hands

Read the article. What did you learn from it?

How might you be able to improve your practice or that of your colleagues?

Write a summary of the technique and demonstrate good hand-washing to your supervisor.

AC 4.2 Demonstrate ways to ensure that own health and hygiene do not pose a risk to others at work

As a health and social care worker you probably work in environments that potentially pose risks, and so it is important that you take care of yourself and in turn do not pose a risk to service users, colleagues and members of the public.

Policies and procedures, induction and updated training are all in place to support you to maintain your health and hygiene.

We know that it is possible to 'carry' infections from place to place and therefore you must be vigilant if you or someone you have contact with has an infection that can passed on from one person to another. This includes diarrhoea and vomiting, and colds and flu.

If you do have diarrhoea and vomiting you must not go into your place of work and you should be 48 hours clear before returning to work. If the person(s) you support have diarrhoea and vomiting, this should be reported to your manager or supervisor.

There are other diseases that you should be aware of and seek advice about if you either contract them or have contact with someone who is suffering from them. These include chicken pox, German measles and mumps. This is important so that cross infection can be prevented.

Other ways to prevent infection and ensure you do not pose a risk to others

You can also prevent the spread of infection in other ways, so it is important to:

- Wear disposable gloves and protective clothing (PPE) when dealing with bodily fluids.
- Ensure your clothing is appropriate for your role. It is likely your organisation has a dress code.

- Ensure there are not any sharp objects such as pens and pencils that could be a hazard for individuals. For example, objects could accidentally harm the individual.
- Wear appropriate clothing including shoes. Heels can be a hazard for both you and a risk to others. It is preferable to wear flat shoes with no sling backs or open toes.
- Wear protective clothing (PPE) See unit HSC 2015 for more information.
- Deal with waste, ensuring the correct bags are used to dispose of this.
- Long hair or headscarves are tied back.
- Not wear jewellery except a plain wedding band (there may be restrictions on this set by your workplace).
- Ensure you clean any equipment you use.
- Follow food hygiene and safety procedures – this will include wearing appropriate clothing like a white coat and hat in a kitchen area. Always wash your hands before and after handling food.
- Take special precautions, such as in cases of food poisoning.

See Unit ICO2 for more information on infection control.

Case study

4.2 Own health and hygiene

Jim, the care support worker, has been to visit his niece. She is unwell with diarrhoea and vomiting. Jim goes home and has the same symptoms within several hours.

He is worried because he knows they are short staffed at work and thinks he should go in.

What should he do and why?

Evidence activity

4.2 Health and hygiene

Draw up a table of the various methods you can use to manage your own health and hygiene.

LO5 Be able to move and handle equipment and other objects safely

AC 5.1 Identify legislation that relates to moving and handling

Moving and handling is often a key aspect of our work in health and social care. This might include moving equipment, laundry, or assisting service users to move (walk, sit in a chair, transfer from bed to chair, etc.).

Care workers who are not appropriately trained or do not follow the correct procedure can put themselves and the service user at risk. Poor practice leads to:

- back pain or injury
- accidents
- anxiety – the service user may feel that the care worker lacks the right skills and does not have confidence in their ability to help them in a competent way.

Legislation that relates to moving and handling includes:

- Health and Safety at Work etc. Act 1974
- Manual Handling Operations Regulations 1992 (amended 2002)
- Management of Health and Safety at Work Regulations
- Lifting Operations and Lifting Equipment Regulations 1998.

See AC 1.1 for information on these.

The legislation deals with:

- risk assessment
- ensuring equipment is used for the intended purpose
- ensuring that the equipment is maintained in a safe condition.

Evidence activity

5.1 Moving and handling legislation

Think about the type of moving and handling activities you carry out at work.

Refer to the legislation above and write some bullet point notes on the main points of the legislation.

Use this to give a brief information session in a staff meeting.

AC 5.2 Explain principles for moving and handling equipment and other objects safely

We use moving and handling equipment to transfer objects and people safely. We no longer refer to 'lifting' because this should always be avoided when dealing with people or any heavy object. Equipment is used to lift a full weight, or move someone, or to enable the individual to maintain their independence.

There are basic principles to think about when moving and handling safely.

Recognise and assess the risks and use the following precautions to reduce the risks:

- Ensure all staff are clear about their roles and responsibilities.
- Ensure that all people carry out the procedures correctly.
- Avoid any handling that might result in injury. Injury or pain should not be caused to the worker or the individual.
- Encourage individuals to do as much for themselves (to actively participate).
- Employers have a responsibility to provide lifting and handling equipment, but it is your duty to use this safely.
- Ensure that the handling is necessary and look for safe alternatives, including the use of equipment.

- Ensure the service user has been consulted throughout the process and is able to participate safely – for example, they are able to understand instructions, or express any discomfort they may be feeling. You should reassure them and talk them through the process every time you are engaged in moving them because it can be a frightening and sometimes embarrassing experience.
- Ensure you have enough space to move.
- Ensure the floor surfaces are safe to move on.
- Use brakes on wheelchairs, hoists, etc.
- If you are working as a pair, ensure you are both clear about the sequence of events – agree to begin hoisting on the word 'go', for example.
- If the situation changes or you are concerned about the process, consult your manager or supervisor for advice.

Evidence activity

5.2 Principles for moving and handling equipment

Think of an example of a piece of equipment used to:

- lift an object or a person
- move a person safely from one place to another
- enable a person to move about independently.

AC 5.3 Move and handle equipment or other objects safely

Due to health and safety regulations the techniques for moving and handling have changed a great deal over recent years. This is to protect both the service user and the member of staff.

Case study

5.3 Move and handle

You are working with Jim and are supporting a service user to have a bath. This involves using a hoist. When you start to use the hoist you realise that it is faulty. Jim suggests you carry on by lifting the person into the bath together.

There are two major concerns in this scenario. What are they and what course of action should you have taken?

There is a variety of specialised equipment that can be used. The physiotherapist will usually assess the situation to establish the most suitable type of equipment: This includes:

- Hoists, which are designed to help transfer a person from bed to chair, wheelchair to bath, etc.
- slide boards
- banana (transfer) boards.

In your place of work there could be a wide variety of equipment. Each individual is assessed in terms of the equipment they require to support them and it is crucial that you do not use any equipment before being trained in its use. You must also never support an individual with a piece of equipment unless an assessment has been carried out. For example, if an individual always uses a stick to walk with, do not offer them a Zimmer frame if you think they are struggling – this needs to be correctly assessed. It is your responsibility to bring the problem to the attention of your manager or supervisor.

Before and during moving and handling

You should always be trained in moving and handling people before supporting anyone with moving from one place to another (bed to chair, for example). Once you have been trained and assessed as being competent (able to do the job properly) you should read

Figure 8.3 It is important to use the proper techniques for moving people

your organisation's policies and procedures, familiarise yourself with the equipment you will be using and make sure you have read and understood the moving and handling care plans for each individual. If the care plan says that two people must work together to help the person to move, ensure you have agreed first how you will do this so that you are working as a team. You should ask for advice if unsure, so you know how to carry out the manoeuvre safely and correctly. Any changes should be reported immediately, or if you are concerned for the safety of the individual during a transfer, so that the situation can be reassessed and an amended care plan written. Most care plans include risk assessments to help you understand and deal with any risks when moving an individual. Such risks might include having variable mobility – so they may be steadier on their feet on some days.

LO6 Know how to handle hazardous substances and materials

AC 6.1 Identify hazardous substances and materials that may be found in the work setting

Substances and materials that are hazardous and found in the workplace (including the individual's own home) include:

- chemicals (including cleaning products containing chemicals)
- fumes

Key term

COSHH stands for Control of Substances Hazardous to Health.

- dust
- gas
- germs
- asbestos
- lead.

Refer to 'Working with substances hazardous to health: A brief guide to **COSHH**' (HSE, 2012).

Sometimes we assume normal everyday items are not hazardous, but in fact household items like paint, washing up liquid and bleach are potentially hazardous if not stored in the correct way or are used for the wrong purposes.

AC 6.2 Describe safe practices for:

- **storing hazardous substances**
- **using hazardous substances**
- **disposing of hazardous substances and materials.**

Safe practices for storing hazardous substances

The COSHH regulations identify safe practice and guidance about the storage of hazardous substances. Safe storage includes:

- always store the substance in its original container – never 'decant' washing up liquid, etc. into a different container
- if necessary, ensuring substances are stored in a well-ventilated area to prevent fumes building up and increasing the risk of explosion or fire
- not storing items on high shelves so they are difficult to reach and could fall off
- storing substances in a locked area to prevent vulnerable people accessing them
- following manufacturers' instructions for safe storage.

Describe safe practices for using hazardous substances

All potentially hazardous substances carry warning labels. Check the label on hazardous substances as this will tell you how to use them and what to do if you spill the substance. You should also have a risk assessment at hand – this is "Control of Substances Hazardous to Health" (COSHH). You should NOT use any hazardous substance unless there is such a risk assessment.

COSHH regulations require your employer to:

- have procedures in place to store hazardous substances safely
- use and dispose of them safely
- provide protective (PPE) clothing such as gloves or goggles that keeps you safe from the hazardous substances.

Figure 8.4 Be aware of warning labels

You must also take responsibility for your own safety and therefore you must wear protective clothing when dealing with hazardous materials. You must make sure you know what you are using and how to use it.

Figure 8.5 shows a burn inflicted by a hazardous substance – the worker was not wearing the correct protective clothing, nor had they questioned whether it was appropriate to use the substance.

Safe practices for disposing of hazardous substances and materials

- Faeces and urine
- Blood
- Chemicals
- Sharps
- Soiled linen
- Clinical waste.

All of the above can be described as hazardous substances because they have a potentially harmful effect if not disposed of correctly.

- Bodily fluids: You should always use protective clothing when dealing with any bodily fluid and ensure you safely dispose of the apron and gloves and wash your hands before supporting another individual.

Most organisations provide guidance on how to clean areas that have been contaminated by blood, and urine, for example. If you work in a care home, use the **sluice facilities**, and if you work in an individual's own home, ensure the toilet and bathroom are thoroughly cleaned with bleach. Check instructions about how to dilute the bleach and do not mix one chemical with another, e.g. bleach and toilet cleaner, as this can produce dangerous fumes.

- Sharps (syringes, needles, hypodermic needles) should ALWAYS be disposed of in a yellow sharps bin. NEVER handle a needle that does not have a cover over the needle tip.

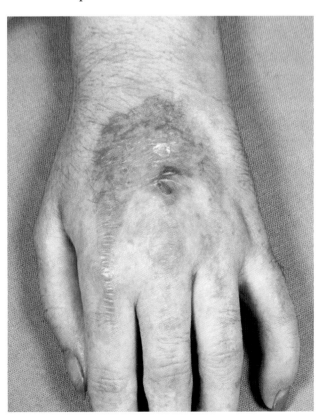

Figure 8.5 A burn as a result of using a hazardous substance

- Soiled linen must always be handled wearing disposable gloves- you should change gloves for each individual's linen. Never place soiled linen on the floor, and transfer to the sluice as soon as possible.
- Always cover commode pans when taking them to be emptied, and use the recommended cleaning solutions and methods. If in doubt, seek advice from your supervisor.
- Some establishments and all hospitals use disposable bed pans. Ensure you have been shown how to use the macerator (sanitary waste disposal unit).

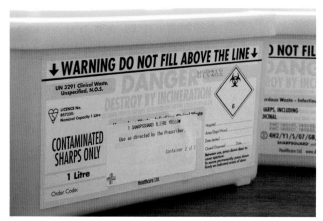

Figure 8.6 Needles must be placed in the sharps bin after use

Evidence activity

6.2 Safe practices

Make a list of all the hazardous substances you come into contact with at work and describe how to dispose of them. What are the safe practices to use for:

- storing hazardous substances
- using hazardous substances
- disposing of hazardous substances and materials.

LO7 Understand how to promote fire safety in the work setting

AC 7.1 Describe practices that prevent fires from:

- **starting**
- **spreading.**

Preventing a fire from starting

The most effective way of fire prevention is to ensure you have systems in place to stop the fire from starting in the first place.

Fire needs three things:

- oxygen
- fuel – this can be gas, wood or paper, fabrics, etc.
- heat – this can be an electric or gas fire, cigarettes, sparks.

See AC 7.2 for more information on procedures to follow in the event of a fire.

Flammable materials

All flammable material (for example furniture) should be checked for British Safety Standards and all flammable liquids should be stored safely away from possible sources of fire. Do not store large quantities of flammable liquids if possible and make sure they are in a well-ventilated area.

Do not use faulty electrical equipment and if you find a fault, report it immediately. If you work in the service user's home, advise them not to use the equipment and put it away or dispose of it with their permission.

Smoking

Smoking is not permitted in communal and public areas, but this is not the case in the individual's home. If they do smoke ensure that an adequate risk assessment is in place and you are very clear about what to do if you think there is a fire risk.

Vigilance and risk assessment

Vigilance in any environment is also key to fire prevention. Be aware of new hazards and

Research and investigate

8.1 Preventing fires

Look into the different health and safety symbols and marks. For example, what does the British Standard Safety Mark for non-flammable furniture look like?

the policy for reporting and dealing with them. Ensure you are aware of those people most at risk and that you know what the evacuation plan is.

There may also be risk assessments for more vulnerable individuals – for example, those with poor mobility.

Training

Fire safety training is also crucial. Ensure you keep updated and ask for advice if you are unsure of any procedures.

Fire safety check

If you work in a service user's home it is worth while discussing with them a fire safety check from the local fire service. The service is keen to do this, particularly for vulnerable, housebound people. They will check and fit fire and/or smoke detectors.

Preventing a fire from spreading

If you discover a fire in its early stages you may be able to contain it by using the appropriate fire extinguisher. If you are not confident you cannot put out the fire then raise the alarm

immediately, summon the fire service and evacuate the area. You should familiarise yourself with fire fighting equipment, including the use of extinguishers and fire blankets.

Figure 8.7 Different fire extinguishers have different uses

Evidence activity

7.1 Preventing fires

Carry out a survey in your place of work (if this is an establishment) or think about the home of a vulnerable service user.

Make a note of any potential fire risks and bring them to the attention of your supervisor or line manager.

Discuss an action plan to be put in place.

Research and investigate

7.1 Fire extinguishers

Go to **www.extinguisheradvice.org.uk** and research the different types of extinguishers. Learn more about their uses and purposes, danger points and advice on how to use them.

Remember that fire produces smoke, fumes and explosions and therefore you must never assume it is a simple matter of putting out a fire in a waste bin, for example. There could be an aerosol can in the bin, which could explode.

Fire spreads when oxygen feeds it, so as you leave the building close all doors to stop the spread. NEVER wedge fire doors open.

AC 7.2 Outline emergency procedures to be followed in the event of a fire in the work setting

All workplaces have a fire procedure and it is one of the first things you should familiarise yourself with when you start in a new job. You should:

- Get to know the building and where hazardous substances are stored.
- Ensure you know the correct address, including the postcode.
- Find the fire doors.
- Locate the fire alarm points.
- Locate the fire assembly point/s outside the building.
- Check if you have a 'signing in' register for all staff and visitors – the fire service could waste valuable time looking for someone who has already left the building.
- Locate the fire extinguishers and ensure you know which types of fire they can extinguish – for example, never use a water extinguisher on an electric fire. All extinguishers have written guidance for use on the side.

Remember:

Keep calm and do not run, you could cause panic. Sound the alarm.

The safety of everyone is the most important thing to remember and therefore unless you are 100% sure you can extinguish the fire – using the correct fire extinguisher – dial 999 immediately.

- You will be asked which service you require. Answer clearly and concisely (do not try to tell a long story). The call handler will want to know your name and address and the location of the fire, e.g. 'ground floor lounge', and how many people could be affected. Make it clear that the people are vulnerable and some may not be able to evacuate the building without help. They will also need to know if anyone is trapped and where they are.

- The person in charge of the building may give you instructions to start moving people out. Fire doors are designed to keep the fire back and you would only be expected to start evacuating people yourself if there was a risk the fire door would not be enough protection. It is crucial that you check all these arrangements out now, so that you are prepared.
- Do not use the lift.
- Take mobile people out of the nearest exits and if people cannot be moved, close their bedroom door after reassuring them that they are safe as the fire service is on its way.
- Do not stay in the building longer than necessary – the fire and rescue service need to rescue the vulnerable service users, not able bodied staff.
- Do not re-enter the building. There could be risk of explosion or smoke and fumes affecting you before you could safely leave.

Some buildings have an automatic phone line to the fire and rescue service which alerts them when the fire alarm goes off. However, even if this is the case you should still dial 999 as the line may be damaged or not in use.

Remember:

- Always respond to fire alarms unless you are fully aware it is a test.
- Ensure you have regular fire drills.

You will also need to ensure that you have the fire register with you when you evacuate the building. This includes the visitors' register, the list of staff on duty and the register of all residents currently in the building so you and the fire service can account for everyone.

Evidence activity

7.2 Emergency procedures

Refresh your memory about fire procedures. Investigate who the local fire safety officer is and ask for advice in producing a fire safety guidance leaflet for your service users.

AC 7.3 Explain the importance of maintaining clear evacuation routes at all times

All public buildings have particular fire escape routes and all fire doors should have signs to inform you they are the designated fire proof doors that close automatically in the event of a fire.

Evacuation routes should:

- be free from obstacles such as unused equipment, to ensure the way is not blocked – valuable time is wasted if you have to remove obstacles
- have a safe surface to walk on so there are no trip hazards
- have handrails to provide support for people who may be unsteady
- be wide enough to enable people in wheelchairs to be evacuated safely
- be well lit so anyone with poor sight can find their way more easily
- be well signposted so that staff, service users and visitors are aware of the escape routes.

Evidence activity

7.3 Clear evacuation routes

Imagine that you are working in a care home. When you check the evacuation route at the back of the building you discover it is being used as a storage area for refuse to be disposed of at the end of the day. Your colleague tells you it doesn't matter as he always removes the refuse at night and anyway, no one would use that corridor.

Do you think he is right?

What action might you take and what guidance could you read to help you?

LO8 Be able to implement security measures in the work setting

AC 8.1 Use agreed ways of working for checking the identity of anyone requesting access to:

- premises
- information.

Key terms

Agreed ways of working include procedures and agreed standards of conduct in a place of work.

Premises include both health and social care establishments and the service user's home. As a health and social care worker you have a duty of care to ensure they are not exposed to unwanted visitors. This might include people who can take advantage of a vulnerable person and

Individuals have a right to feel secure in the setting. In a health and social care setting, security can mean that individuals feel safe and secure against abuse, that their property is secure, and that they feel secure against the threat of unwanted visitors.

Basic rules

There are basic rules you should follow when dealing with anyone who is requesting access to the premises:

- Check whether the person was expected.
- Ask for their identification.
- Do not let them into private areas of the building until you are sure they have a genuine reason to be there.
- If they are at the door of a service user's home, ensure they cannot see inside – some bogus callers are checking the property for an opportunity to burgle.
- If you are concerned, call the police and make sure you can identify the caller.

All visitors to an establishment should sign the visitors' book and wear their identification. It also helps if you can provide a badge that identifies them as a visitor.

Callers and visitors

- Cold callers – people who claim to be salespeople who want to discuss a service or sale of goods with you. They call without invitation and can catch people 'off guard'. You can support the individual by discussing the risks involved and consulting with Trading Standards who can offer advice and information about cold and bogus callers.

- Bogus callers – people who falsely claim they are repair men, meter readers, etc. You should always ask for identification and if you are at all suspicious tell them it is not a convenient time. A genuine person will come back another day and in the meantime you can contact the organisation they claim they are from. If they are indeed bogus callers, alert Trading Standards who liaise with the police in these matters.
- People who have already been requested not to visit – this might be a relative or unwanted salesperson. They do not have an automatic right of entry and you can refuse to let them in until you have checked that it has been agreed they can visit. This should have been discussed with your manager already. When dealing with these situations always remain firm and polite. Do not get drawn into arguments and calmly explain that the person they want to visit has chosen not to see them and that is their right. If they persist, ask them to wait in a safe place and ask for the support of a more senior person.
- Remember – you are not automatically obliged to admit entry to visitors.

Information

All personal information is protected by the **Data Protection Act 1998**. Information can only be shared with the permission of the individual and on a 'need-to-know' basis.

Be very careful you do not talk about service users in front of other people, and store their information in a secure place.

Advising individuals who live in their own homes

You should advise individuals who live in their own homes about the importance of checking the identity of people at the door. There are also schemes which provide smoke alarms and security devices. Trading Standards offer advice and support, as do the fire services in most areas.

See AC 8.2 for more information on security. There may be some overlap in this unit, and AC 8.2 measures for security, but this is part of checking identity.

AC 8.2 Implement measures to protect own security and the security of others in the work setting

We have discussed how we can authorise visitors who wish to gain entrance; we can explore other measures to protect security.

Own security

Most organisations have a "zero" tolerance policy for violence and aggression towards staff from members of the public. It is important to have training in how to deal with and de-escalate challenging situations. Ensure you are aware of any alarm systems in place. If you know you may come into contact with a potentially difficult situation, alert a colleague to be your "back up" – they may need to be just out of sight but close enough to come to your aid. If the situation escalates, remove yourself and if appropriate, call the police and ensure your manager is made aware.

Managing behaviour that challenges from individuals that we support is an entirely different matter and you must have training in how to support them effectively, for example, a person living with dementia may be aggressive but this is likely to be caused by their own fear or inability to express themselves clearly.

Security of others

We can protect the security of others in a care setting or in their own home by using different strategies.

- You should always familiarise yourself with the security arrangements in your work setting, and if you support individuals living in the community check if there are neighbourhood watch schemes or other initiatives.
- Most organisations expect their staff to wear identity badges – always show them to visitors or new service users – do not wait to be asked.
- Ensure that any locked areas are not accessed by people who do not have authority to do so – ask for their identification and if in doubt, check first with a more senior member of staff. Visitors are often issued with an official visitors' badge.
- The individuals you support are more vulnerable because of their disability, or mental health needs or general frailty. Be aware that they can be more likely to be exposed to exploitation or hate crime, for example. Check with your manager or supervisor if it would be helpful to make contact with community police officers if there are particularly vulnerable people living alone. This may be done by the individual's care co-ordinator and might be part of their care plan, so always check first, particularly as you also require the permission of the individual or in some circumstances their family to alert the police.
- When individuals live in a collective care setting like a care home we must respect their right to privacy (for example, in their bedrooms) but also ensure that the security of the building is maintained. This means being vigilant, checking identification, ensuring you are aware of any visitors and respecting the rights of the individual not to see visitors.

Property

In a collective care setting there will be lockable facilities for the safekeeping of valuables. It is usually good practice to make an inventory of property when the individual is admitted. Remember to describe jewellery using the colour, for example 'yellow metal ring with white stone' – do not write gold ring with diamond as this is making an assumption.

If you have concerns about the safety of the individual's property, inform your line manager. Sometimes people living with dementia will 'lose' items and think they have been stolen. Although you must respect this fear, you should also look at the facts and check the item has not been misplaced. Be vigilant-if you think items are missing, this must be reported because of the vulnerability of the individual.

Other measures

- DBS – this used to be the Criminal Records Bureau checks and is now the Disclosure and Barring Service. All those who work with vulnerable people and children are subject to this check, to ensure that they are suitable for the role. You probably have personal experience of such a check.
- If you are a nurse, therapist, doctor or social worker you will also be required to register with your professional organisation, to ensure you work within its code of conduct.
- As well as processes to ensure people work safely, there are practical steps that can be taken to secure a building, including security key pads, CCTV, burglar alarms, visitors' books, panic alarms, walkie talkies and pagers.

Evidence activity

8.2 Measures

Think about your work situation.

What measures are there to make sure you are safe? How could these be improved?

AC 8.3 Explain the importance of ensuring that others are aware of own whereabouts

You have a responsibility to keep yourself safe, but equally your employer should ensure there are tough procedures in place so that relevant risk assessments and safety measures are there to protect you.

It is likely that your organisation has a 'lone working' policy, particularly if they employ people who work in the community, although lone working also applies to anyone who is working alone in a building.

If you work alone you should:

- ensure there are no risks involved if you are visiting a new service user (e.g. behaviour that challenges)
- check the address and that there are no problems in terms of safety, e.g. access. Is it a remote road or an unlit area?
- use the signing out procedure and indicate where you are going, who you are seeing and the time you are expected back so that you can be found in case there are any problems or concerns
- if you feel you need more support, ask a colleague to ring you on your mobile phone (make sure it is charged!) at a certain time
- make sure you also leave the landline number of the address you are visiting in case there is no mobile reception
- ensure your car is in good repair to prevent it breaking down in remote or risky areas
- make sure you have enough petrol to get you back safely
- if you are working alone in a building, make sure a colleague knows you are there and agree that you will ring them as you leave
- use the 'buddy system' when working alone in the community, especially after 'office hours'
- carry a personal alarm or panic button.

The Suzy Lamplugh Trust has more tips and information: **www.suzylamplugh.org**

Evidence activity

8.3 Whereabouts

Think about the risks associated with lone working.

Write a list and then check whether your organisation has a policy or procedure to manage those risks.

If necessary, discuss this with your supervisor or line manager.

LO9 Know how to manage own stress

AC 9.1 Identify common signs and indicators of stress

Key term

Stress means pressure or tension. It can have positive as well as negative effects, but in this unit the word is used to refer to negative stress.

We all experience **stress** to a greater or lesser extent and the term is often used loosely to describe the experience of being under pressure. However, stress actually describes feelings of anxiety and possibly depression that do not easily go away. We might have a difficult day at work but once we get home we feel better and are able to relax. Experiencing stress often means that the person cannot relax or 'switch off'.

Common signs and indicators of stress are similar to those of depression. Below are some of the emotional and physical signs and indicators of stress.

Emotional
This can include:

- poor sleep pattern
- early waking
- over-attention to detail
- lack of concentration
- feelings of being overwhelmed
- tearfulness

Evidence activity

9.1 Stress

Think about situations that might have triggered some of these feelings.

How did you cope with this?

Think about how you could support colleagues who may experience some of these feelings.

- irritability
- feelings of dread and constant worry.

Physical

This can include:

- tiredness
- chest pains
- aches and pains
- more likely to get colds
- loss of appetite.

AC 9.2 Identify circumstances that tend to trigger own stress

In the previous exercise you have already begun to identify some triggers. Others you may or may not have experienced include:

- financial worries – this can include whether you are able to pay the rent or mortgage, or whether you are able to afford this month's bills
- life events, relationship difficulties or bereavement
- lack of sleep, work pressures or feeling unsettled at work – job roles may be changing; there may be new expectations and responsibilities you have to manage; the hours you have to work may also be an issue
- lack of support from your manager, colleagues, friends or family – feelings of being abandoned or alone
- juggling work and home life – feeling that you have conflicting responsibilities and you are having to please everyone
- lack of job satisfaction, frustration with colleagues or lack or career progression. You may also be worried about redundancy or retirement
- dealing with unfamiliar situations or people.

Evidence activity

9.2 Triggers

Look at the above list. Can you identify with any of these triggers?

Talk to a trusted colleague about the things that would trigger their stress. Discuss some coping strategies to support one another.

AC 9.3 Describe ways to manage own stress

Work/life balance

'Work/life balance' is a phrase commonly used today – it simply means that to manage our own well-being we should aim to have a balance between our work and home lives so that one does not overtake the other. Most people would say that their work life can take over, particularly if they have deadlines to meet or they are short staffed at work.

Managing stress

Stress can be managed in many ways. Many organisations will undertake a stress risk assessment with staff to establish their level of stress.

Positive strategies include:

- taking your break entitlement
- taking regular holidays
- debriefing after experiencing a difficult situation at work
- being clear about the expectations of your role
- prioritising workload and organising your time
- having regular supervision and talks with your manager. Telling your manager if you begin to feel anxious – it may be that some of your work can be shared, or you can do something different for a while to give you a 'break'
- talking to friends or families about what is worrying you
- taking part in physical activity or exercise which can change your mood because of the **endorphins** that are released during physical activity
- eating healthily
- enjoying a hobby
- practising mindfulness – this means being in the moment and not making the problem or issue bigger than it is by thinking 'what if…'
- practicing other relaxation techniques such as that can help you to be calmer and relax
- trying to cut down the tasks into manageable sizes.

Accessing support

Your workplace may have a policy for addressing stress. If you feel that your work role is one or the main reason for you experiencing stress, or personal circumstances are affecting you and your work, there are several courses of action you can take (particularly if you feel you cannot talk to your family or friends):

- If possible, explain how you are feeling to your manager or supervisor because your stress may also be having an impact on your performance at work.
- Seek advice and support from your GP. They can signpost you to organisations that can help or they may suggest strategies you can try for yourself, like 'mindfulness'.
- It is important that you seek help so the first step is to share your anxieties with a trusted friend, colleague or family member. Seek professional help as they can help you to access the correct support for you.
- Talk to your manager as soon as possible so that you can consider your work role and it may then be possible to make some adjustments until you begin to feel better. For example you may be able to change your shift pattern or work alongside a more experienced team member.

Evidence activity

9.3 Managing stress

Some people rely on alcohol, cigarettes or food to alleviate stress. What do you think the dangers of doing this are?

Look at the previous list and discuss why they are more positive ways of reducing stress.

There are professional people who can help you with stress. These include your GP, your manager or supervisor, your personnel (or Human Resources Department).

Legislation

Health and safety at Work Act (HASAWA) 1974

Management of Health and Safety at Work Regulations 1999

Manual Handling Operations Regulations amended 2002

Provision and Use of Work Equipment Regulations 1998

Personal Protective Equipment at Work Regulations 1992

Reporting of Injuries, Diseases and Dangerous Occurrences Regulations (RIDDOR) 1995

Control of Substances Hazardous to Health Regulations (COSHH) 2002

Regulatory Reform (Fire Safety) Order 2005

Health and Safety (First Aid) Regulations 1981

Food Safety Act 1990 and the Food Hygiene (England) Regulations 2006

Lifting Operations and Lifting Equipment Regulations 1998

Data Protection Act 1998

Useful resources

Websites

Organisational policies and procedures
www.nidirect.gov.uk/employees

Health and Safety Executive
www.hse.gov.uk

Public Health England
www.hpa.org.uk

Skills for Health
www.skillsforhealth.org.uk

Skills for Care
www.skillsforcare.org.uk

Information for public services
www.direct.gov.uk

Handle information in health and social care settings

This unit is worth 1 credit

What are you finding out?

This unit is about handling information and will help you to understand why and how information should be handled in a secure and sensitive way.

You will be finding out about the legislation (laws) that govern the ways in which we must record, store and share information about other people; how to store information in a secure way and why this must be done, using guidance and information to help you, as well as working within agreed ways of working (using organisational policies and procedures); how to raise a concern when you are worried about the way

a piece of information has been recorded or stored or shared with others; and the importance of keeping records up to date and accurate.

By the end of this unit you will:

1 Understand the need for secure handling of information in health and social care settings
2 Know how to access support for handling information
3 Be able to handle information in accordance with agreed ways of working.

Links to Level 2 Certificate in Preparing to work in Adult Social Care

HSC 028 Assessment Criteria	Unit PWCS28
AC1.1	AC1.1
AC1.2	AC1.2
AC2.1	AC2.1

LO1 Understand the need for secure handling of information in health and social care settings

AC 1.1 Identify the legislation that relates to the recording, storage and sharing of information in health and social care

Information and data

We all have access to information about other people, whether it is a parent and child, a teacher, a pupil, a doctor, a patient, or a service user or social care support worker. As information technology becomes more and more sophisticated and there are more ways to share information over the internet, so the risk of information going missing, or being shared inappropriately or illegally, increases.

It is therefore important that there is legislation to guide and reinforce or support the way we record, store and share information about individuals. We might also refer to this information as '**personal data**'. The Data Protection Act 1998 is the law that refers to data as information about individuals. The Freedom of Information Act refers to information held by public sector organisations (like the NHS) relating to activities.

> **Key term**
>
> Personal data includes information about the individual's age, address, medical or mental health history, services received as well as care plans, case notes etc.

Recording

We record information about service users in written format, either electronic or as 'hard copy' (paper). The law relates to *all* types of recording including assessments, correspondence and any records of contacts with individuals, and there are principles we should adopt when we record information about the individual, bearing in mind they have the right to read what we record.

The main principles of good recording include:

- accuracy (do not use guess work – record factual information)
- remaining non-judgemental – beware of the language you use, for example 'A behaves in this way because she has red hair'
- not expressing a personal opinion – if you are saying something that is based on your opinion, ensure you record this to be the case and check with others that it reasonable to record this – for example, you might say 'In my opinion, A misses her dog because the last time this situation occurred she told me she was missing her dog'

- not using abbreviations that the person would not understand – for example 'MDT' which should say 'Multidisciplinary Team meeting'
- being objective – be factual and do not impose your own values on the individual's behaviour
- on a **need-to-know basis** – do not include unnecessary detail, only state the facts that are required and do not 'decorate' with a lot of unnecessary descriptions if they do not add to the value to the account.

Storage

All records must be stored safely because they relate to the personal history and details of individuals. They are therefore not to be shared with anyone but those people who are authorised or have permission to see them.

For example:

- Computers should be locked when not in use.
- Passwords should not be shared.
- Access should be limited to staff who, because of their role, are required to see the individual's information.
- Information should be marked 'confidential'.
- Paper information should be stored in locked cabinets in a locked room.
- Records can be destroyed only after a certain length of time.

Sharing

Think about the variety of information that is shared. We share information with other professionals, but this should only be on a need-to-know basis – this means you should not talk about people unnecessarily – for example, tell everyone in the office about an event if they are not directly involved with the individual. Equally, you should not share written records unless the person they are being shared with is authorised to see them.

For example:

- medical records
- social care information
- information about criminal records

Key term

A **need-to-know basis** means information should not be shared unless it is in the best interests of the individual and should only shared with those people who need (in order to support the person) to know that information.

- information about risk registers
- financial information.

Data Protection Act 1998 (DPA)

This law protects individuals and the way information about them is used. It relates to people living in the UK. All recorded information about the individual is subject to the DPA.

The main principles (rules) include:

- Service user information must be confidential and can only be accessed with their consent (see the next page for more on confidentiality).
- Service users must know what records are being kept and why the data is kept.
- All personal data must be accurate and kept up to date.
- All personal data must not be kept for any longer than is necessary.
- All personal data is processed in accordance with the person's rights. They have the rights to have data about themselves removed.
- All personal data must be kept secure at all times.
- Information gathered should only relate to the purpose it is needed for.

The Data Protection Act relates mainly to information about identifiable individuals, i.e. the individuals who use our services and who are identified on the systems of the organisation e.g. NHS records, social care records, housing records and education records. It gives people the right to see information that has been recorded about them.

Freedom of Information Act 2000 (FOI)

This gives people the right to ask organisations like the NHS and the Local Authority for the information they have about them as well as the services they provide. If the organisation decides to withhold information to protect various interests, the person must be made aware of it. The FOI Act relates to organisations releasing information about services and statistics – for example, a member of the public might ask for information from their local health provider about the number of people treated for a particular disease – they cannot ask about individuals but they can ask for statistics about the number of people.

Human Rights Act 1998

This gives the individual the right to respect for their private and family life. It also means that personal information about you should be kept securely and not shared without your permission, except in certain circumstances where it might cause risk to the general public.

Confidentiality

When we introduce a person into our service we should be very clear about the rules of confidentiality and explain carefully to them how and why we may, on some occasions, be required to share information about them. People usually understand this and we must ask them to agree to sign an information sharing/confidentiality agreement. It is equally important that we do not share information verbally without the person's permission.

Information can relate either to the individual, or to a company or organisation.

Caldicott

In 1997 Dame Caldicott reviewed the way information about patients was transferred from NHS organisations to other NHS and non-NHS organisations. She emphasised six major principles:

1 Justify the purpose(s) for using patient data. This means that we have to be accountable for using information about people.
2 Don't use patient-identifiable information unless it is absolutely necessary. This means that we should use information about people only when there is no other option,

particularly as the person's identity will be revealed in the process.
3 Use the minimum necessary patient-identifiable information. This means that we only use information that relates to the issue we are dealing with – for example, if the dentist requires a person's dental records we would not expect him to receive a record of their postnatal care.
4 Access to patient-identifiable information should be on a strict need-to-know basis. This means that we only share information that is necessary – and release it only to those people who need it. The dentist, on a need-to-know basis, does not need to know about a woman's postnatal care, but does need to know that she has been treated for gum disease.
5 Everyone should be aware of their responsibilities to maintain confidentiality. When we have a confidentiality policy it will be safe only if all members of staff are aware of it and use it.
6 Understand and comply with the law, in particular the Data Protection Act. It is very important to understand that the policies and procedures in our workplace that relate to sharing information are based on law.

Note: The Information Commissioner's Office's role is to uphold information rights in the public interest. They cover both the Data Protection Act and the FOI Act.

Evidence activity

1.1 Legislation

Look at the policies and procedures in your organisation that relate to the recording, storage and sharing of information. Can you identify how these relate to the DPA, Caldicott and FOI Act?

AC 1.2 Explain why it is important to have secure systems for recording and storing information in a health and social care setting

Secure systems for both recording and storing information should mean that there is a common standard that all staff follow.

This means that all staff are aware of and ensure they maintain the rules of confidentiality, and that they make sure important information is shared in a timely way with staff on a need-to-know basis.

Why is it important to have secure systems for recording and storing information?

Both service users and staff's private information should be protected from unauthorised viewing.

It is important to have secure systems because:

- Individuals share information with you in confidence. This may be private information, and may include details about their medical history, background, family or they may tell you about financial matters. Your role and duty is to the individual, it is important that they know the information that they tell you will not be shared. It is therefore your duty to ensure this information is recorded and stored safely and securely.
- Information should only be available for those who need to know, so that access to information is controlled carefully and not widely distributed when this is unnecessary and would breach confidentiality.
- There could be a risk of **identity theft**.
- The organisation should comply with legislation such as the Data Protection Act 1998.
- Confidentiality must be protected.

How can you ensure this?

- Be careful how you record and store information, including files notes and any other written documents or otherwise.
- Information should be recorded in a location where confidentiality can be maintained, not in public view.

> ### Key term
>
> **Identity theft** is when your personal details are stolen and identity fraud is when those details are used to commit fraud.

- Try not to take files home with you or outside of your workplace. There is a risk that you could lose them, or they could be stolen. Patient records can however be removed from the workplace, but should be 'tracked' and locked in the car boot when not in use – they should also be held in a particular carrier that is issued by the organisation. You may also need to keep files at an individual's homes if you are working there, but again, ensure that you treat this carefully so that it cannot be accessed by others such as people who may be visiting.

All information including electronic data should be stored safely – see a computerised recording on page 170. You should also check your setting's policy on this.

- Any information 'informally' recorded on scraps of paper or personal notebooks should be transferred to the approved record, and notes etc. should be shredded.
- Ensure information is locked and stored safely.

Confidentiality

Individual information should be passed on only with the person's permission, but if the information is going to pose a risk, it should be passed on to the senior person.

It is important to have a secure system for recording to ensure a balanced, clear and accurate picture of the individual's situation, written in a manner that can be easily understood.

If you, as the care support worker, think that you have to breach the confidentiality of the individual, you must record your interaction with an action plan explaining the reasons for the breach. This would normally be a situation where the individual disclosed a serious risk, or a **safeguarding** issue. Normally, you would explain to the person that it is in their best interests to share this information with a more senior person so that the problem can be addressed.

Manual and computerised recording

Manual recording means that we use paper records. Most organisations use computer records, but in some cases staff may use a written assessment format first, then transfer this onto a computer. Paper records may still be used in some areas instead of computer records – if there is a combination of paper and computer records, it is important that this is recorded, so that everyone is aware they may need to consult both paper and electronic records. All paper records are held in relevant files in a locked metal filing cabinet. Keys must be held safely and only those people with permission should access the keys. Never give the keys to someone unless you have permission to do so.

In the case of computerised recording, it is important to keep computerised information safe. This should be done using a secure password that you remember, never write it down. It is also important to use a password that is not obvious and to change it regularly. Firewalls and anti-virus software should also be installed.

Key term

Safeguarding: health and social care play an important role in the protection of vulnerable people before harm has happened and after it has happened.

Evidence activity

1.2 Secure systems

List all the records you keep in your workplace and where you store them.

Assess whether they comply (meet) the requirements of the law and internal policies.

Draw any issues to the attention of your manager.

LO2 Know how to access support for handling information

AC 2.1 Describe how to access guidance, information and advice about handling information

In most workplaces, advice and guidance can be obtained in several ways. These include:

- **Line manager or supervisor**: if you are in doubt – for example, because you feel under pressure about dealing with a query about a service user/individual, you should consult your line manager or supervisor.
- **Policies and procedures**: all organisations will have policies and procedures to guide you. You should read them as part of your **induction**.
- **Through supervision**: issues about records, data and confidentiality can be discussed with your supervisor and advice and guidance can be recorded as part of your personal development plan.
- **Through 'reflective practice'**: this is an exercise where you and others can analyse a situation and think about what went right or wrong, why it happened, what you have learned from the situation and how you can improve your practice.
- **Through training**: ask for further training if you feel you do not have enough knowledge and skills in accessing guidance and advice or handling information. This might be through learning, or time set aside to read the policies and procedures. You may find it helpful to discuss particular scenarios.

Key term

Induction is a set period of time when you are new to a service and are given training and support to help you learn about the service and settle in. This might include attending training, shadowing experienced staff, and e-learning.

Codes of practice: the Health and Care Professions Council and the Nursing and Midwifery Council are two professional organisations whose codes of practice include standards about handling information. These standards include:

- You must keep accurate records.
- You must keep records for everyone for whom you provide care or services.
- You must complete all records promptly.
- If you are using paper-based records, they must be clearly written and easy to read, and you should sign and date all entries.
- You must protect information in records from being lost, damaged and accessed by someone without appropriate authority, or tampered with.
- If you update a record, you must not delete information that was previously there, or make that information difficult to read.
- You must respect the confidentiality of service users.
- You must treat information about service users as confidential and use it only for the purposes they have provided it for.
- You must not knowingly release any personal or confidential information to anyone who is not entitled to it.
- You should check that people who ask for information are entitled to it.
- You must only use information about a service user to continue to care for that person, or for purposes where that person has given you permission to use the information or the law allows you to do so.
- You must also keep to the conditions of any relevant data protection laws and always follow best practice for handling confidential information.
- You must keep up to date as laws and procedures can change.

© HCPC 2012 Health and Care Professions Council (UK): hcpc-uk.org

AC 2.2 Explain what actions to take when there are concerns over the recording, storing or sharing of information

Concerns about recording, storing or sharing information may come from different sources, for example:

- A supervisor may notice that an entry in a care record has not been signed by the care support worker. This is a concern because as professionals we are held responsible and accountable for what we record about a service user. This is partly why all recording should be accurate and objective.

Figure 9.1 Confidential information must remain confidential

- The team secretary may be concerned because she discovers that a member of staff has left a patient's personal file on her desk, hoping that the secretary will file it for her. She should bring this to the attention of the responsible member of staff and, if necessary, escalate it to the manger if her concern is not responded to. All personal information is confidential and should not be left open to view but stored in a secure place.
- A care home resident complains to the home manager that she overheard two care support workers talking about another resident in a public area. The information they were sharing was very sensitive and the resident's right to confidentiality was being ignored. The manager should take this complaint seriously and talk to the staff to find out why they were discussing the resident and check what they understand about confidentiality.

Steps to take

If you have concerns you must take action. You may:

- Talk to a senior member of staff, your supervisor or line manager in the first instance.
- Ensure you record it.
- If you have a serious concern, you must 'escalate' your concern to a more senior manager, and if they are not available, find out who is the 'duty' manager.
- Some concerns cannot wait – for example, concerns about sharing information about the abuse of a service user.
- If the information has to do with a service user's privacy, obtain consent from the service user before passing on the information, except when the information poses a risk to them. In this situation you have a **duty of care** to share information with the appropriate person, normally your supervisor or line manager – you also have the right to take your concerns to the CQC or a Director of your organisation, but it is advisable to ensure that you have initially raised it with your manager so they are aware of your course of action (unless your concern is about them).

Make sure that information about a service user is not discussed in front of another service user because it is against confidentiality law.

There are some occasions when you may need to approach the regulatory body, such as the Care Quality Commission. If you work in a large NHS or social care organisation you will also probably have an **information governance** department and they will support and guide you.

Key terms

Escalate means to increase the intensity or seriousness of a situation.

Duty of care describes what you are obliged to do in your role as a health or social care worker – for your service users, patients, colleagues and in the public interest. Everyone has a duty of care – it is not voluntary.

Information governance (IG) departments make sure that there are necessary safeguards for, and appropriate use of, patient and personal information.

Research and investigate

2.2 Duty of care

Use a search engine to research 'duty of care' and 'information governance'.

Produce a leaflet for your staff induction pack that explains how we all have a duty of care to protect individuals when there are concerns about recording, sharing and storing information.

Evidence activity

2.2 Recording, storing or sharing information

Write a step-by-step list of the steps you can take and who you can talk to if you are concerned about recording, storing or sharing information.

LO3 Be able to handle information in accordance with agreed ways of working

AC 3.1 Keep records that are up to date, complete, accurate and legible

Health and social care records relating to individuals are legal records and the person has the right to access their own records. They may also be used as a historical document in future, or shared with other agencies. With this in mind, it is important that records are clearly written and presented so others can read them. They should be:

- Accurate – if you are not sure of all the details, check, don't guess. They must be an accurate account and you should be able to have the evidence to back up your account.
- They should be facts, not your personal opinion. Do not generalise – if Ella does not eat lunch, do not say 'refused lunch', or 'was not hungry.' State the FACT – it may be that Ella did not eat because she felt unwell or did not like the meal, so write that Ella did not eat her meal.
- Legible – this is a legal document and therefore it should be possible to read it easily.
- They should include relevant points – think about how you describe relevant?
- They should be presented in an accessible, clear, concise format. This could be clear paragraphs, or a bulleted list. This will also save time for the worker reading them.
- If they are written notes, make sure your handwriting is clear, again saving time for the next person who reads these. They should be able to read with ease. If they are unable to read the information, they may also miss key pieces of information.
- up to date (complete) – most organisations have standards that staff must keep.

A record must be:

- Complete – it should be completed as soon as possible after a contact with a service user or patient. It is unacceptable to complete a record several days after the contact – things can be forgotten, or there may have been other developments and if the record is not up to date crucial information may be missed.
- Dated – records should be chronological (in date order) so that a picture of the situation can be built up and a record kept of the sequence of events. Sometimes it is important for legal reasons (for example, the date you found a bruise on a resident in matters of safeguarding).
- Signed – computer records create electronic signatures when you log in and are registered to an account. Written signatures on paper records must also be used. This is to ensure our **accountability** for the records we have created.

Key term

Accountability is taking professional responsibility for our actions.

Evidence activity

3.1 Records

Mr James is admitted to the ward because he has a chest infection. He is rather confused about his surroundings and why he is in hospital. The health care assistant (HCA) tries to help him with his personal care, but because he is frightened he grabs her arm and pushes her away.

The HCA writes in his notes that Mr James was 'aggressive' towards her. Do you think this is:

1 Accurate?
2 Factual?
3 Helpful for Mr James or other staff?

Think about this situation.

AC 3.2 Follow agreed ways of working (policies and procedures) for:

- **recording information**
- **storing information**
- **sharing information.**

Key term

Agreed ways of working means working within the policies and procedures in your workplace.

Recording information

See AC 3.1 for information on how to ensure information you record is complete, accurate and legible.

Storing information

Common methods of communication include:

- Communication or message books (daily logs)
- Care plans
- Intervention plans
- Observation charts.

All these methods of communication should be stored in a secure place – a communication book should be locked away at night and when in use during the day, kept in a discreet place where it cannot be read by visitors. If residents or patients are referred to in the book, there should only be a reference to read the personal record. Entries that disclose personal information should be discouraged. Individuals should have a confidential personal record and there should not be any collective entries about different individuals in a communication book.

Individuals' records should be replaced in their personal file when not in use and never left in a public area. If you are transporting records, check your procedure. It is likely that you are advised to use a method that anonymises the records – for example you may be advised to use plain folders. If you are travelling by car, personal records should be locked in your boot. Individuals' files should normally be stored in a locked, fireproof filing cabinet.

All organisations will have a policy about confidentiality and it is very important that you familiarise yourself with it as soon as possible. Be vigilant and support colleagues about confidentiality. Put confidential information away safely, do not leave computers unattended if information is on the screen.

Sharing information

Confidentiality

Sharing information is bound by the rules of confidentiality. Remember, confidentiality is not about keeping a 'secret'. Personal information should not be shared without the consent of the individual, and details should not be disclosed simply upon request from another person, even if they appear 'official'. If you are at all in doubt, ask for the person's official identification.

Information should be shared on a 'need-to-know' basis only, so ensure the person has a right to that information professionally or personally. Never tell individuals everything they tell you is a 'secret' – you must be clear that for their well-being this information will be shared with some other people.

There may be times when someone tells you something in confidence and asks that it isn't shared. You must use your professional judgement. If you assess that it will not be harmful to keep their confidence, do so. If you are not sure, you could talk about the scenario as a 'hypothetical' situation with your manager. This means you do not reveal the person's name but might ask, 'What would you do if someone said this to you?'

There are times when it is necessary to pass on information. If you realise the disclosure is serious and affects the person's well-being, you must explain to them that although you are not going to tell all your colleagues, you do need to share this with a manager as it is serious. Sometimes people say, ' I want to tell you a secret' – advise them gently that you are pleased they can confide in you but that it may be you will have to share the information, particularly if they are going to need help and support. You must therefore make it clear the information will be passed on but also explain the reasons why, for example, if the person has disclosed that they have been hurt or abused by another or has had money stolen. In these circumstances you will need to undertake a risk assessment – this might be on the spot when you are balancing the need to share the information against the privacy of the individual. If medical information is to be passed from one organisation to another there will be a process for doing this. Never share an individual's information just because you are asked – always check whether this is appropriate and what steps have to be taken to do so.

When you record all contacts, conversations, interventions and care plans, ensure you sign them. Write in black ink.

Care plans or observation plans should be reviewed after a specified period. You might review a fluid chart daily, or a care plan weekly or three-monthly. Make sure you find out what is expected of you.

Figure 9.2 The dilemma of confidentiality versus concerns

Legislation

The Data Protection Act 1998

Human Rights Act 1998

Freedom of Information Act 2000

Evidence activity

3.2 Recording, storing, sharing information

You find a written note about a service user in the waste bin. It is crumpled up.

You draw it to your colleague's attention – they say it is OK because the paper isn't an official record and it is crumpled up and in a bin in a secure office.

What course of action should you take?

Useful resources

Websites

Government services and information

www.gov.uk

Health and social care information centre

systems.hscic.gov.uk

Optional
Group B Units

Unit DEM 201

Dementia awareness

This unit is worth 2 credits

What are you finding out?

Dementia is the term used to describe the symptoms caused by certain diseases or conditions of the brain. Dementia is called an 'organic' condition because it affects the structure of the organ – the brain – and how it can operate. This is why dementia can affect younger as well as older people. It is not a condition that is necessarily part of getting older.

There are many types of dementia and in this unit we will look at the most common types, those you are most likely to come across in your work setting.

We will explore the effect dementia can have on the individual and how it is viewed by society. We

will go on to understand the person's experience of dementia.

By the end of the unit you will:

1 Understand what dementia is
2 Understand key features of the theoretical models of dementia
3 Know the most common types of dementia and their causes
4 Understand factors relating to an individual's experience of dementia.

LO1 Understand what dementia is

AC 1.1 Explain what is meant by the term 'dementia'

Dementia and the human brain

Dementia is a condition of the brain. The brain is part of the body's nervous system. This is a network of nerve **cells** that carry 'messages' to different parts of the body. The brain has billions of nerve cells connected by **dendrites**.

The brain constantly passes messages and this is how it controls our activities, such as solving problems, walking, eating or understanding instructions.

Death of nerve cells

When someone has dementia they are experiencing the death of nerve cells in their brain. These cannot be replaced, which means that dementia is a progressive disease – it gets worse over time and cannot be reversed. It can affect younger as well as older adults.

It is estimated that there are currently 820,000 people diagnosed with dementia in the UK (Alzheimer's Research Trust 2010), and this will rise to over 1 million by 2025. Dementia is not a natural part of aging, although the chances of developing it increase with age. People in their mid-life can also be affected – people in their thirties have been diagnosed. It can affect anyone from any race, social or class background or location. It is a **long-term condition**.

The signs or symptoms will vary and this depends on the type of dementia the person experiences. It is important to remember that each person's experience of dementia is unique to them. See AC 1.2 for more information on the common symptoms of dementia.

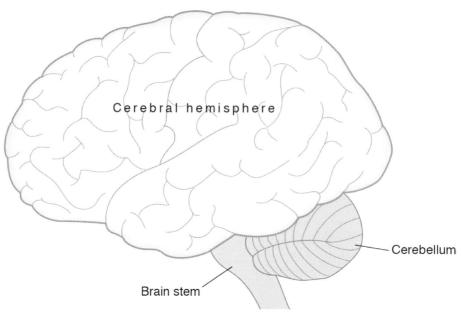

Cerebral hemisphere

Cerebellum

Brain stem

Figure 10.1 The human brain

Evidence activity

1.1 Supporting people with dementia

Dementia is an 'umbrella' term for a set of symptoms. Describe some of these symptoms. How do you define dementia? How has this been affected by your role? Think about an occasion where you may have cared for supported someone with dementia. How did it make you feel?

We have looked at what is meant by dementia and we have looked at the common symptoms. What emotions do you think a person will feel when they are first diagnosed?

How can:

1 We as care workers support them?
2 Family and friends help?

Research and investigate

1.1 What is meant by dementia?

Make a note of the key definition of dementia. The Alzheimer's Society website or the National Dementia Strategy 2009 can help you do this. How have these helped you to better understand what is meant by dementia?

AC 1.2 Describe the key functions of the brain that are affected by dementia

Common symptoms of dementia include:

- memory loss (particularly short-term memory)
- disorientation – people with dementia become more confused about time, place and people
- difficulties with communication, thinking, judgement and **perception** – these are called **cognitive abilities**

- changes in behaviour – people can become withdrawn, or suspicious or agitated or restless
- lack of physical co-ordination – the ability to sequence things, i.e. put them in the right order, or see things at the right level.

In short-term memory, the memories are the most recent and help us to remember new experiences and thoughts. Short-term memory also helps us to learn new things.

In long-term memory, the memories are from past events.

Loss of memory

This is the most common feature of dementia and can cause the most difficulties and anxieties for the person living with the condition. They will probably find that their short-term memory is affected first, with their most recent memories disappearing.

Memory is able to work in various ways:

- It can record new information – for example, a new name or idea.
- It can store and retrieve this information, so you can find it later (a bit like a filing cabinet or memory stick).

We rely on our memory to learn and store new things. This is very difficult for the person with dementia because the (temporal) part of the brain responsible for learning and interpreting (making sense) of new information is affected by the dementia. The person therefore relies on their long-term memory and often responds to emotions stored with those memories.

This is why, for example, a person with dementia may not be able to remember your name, but they can tell you the name of their teacher from 50 years ago.

Figure 10.2 Memory is a bit like a filing cabinet

The Temporal Lobe (part) is responsible for visual and auditory recognition, (seeing and hearing) and has a role in memory too because the part of the brain called the hippocampus makes new memories and helps us to remember places. The hippocampus is part of the temporal lobe.

Other effects of dementia

Each section of our brain is responsible for certain functions. Dementia can affect the brain in different ways, and depending on which parts are affected, people may experience more or less of the symptoms described below:

- **Emotion** – difficulty controlling emotions, or understanding the emotions of others; for example, not reacting to another person's sadness.
- **Thought** – not being able to arrange and understand thoughts as logically; for example, not being able to follow a conversation and join in.
- **Planning** – not being able to see a project through; for example, organise a shopping trip.
- **Interpreting the world** – not understanding situations in the same way as before; for example, thinking that you are in a hotel when in fact you are in hospital.
- **Speech and language** – not being able to find the correct words and not being able to understand what is being said; for example, describing an object rather than using the correct word.

Evidence activity

1.2 Key functions of the brain affected by dementia

Describe some of the ways poor short-term memory can affect the day-to-day life of a person living with dementia and discuss with colleagues some of the ways you may be able to help them.

Find a diagram of the brain and make a brief list of how different parts of the brain control how we function.

The main parts of the brain are called lobes, cerebellum, limbic system and brain stem.

Figure 10.3 People with dementia may also experience depression

- **Mathematical ability** – not being able to do arithmetic; for example, not understanding whether you have been given the correct change.
- **Reading and writing** – finding it difficult to express thoughts on paper; for example, not being able to read a shopping list or fill in a form.
- **Judging distance (spatial ability)** – not being able to work out how near or far an object is; for example, sitting on the floor rather than on a chair.
- **Sequencing** – not being able to put things in the right order; for example, not being able to dress correctly.
- **Movement and co-ordination** – not being able to avoid objects or catch a ball.
- **Sensing heat, cold, touch and pain** – for example, not being able to keep yourself safe because you are unaware of the heat or the pain.

AC 1.3 Explain why depression, delirium and age-related memory impairment may be mistaken for dementia

Depression

Depression and dementia are not the same. People living with or without dementia can experience depression. We can all feel 'blue' or fed up at times – this is normal because we usually feel better after a time.

Depression is different

People who experience **depression** (see page 183 for definition) can have feelings of hopelessness that do not go away. They may have low self-esteem, and feelings of guilt and sadness as well as thoughts of self-harm and death. Depression can make people agitated or restless, and anxious. They may sleep too much or be wakeful at night. They often lose interest in the world around them.

Another symptom of depression is that they may forget or be unable to concentrate. These symptoms can therefore be confused with those of dementia.

People living with dementia may also experience depression, possibly as a reaction to their condition and the effect it is having on their everyday life.

Possible depression in anyone **must** be taken seriously at all times and if you are worried or concerned that someone appears to have the symptoms, you must seek advice and support for them.

Delirium

The symptoms of delirium are very similar to those of dementia. People with dementia who are ill are more at risk of developing **delirium**.

The main symptoms of delirium are fluctuating or unstable alertness (being alternately sleepy and awake), changes in sleep pattern, disorganised thoughts and **hallucinations** and **delusions**. People can be agitated, restless or withdrawn. They may find it difficult to concentrate and can be very emotional. This is why delirium can also be mistaken for dementia.

Unlike dementia, the onset of delirium is sudden, but it can take weeks and sometimes months to get better. It is important to be particularly observant when a person with dementia is ill, especially if they have an infection or are taking more than four types of medication. This is termed **polypharmacy**.

Some of the main causes of delirium are:

- pain
- infection
- constipation
- dehydration – being too hot and not drinking enough
- polypharmacy.

Age-related memory impairment

We can all find it difficult to remember things sometimes.

As we get older this problem is more likely to increase and it is natural for people to assume they are developing a dementia-type illness. Some memory loss can be caused by medication, depression and physical illnesses like **diabetes** or **pernicious anaemia**.

However, for most of us this will be a normal part of the ageing process. This age-related memory impairment is sometimes called '**Mild Cognitive Impairment**' and there are theories that a healthy diet, exercise and 'brain training' can help slow the onset.

Key terms

Depression is not just a matter of feeling 'sad' – depression can have a range of symptoms, ranging from lasting feelings of sadness and hopelessness, to losing interest in the things you used to enjoy and feeling very tearful.

There can be physical symptoms too, such as feeling constantly tired, sleeping badly, having no appetite or sex drive, and complaining of various aches and pains.

Delirium can be caused by a variety of factors including pain, infections, dehydration, too much medication and change of environment. It is not a mental illness but rather a change in mental status when the person can become very confused, withdrawn or agitated. The person can recover from delirium but it can seriously affect a person with dementia who may find more difficulty in fully recovering.

Hallucinations happen when someone sees, hears, smells, tastes or feels things that do not exist outside their mind.

Delusions are when a person believes something impossible despite all the evidence. There are different types of delusions – for example, feeling persecuted, thinking that someone is 'after you' when there is absolutely no evidence of this. This can be very distressing for the person.

Polypharmacy means multiple medications.

Diabetes is a lifelong condition in which the person's blood sugar levels are too high and have to be controlled.

Pernicious anaemia is when the body cannot absorb vitamin B12, which then affects the red blood cells carrying oxygen around the body. As a result the person can become breathless and there can also be neurological changes, including the onset of dementia.

Mild cognitive impairment is a mild level of forgetfulness or ability to concentrate – it is not the same as dementia.

It is only when memory loss begins to stop a person from carrying out their normal activities of daily living that they should seek advice and treatment.

Case study

1.3 Mrs Jones

Mrs Jones has been admitted to hospital with a chest infection. As her care worker, you visit her. She seems very sleepy and cannot remember your name. She asks you to 'fetch her slippers from the bedroom'.

What do you think is happening to Mrs Jones?

Are there any ways in which you can help the nursing staff plan her care?

Figure 10.4 The medical model of dementia must be dealt with by medical experts

Evidence activities

1.3 Dementia, delirium, memory loss, depression

Complete a table that demonstrates your understanding of the main symptoms and differences between dementia, delirium, memory loss and depression.

	Similarities with dementia	Differences
Depression		
Delirium		
Age-related memory impairment		

LO2 Understand key features of the theoretical models of dementia

AC 2.1 Outline the medical model of dementia

Evidence activity

2.1 Medical model of dementia

Think about the advantages and disadvantages of describing dementia only as a disease that has to be 'treated'.

What effect do you think this could have on the person living with dementia?

Key terms

Medical model defines illness and disabilities in terms of the physical or biological effects, and does not take into account other aspects such as environment or the individual's social situation.

The 'medical model' of dementia describes the physical problems of the condition, for example, being unsteady, being unable to talk, being unable to wash or dress or eat independently. It uses this description to define the person and the problems they come across in everyday life. Because it is viewed mainly as a 'disease', it is seen as a problem that can only be dealt with by medical experts. The 'patient' who 'suffers' from dementia must be treated and cared for. This is a view that sees the disease in control of the person, and does not particularly take into account all the other elements in the life of the person with dementia. This is not a person-centred model.

AC 2.2 Outline the social model of dementia

The 'social model' of dementia thinks about society's attitude to dementia. It describes the barriers that society can make for people with dementia (or other disabilities). These barriers can stop people fulfilling their potential.

For example, a person living with dementia may be perfectly capable of going shopping independently, but a 'well-meaning' neighbour or family member will try to persuade them not to, simply because of the diagnosis of dementia rather than looking at the person's individual abilities regardless of their dementia.

The social model does not see the person with the illness or disease as the problem; it sees society as the problem. The social model emphasises that we must see the person first, that we should understand the experience of the person with dementia and by doing so, society should ensure people are able to access person-centred services and support.

The 'National Dementia Strategy 2009' (Department of Health) supports the social model of dementia. It talks about 'living well with dementia'. This is reinforced by the Prime Minister's Challenge in 2012 which asks all organisations to support 'dementia friendly' communities and introduced the idea of 'dementia friends'.

Research and investigate

2.2 The Social Model of dementia

Find out about the Dementia Friends national campaign. How does this fit in with the social model of dementia? What is the aim of the campaign?

Evidence activity

2.2 The Social Model of dementia

What is the social model of dementia?

Describe one way in which you think society's attitude to dementia is changing.

AC 2.3 Explain why dementia should be viewed as a disability

As we have read, the medical model concentrates on what the person cannot do rather than what is possible for them. The social model of dementia developed because people with **disabilities** disagreed with this idea and were unhappy about the effect it was having on their lives.

They argued that labels such as 'disabled' or 'limited' not only **stigmatised** them but also did not take into account their personhood, their skills and abilities. Being given a 'label' can also create barriers to some parts of society like housing, social events, transport and education. The Equality Act 2010 was passed to stop these barriers being accepted as a normal part of the way we view and treat people living with any disability. For example, there is now a social responsibility to ensure people with a disability are able to access buildings and on a bigger scale, and when a local authority is making strategic decisions (decisions about the services the local authority should supply) they must take into account equality of access for anyone with a disability.

Key terms

Disability is a physical or mental impairment that affects a person's ability to carry out everyday tasks.

Stigma means assuming that a person is defined by the way they look or the illness or disability they may experience. Stigma puts a negative label on people.

2.3 Dementia as a disability

The Equality Act 2010 says that a person with a disability is discriminated against if an association treats them less favourably than it treats others.

Why do you think people living with dementia may be treated differently or are not seen as equal to people who do not have dementia? Give some reasons why this might be the case.

Give an example of where you think a person living with dementia might be treated less favourably.

LO3 Know the most common types of dementia and their causes

AC 3.1 List and AC 3.2 describe the likely signs and symptoms of the most common causes of dementia

Dementia is an 'umbrella' term, which describes a disease of the brain. There are many types of dementia. The most common are Alzheimer's disease and Vascular dementia.

Alzheimer's disease (AD)

This is the most common type of dementia. It causes **tangles** and **plaques** in the brain that lead to the death of brain cells. It is progressive, affecting more parts of the brain over time. There is also a general loss of brain cells and brain matter (**tissue**) shrinks. AD is usually slow and gradual.

Signs and symptoms

Alzheimer's disease affects the ability to remember, speak and think clearly. In the early stages the person may be mildly forgetful; they may have problems finding the right words and lose interest in hobbies, etc.

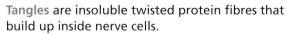

Key terms

Tangles are insoluble twisted protein fibres that build up inside nerve cells.

Plaques are protein deposits that build up around nerve cells.

Tissue a structure of similar cells.

Vascular relates to, affects, or consists of a vessel or vessels, especially those carrying blood.

As the disease progresses, memory loss and finding the right words while speaking become worse. The person may be confused by new surroundings and have trouble recognising familiar people and places. They find difficulty undertaking everyday tasks like dressing or preparing a drink.

In the later stages the person can become completely dependent on others, and have difficulty eating and walking, controlling bodily functions and understanding their environment.

Vascular dementia

This is the second most common type of dementia. It is caused by blockages in blood supply to the brain. The lack of blood and oxygen supply to nerve cells means they die. Areas of the brain damaged this way are called 'infarcts'. **Vascular** dementia is sometimes called 'multi-infarct dementia' and is due to a series of strokes.

Signs and symptoms

People with Vascular dementia have symptoms similar to other dementias, but in particular, they have problems concentrating and communicating. There may be a 'step-like' progression of the dementia. The person may have a stroke causing some worsening and then a settling of symptoms followed by another dip because of a stroke.

The person may become restless, they may walk about more than usual and struggle with memory problems and incontinence. Vascular dementia tends to affect particular areas of the brain, which means the person may retain more insight into their situation and hence become depressed.

Dementia with Lewy bodies (DLB)

This type of dementia is less common – up to **15 to 20** per cent of people diagnosed with dementia will have DLB. It is a result of small round protein deposits found in nerve cells. The protein deposits in the brain stop chemical messages working.

Signs and symptoms

People with DLB can have symptoms similar to those of AD. They may have problems with attention, alertness and **disorientation**, as well as being unable to plan ahead. They may develop the symptoms of Parkinson's disease, including loss of facial expression, slowness and rigidity of limbs and changes in strength and tone of voice. DLB can be variable from day to day. Tasks that a person completed yesterday may be impossible for them today. This is why someone with DLB can sometimes be labelled as' lazy' or 'manipulative'.

Frontal-temporal dementia (FTD)

This is less common – about 5 per cent of people living with dementia have FTD. It damages the front parts (frontal lobes) of the brain that are responsible for our behaviour, emotions and language.

Signs and symptoms

The person can experience changes in their personality and behaviour. They may lose the ability to empathise with others (see things from the other person's point of view). It may affect the person by changing them from being introverted or reserved to being extroverted or loud, or vice versa.

This means that the person experiencing FTD can become **disinhibited**, and as a result may make insensitive and rude comments. Their social skills can become blunted (for example the person may be more outspoken or rude to other people) and they can develop particular routines or rituals. They may have language difficulties, with '**pressure of speech**', using many words to describe a simple concept, or speak less and less. They are also more likely to overeat and develop a 'sweet tooth'.

Korsakoff's syndrome (KS)

This is caused by a lack of vitamin B1 (thiamine) which damages the brain and nervous system and is usually associated with drinking a lot of alcohol over a long period of time. Alcohol can inflame the stomach lining, which prevents the body from absorbing vitamin B1. Many people who drink heavily also tend to have a poor diet and so do not make up for the lack of vitamin B1. About 2 per cent of people with dementia will have KS.

Signs and symptoms

The main symptom is memory loss, particularly those things that happened after the onset of the condition. Other symptoms include difficulty in learning new information and skills, personality changes, for example from being a quiet to a talkative person, and repetitive behaviour. The person may not realise they have the condition and will invent things to cover the gaps in their memory. This is called 'confabulation'.

Creutzfeldt-Jakob disease (CJD)

This is a type of prion disease. Prions are proteins that are found on the surface of nerve cells in the brain but cause progressive nerve damage if they become faulty. CJD is quite rare. It is also referred to as 'Mad Cow disease.'

Key terms

Disorientation means not recognising or understanding where you are or who the people around you are, or not knowing the time or date.

Disinhibited means not being able to control our own behaviour – not behaving appropriately in public, for example. This may include undressing, being over-friendly or rude to other people.

Pressure of speech describes the way a person may talk very fast and loud and may go over the subject repeatedly.

Signs and symptoms

There are changes in personality, depression and loss of interest in life. As the condition progresses there can be confusion, memory loss, anxiety, delusions, loss of balance, difficulty in hearing and seeing, speech loss and paralysis.

Person-centred care

Although it is helpful to understand the nature and causes of the different types of dementia, it is more important to see the person and not the condition first. Each person will be different and we must not make assumptions that they will behave in any particular way because they have a certain type of dementia. This is the essence of person-centred care.

Evidence activities

3.1 List signs and symptoms

Produce a poster for colleagues explaining the main types of dementia and how they may affect an individual. Make sure you include the signs and symptoms of each one.

3.2 Describe signs and symptoms

You are supporting a person who has been diagnosed with Alzheimer's disease. You have been asked to explain some of the reasons for their behaviour to a relative and to think about ways the relative can help the person with dementia. What would you say to the relative?

Figure 10.5 See the person, not the condition, first

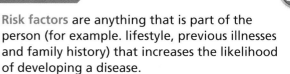 **AC 3.3** and **AC 3.4** Outline the risk factors for the most common causes of dementia and identify prevalence rates for the different types of dementia

Remember that **risk factors** and **prevalence** relate to people who are diagnosed with dementia. We know that there are significant numbers of people who, for many reasons, may not yet be diagnosed.

Key terms

Risk factors are anything that is part of the person (for example. lifestyle, previous illnesses and family history) that increases the likelihood of developing a disease.

Prevalence is the number or proportion or percentage of the general population who have a particular condition.

Did you know?

- Alzheimer's disease or Vascular dementia: **75 per cent** of people with dementia have either or a combination of both.
- There are over **11,500** people with dementia from black or minority ethnic groups.
- In the UK there are currently at least **15,000** people under the age of 65 with dementia.
- **60,000** deaths a year are directly attributable to dementia.
- **Two thirds** of people with dementia live in the community.
- **64 per cent** of people living in care homes have a form of dementia.

Risk factors associated with dementia

- Age: **33 per cent** of people over the age of 95 have dementia. The proportion of people aged 85 and over with dementia is between **25 per cent** and **35 per cent**.

- Gender: About **two thirds** of people with dementia are women. However women have a longer life expectancy than men.

- Education: Educated people have been found to have less nerve damage. There is a theory that people who have been educated to higher levels are able to use their brains more to compensate for some of the side effects of dementia.

- Lung and heart conditions can affect the blood and oxygen supply to the brain. The brain is damaged when it does not get the right supply of oxygen, which can cause conditions such as dementia.

- Vitamin B deficiency anaemia causes red blood cells which carry oxygen around the body to function abnormally, potentially causing damage to the nervous system.

- An unhealthy lifestyle, including heavy smoking, drinking and obesity, can affect the circulation and therefore the blood supply to the brain causing damage.

- A history of stroke, high blood pressure and cholesterol may make someone more likely to get dementia.

- Learning difficulties like Down's syndrome: studies have shown that people with Down's syndrome develop the plaques and tangles associated with Alzheimer's disease.

- A family history of dementia may make you more at risk of developing dementia.

LO4 Understand factors relating to an individual's experience of dementia

AC 4.1 Describe how different individuals may experience living with dementia depending on age, type of dementia, and level of ability and disability

How does growing older while experiencing dementia affect the person? The likelihood of dementia increases with age because as we get older we are all more likely to experience different conditions. However, this does not mean that dementia is a natural part of being older – it is a disease of the brain that can affect younger as well as older people.

Older people with symptoms of dementia may be discriminated against because dementia is dismissed as a 'normal' part of ageing.

They may have difficulty gaining access to the right services and support to suit them.

Evidence activities

3.3 Risk factors
Produce a poster to display in a public area that gives some tips on a healthy lifestyle. The title of the poster is 'Look after your heart and look after your head'. Think about how you can tell people about the risk factors for the most common causes of dementia.

3.4 Prevalence rates
Think about why there are still people who have not been diagnosed with dementia. Discuss with colleagues whether this is connected to the prevalence rates (number of cases).

Are there more people with dementia in certain groups but we just don't know about them?

Why do you think some people may not want to be assessed for dementia?

Evidence activity

4.1 Different experiences of dementia
Think about the people you know who may have been diagnosed with dementia. What are their different experiences?

What skills and personal qualities do they have? What sorts of things do they struggle with?

Discuss with colleagues how you can support a person with dementia who experiences a level of disability.

The stigma associated with ageing and dementia can mean that older people's views and needs are not taken as seriously, or it is assumed they have certain needs or want to make certain choices. This is called '**perceived needs**' – when we do not offer real choice or understand the situation from the person's point of view, but try to fit them into a service rather than shape a service around them, which is called '**personalisation**'.

Effects on the carer

The carer for the person with dementia is often the husband, wife or partner and as an older person themselves may have their own health needs too. It is very important that we recognise this and ensure that the carer is also offered advice and support when necessary.

Children of people with dementia may also be older and find difficulty coping with both the physical or emotional aspects of caring. Sons and daughters are likely to have children of their own, jobs and other commitments and might struggle to fit the caring role in. This can lead to feelings of guilt or frustration.

Key terms

Perceived need is when other people decide what the individual's need is without consulting them, making assumptions about what is needed.

Personalisation is described by the Department of Health as meaning that 'every person who receives support, whether provided by health or social services or funded by themselves, will have choice and control over the shape of that support in all care settings'.

Time to think

4.1 Services that support older carers
Think about the problems an older carer may encounter. Investigate the types of services in your area that support older carers.

The carer could also be a son or daughter who has to work and juggle the role of a carer with a full time job and a family to support.

Being diagnosed with dementia at an earlier age brings with it very different problems. Younger people in their forties or fifties are often unprepared for such a diagnosis and unless given support from the beginning can quickly feel that all hope is lost. They can feel shock because like many people they have assumed that dementia was something that only happens to older people.

They may still have a job and children at school. Financial and family concerns add to the pressure of the diagnosis. They may have been planning their retirement or embarking on a new venture. Because as a society we still associate dementia with older people, there is limited public and professional awareness and understanding of young onset dementia and this can make it difficult for younger people with dementia to find appropriate support tailored to their needs. The Dementia Friends campaign discussed in AC 2.2 aims to recruit volunteers who will support people with dementia in carrying on with their hobbies and activities. It is widely recognised now that traditional services like day care do not meet needs of many people. We all want to remain in our own communities doing the things that have always interested us for as long as possible.

How different individuals may experience living with dementia depending on the type of dementia

Dementia is associated with the decline of the brain's capacity to process information. This decline can have profound effects on a person's ability to carry out daily activities, communicate, make sense of the world and make judgements.

Figure 10.6 Elderly people should be encouraged to carry on with their hobbies and activities

Day-to-day activities that can be affected include:

- putting letters, words and sentences together in order to read and write
- combining numbers to make calculations
- co-ordinating movements, for example dressing, using implements, walking
- locating objects within a space, for example reaching for something
- thinking, planning and learning new tasks such as shopping and cooking
- performing particular activities because of lack of motivation (apathy)
- problems with the 'communication cycle' – inability to use the correct word may result in an individual finding it hard to understand the message as well as to respond
- misperceptions – this is when the person misinterprets pictures, etc., for example mistaking patterns on the carpet for holes
- misidentifications – when the person cannot perceive the difference between people, for example mistaking their son for their husband; this is also due to problems with memory – the memory is remembering the past person: the husband, rather than the recent memory, the son
- misnaming what is seen

- other visual difficulties – including being unable to perceive depth, contrast between colours and recognising objects
- a failure of insight and judgement – not understanding risk and danger: this leaves a person with dementia vulnerable to exploitation. They may lose money, leave the gas on or lack road sense while driving or crossing the road. They may also not realise they are neglecting their personal hygiene, putting their health and dignity at risk
- losing sense of time – finding it hard to anticipate what is happening next
- the physical environment – this can also be a problem as it begins to make less sense to the person with dementia.

Level of ability and disability

A person's experience of dementia will be shaped by **internal** and **external factors**. Tom Kitwood talks about **internal factors** like personality and health. For example, if the person has always been confident and optimistic in their approach to life, they may find more positive ways of managing their illness. These are called 'coping strategies'.

Tom Kitwood and Person-centred care

Person-centred care was developed by psychologist Tom Kitwood at the University of Bradford in the 1980s. He said that seeing people with dementia simply in medical terms leads them to be seen as objects rather than people. He explained that people's experience of dementia is not just about their physical health and the brain damage they experience but also about social and psychological factors. This means that you are also affected by your own history and the way you relate to other people. Kitwood said this is the 'personhood' of the individual – it defines who we are as individual people.

When people living with dementia have problems with their physical health, this can have a negative impact on the dementia. Arthritis and an inability to move about may make a further problem like dementia feel worse because the person cannot get about easily and may feel more isolated and restricted to their home. Not being able to hear or see properly can add to their problems – the world can seem a confusing place for the person and if they are also struggling to see or hear properly, this can make this confusion worse.

External factors include the environment the person lives in and their wider social network. Friendships can be lost because other people find it difficult to communicate with the person with dementia. Family relationships change and can become awkward as family members have to take on an increasing caring role. People can drift away and the person with dementia and their carer can feel isolated.

The degree of damage (or the level of disability) will depend on the type of dementia and in some cases like Alzheimer's disease, whether treatment begins in a timely way, to slow down the progress of the condition. The person's experience of dementia may also be influenced by the way the dementia is seen as a disability. If we do not help the person with dementia by adapting their environment, or the way we communicate with them, for example, then we have emphasised the disability rather than supported the person to overcome or manage it.

AC 4.2 Outline the impact that the attitudes and behaviours of others may have on an individual with dementia

Society and the media

'One day I hope that we will treat people with dementia with respect, recognise just how hard they are trying to cope with getting through each day, and provide them with appropriate emotional support, social networks and encouragement.'

Source: Christine Bryden *Dancing with Dementia: My Story of Living Positively with Dementia*, 2005.

Christine Bryden was diagnosed with dementia at the age of 46. She experienced some of the prejudice associated with dementia. Unless we remove the stigma and discrimination shown towards people with dementia and support them instead, they will struggle to cope with their condition and to have their 'personhood' recognised.

The media does not always portray a positive image of living with dementia. The stereotype of the person as a 'victim' who is unable to have any control is common. Often they depict the person with dementia with images of frail, older people. This attitude is partly due to a lack of knowledge. The more we understand about dementia, the more we can help.

The family and individuals

People cannot be experts in dementia simply because a family member develops the condition. As the person moves along their dementia journey, so will family

Evidence activity

4.1 Different experiences of dementia (2)

Think about how your family, friends and colleagues behave towards people with mental health conditions such as dementia. If they exhibit negative views or attitudes, why do you think this is?

How could you help them in changing these views and attitudes?

Make a list of the ways different individuals may experience living with dementia. Think about the things you have covered in this AC including age, type of dementia and level of ability and disability.

and friends develop their knowledge and understanding. At the beginning of the journey they may feel embarrassed, frustrated and anxious. There can be a sense of 'loss' for the person they once knew. They may reflect a more general view that the person only has themselves to blame, that they should stop behaving in the way they do or pull themselves together.

These attitudes can be very damaging to the person with dementia because they do not recognise the struggle the person is experiencing. As a result the person with dementia can feel isolated and lose their self-confidence and self-esteem. If their communication skills are affected they may also have problems expressing how they feel and become more isolated.

A national response

The National Dementia Strategy 2009 (Department of Health) recognised that more must be done to change the attitude and behaviours of society, including health and social care organisations. The strategy has 17 objectives. The first three deal with how we perceive dementia.

Objective 1: Improving public and professional awareness and understanding of dementia. This sparked a national campaign, which portrayed people 'living well with dementia' and aimed to help the public understand that dementia should not be used to stigmatise people.

Objective 2: Good quality early diagnosis and intervention for all. This encourages GPs and other medical professionals to be more vigilant when assessing people and to refer people to specialist services as soon as possible. The earlier in the condition people receive treatment, the more likely they are to have a positive outcome.

Objective 3: Good quality information for those with diagnosed dementia and their carers. Part of the problem is fear due to a lack of knowledge.

There are many health and social care professionals supporting people with dementia and their carers. Good practice dictates that professionals and the general public become well informed about dementia and the impact it has on the people living

Research and investigate

4.2 The Prime Minister's Challenge

The Prime Minister's Challenge has re-looked at the national dementia strategy and set out new challenges.

Find out more about the Prime Minister's Challenge and think about how this can affect the lives of people living with dementia, their family and carers and those people who work in health and social care as professional carers.

Look at the following list of groups that may and research how their attitudes and behaviours may impact someone with dementia.

- Care workers
- Colleagues
- Managers
- Social Workers
- Occupational Therapists
- GPs
- Speech & Language Therapists
- Physiotherapists
- Pharmacists
- Nurses
- Psychologists
- Admiral Nurses
- Independent Mental Capacity Advocates
- Community Psychiatric Nurses
- Dementia Care Advisors
- Advocates
- Support groups.

with it. If this can be achieved then the stigma and prejudice associated with dementia can be things of the past.

Evidence Activity

4.2 Impact of attitudes and behaviours

Produce an information sheet for colleagues and visitors to your workplace that:

- explains the negative attitudes people can have towards dementia
- describes the impact that these attitudes can have on people living with dementia.

Legislation

The Equality Act 2010

The Care Act 2014

Useful resources

Websites

National Dementia Strategy 2009

Prime Minister's Challenge 2012

You can access these documents at

www.gov.uk

Alzheimer's Society

www.alzheimers.org.uk

Social Care Institute for Excellence (SCIE)

www.scie.org.uk

Bupa

www.bupa.co.uk/understanddementia

Unit LD 201

Understand the context of supporting individuals with learning disabilities

This unit is worth 4 credits

What are you finding out?

According to **Mencap** there are around 1.5 million people who have a learning disability within the United Kingdom. Due to advances in health and social care and the fact that people are living longer, this figure is likely to increase. One of the biggest problems is that other people generally do not understand what it means for someone to have a learning disability – it is not an illness or a disease, and it is not always possible to tell whether a person has such a disability. Having a learning disability does not mean a person has mental health problems; however, some people who have a learning disability may develop mental health problems as a result of inadequate care and discrimination.

A learning disability is not what defines a person, it is merely a label used to diagnose people. Those with learning disabilities are all individuals with the right to the same life chances as other people. These people are individuals just like you and me.

By reading this chapter and completing the activities you will be prepared to demonstrate

your learning and understanding of supporting individuals who have a learning disability in your workplace.

By the end of this unit you will:

1 Understand the legislation and policies that support the human rights and inclusion of individuals with learning disabilities
2 Understand the nature and characteristics of learning disability
3 Understand the historical context of learning disability 4 Understand the basic principles and practice of advocacy, empowerment and active participation in relation to supporting individuals with learning disabilities and their families
4 Understand how views and attitudes impact on the lives of individuals with learning disabilities and their family carers
5 Know how to promote communication with individuals with learning disabilities.

LO1 Understand the legislation and policies that support the human rights and inclusion of individuals with learning disabilities

AC 1.1 Identify legislation and policies that are designed to promote the human rights, inclusion, equal life chances and citizenship of individuals with learning disabilities

Most of the laws that concern people who have a learning disability also apply to other people. The main laws that are likely to make a difference to the lives of people who have learning disabilities are concerned with promoting:

- human rights
- anti-discriminatory behaviour
- **equality**
- **inclusion** and **citizenship**.

Legislation aimed at promoting the human rights, inclusion, equal life chances and citizenship of individuals with learning disabilities includes the following:

- The Human Rights Act 1998 – there are 18 articles or protocols that explain fundamental human rights contained in the European Convention on Human Rights – it is unlawful for public bodies to breach the rights that are set out there.

Key terms

Mencap is the leading UK charity for people who have a learning disability and their families.

Equality relates to being equal, especially having the same political, social and economic rights.

Inclusion is a state of being free from exclusion or from feeling left out.

Citizenship relates to being a citizen of a particular community with the duties, rights and privileges/freedoms of this status.

- The Disability Discrimination Act 1995 – this Act is designed to prevent discrimination on the grounds of disability, in things like being offered a job, education, transport, etc. It means that it is against the law to discriminate against people with disabilities.
- The Mental Capacity Act 2005 – this is designed to protect people who may lack **capacity** (see page 197 for definition) to make some decisions for themselves, and is also meant to help empower them wherever possible. Anyone who works with or cares for an adult who lacks capacity must comply with this Act when making decisions or acting on behalf of that person. The Act states that every adult has the right to make their own decisions and must be assumed to be able to do so unless it can be proved that they cannot. Decisions made on behalf of someone should be done with their best interests at heart, and they should be the least restrictive options, in terms of personal freedom, available.
- The Mental Health Act 2007 – this defines mental disorder in such a way that it could apply to learning disabilities as well as mental illness. However, the Mental Capacity Act is normally more appropriate legislation to refer to for people with learning disabilities.
- The Equality Act 2010 – this brings together various separate pieces of legislation that already existed, including the Disability Discrimination Act, into one Act that promotes equality for all.
- The Health and Social Care Act (2012) – this is a huge reorganisation of the NHS and is wide reaching. It is still being implemented, but some of its consequences may affect people with learning disabilities.

'Valuing people now', published in 2009, was the UK government's three-year strategy for improving the lives of people with learning disabilities and their families by improving services. In particular, the strategy aimed to give adults who have learning disabilities more choice and control over their lives through **person-centred planning**, advocacy and **direct payments**. The government-led approach of 'Valuing people now' has not changed since 2012, as there has not been a replacement or updated strategy put in place. The implication is that continuing to implement the vision set out in 'Valuing people now' lies at a local level, with learning disability partnerships, local authorities and health authorities. While 'Valuing people now' is no longer available on an active government website, you can access it at the national archives – see **http://tinyurl.com/q45gmje**

Organisations that provide support for people who have learning disabilities should have policies in place that aim to reinforce this legislation. These policies should set out the guidelines that all health and social care workers have to adhere to in order to ensure people who have learning disabilities are given the same opportunities as any other member of society.

Key terms

Capacity In this context, this means the ability to understand information that has been given to individuals to make a decision.

Person-centred planning is a process of life planning for individuals, based around the principles of inclusion and the social model of disability.

The direct payments scheme is a UK government initiative in the field of Social Services that gives users money directly to pay for their own care, rather than through the traditional route of a Local Government Authority providing care for them.

Evidence activity

1.1 Legislation

Do some research into the following and write down the main things that each Act contains:

- Mental Capacity Act 2005
- Disability Discrimination Act 1995
- The Human Rights Act 1998

AC 1.2 Explain how this legislation and policies influence the day-to-day experiences of individuals with learning disabilities and their families

Policies are drawn up in line with current legislation, nationally at governmental level and also locally by organisations. Policy makers can influence important decisions that affect people's everyday lives. We have already established that there are around 1.5 million people who have a learning disability in the UK, so all policies will affect them in some way.

Policies should be based on the **social model of disability**, aimed at empowering people. People who have a learning disability are the experts in their own lives and their views are an essential part of creating policies. Involving people throughout the process of policy development will help identify gaps in knowledge and give an indication of whether the policy will work in both the short and the long term. Understanding the perspectives, needs and priorities of people who have learning disabilities will develop better policies and deliver effective services.

The different legislation and policies outlined in AC 1.1 seek to improve the lives of people with disabilities. You should refer to AC 1.1 to find out about the goals and purpose of each of the legislation and policies and how they may impact individuals and their families.

Evidence activity

1.2 How legislation and policies influence individuals and their families

Take a look at the policies within your place of work and make a note of any policies that promote human rights, inclusion, equal life chances and citizenship for the service users for whom you provide support.

How do the policies support these aspects of a person's life? How do they influence people and their families on a daily basis?

LO2 Understand the nature and characteristics of learning disability

AC 2.1 Explain what is meant by 'learning disability'

Defining the term 'learning disability' is not easy because it does not have clear-cut edges. No two people have the same level of 'ability' in the way they learn, and every person's experience of their learning disability will be individual to them.

In medical terms, learning disabilities are known as **neurological disorders**. In simple terms, a learning disability may result when a person's brain development is affected, before they are born, during their birth or in early childhood.

Learning disabilities are lifelong conditions that cannot be cured, and they can have a significant impact on the person's life. People with learning disabilities find it harder than other people to learn, understand and communicate. Some people with a mild learning disability may be able to communicate effectively and look after themselves, but may take a bit longer than usual to learn new skills. Others may not be able to communicate at all and may also have more than one disability.

You may have heard a person's learning disability described as mild, moderate, severe or profound. If you hear these terms being used, it is important to remember that they are not separate 'compartments', they are simply stages along the scale of ability/disability.

Research and investigate

2.1 Defining learning disabilities

Think about the individuals you support. How would you define their learning disability?

Evidence activity

2.1 'Learning disability'

How would you explain what the term 'learning disability' means to a new member of staff within your organisation?

Figure 11.1 Continuum of ability/disability

AC 2.2 Give examples of causes of learning disabilities

Learning disabilities are caused by the way the brain develops, before, during or after birth. There are several factors that can affect the development of the brain.

Before birth (pre-natal)

There are causes that affect the pregnant woman: for example, rubella (german measles), excessive intake of alcohol or tobacco, taking illegal drugs, and listeria (food poisoning).

A child can be born with a learning disability if certain genes are passed on by a parent. This is called an **inherited** learning disability. The two most common causes of inherited learning disability are **Fragile X syndrome** and **Down's syndrome**. These are not learning disabilities in themselves, but people who have Fragile X syndrome are likely to have a learning disability too. All people who have Down's syndrome have some kind of learning disability. Fragile X syndrome is the most common cause of inherited learning disability.

During birth (peri-natal)

One of the most common causes is problems during the birth that stop enough oxygen getting to the brain.

After birth (post-natal) or during childhood

These problems include illness, such as **meningitis**, or injury in early childhood.

Sometimes there is no known cause for a learning disability. There is a lot of information about particular syndromes and conditions. Check out the useful websites given at the end of this chapter.

Key terms

Inherited means passed on to a child from its parents.

Fragile X syndrome is a genetic condition. It can cause many developmental problems including cognitive impairment and learning disabilities.

Down's syndrome is a genetic disorder resulting from the presence of an extra chromosome; children usually, but not always, have learning disabilities.

Meningitis is infection or inflammation of the membranes (meninges) that cover the brain and spinal chord.

Evidence activity

2.2 Causes of learning disabilities

Think about the service users you are supporting at the moment. While respecting confidentiality and using any information that is available to you, identify the cause of their learning disabilities.

Where on the continuum of learning disabilities do your service users sit?

AC 2.3 Describe the medical and social models of disability

Time to think

2.3 Assumptions

It is important at this stage to examine how you feel about people who have a disability.

Think about the assumptions that are commonly made about people who have a disability in general. In a few words, what would you say are common assumptions often made about this section of the population? For example, would you say 'they need help?' or would you say you 'feel sorry for them?' or would you say 'people are disabled because of their environment?'

Models of disability provide a framework for understanding the way in which people with impairments experience their disability. It is commonly accepted that there are two contrasting models of disability within our society. These are known as the 'medical model' and the 'social model'.

The medical model of disability

The medical model views the person who has a disability as the problem. This model states that the person who has a disability should adapt to fit in with society. If the person cannot fit in with society then it is their problem. The emphasis is on the individual's dependence on others, which is backed up by the stereotypes of disability. These lend themselves to pity, fear and patronising attitudes. The main focus is on the disability rather than the person. The medical model highlights that people who are disabled cannot participate in society because their disability prevents them from doing so.

The social model of disability

The social model of disability was developed with the input of people who have a disability. Instead of stressing the disability, the social model centralises the person. It emphasises dignity, independence, choice and privacy. This model makes an important distinction between impairment and disability.

- Impairment is seen as something not working properly with part of the body, mind or senses – for example, a person may have a physical impairment, a sensory impairment or a learning impairment.
- Disability occurs when a person, because of their impairment, is excluded by society from something that other people in society take for granted. That might be the chance to attend an event, access a service or get involved in an activity.

The exclusion may affect a person's choices to live independently, to earn a living, to be kept informed, or just to make choices for themselves.

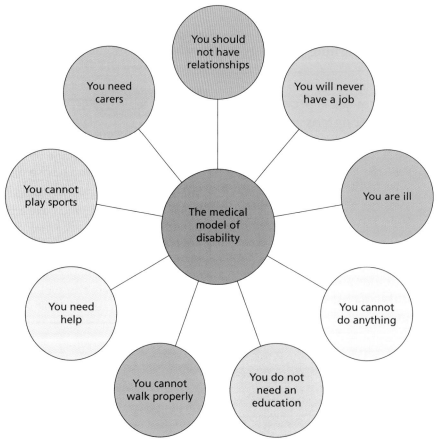

Figure 11.2 The medical model of disability

The social model of disability says that disabilities are created by barriers in society. These barriers generally fall into three categories:

- the environment, including inaccessible buildings and services
- attitudes, including discrimination, prejudice and **stereotyping**
- organisations, including inflexible policies, practices and procedures.

Some people wrongly assume that the impairment causes the disability. However, the social model believes that it is the choices society makes that create the disability. If things are organised differently, these people are enabled – though their impairment has not changed.

Figure 11.3 The social model of disability

Key term

Stereotypes are inaccurate and generalised beliefs, usually held about a group of individuals e.g. all individuals who have dementia have a poor quality of life.

Evidence activity

2.3 Medical and social models of disability

Look at the assumptions you made within the 'Time to think' activity. Would you say your beliefs support the medical model of disability or the social model of disability?

Take a look at the environment in which you work. Are there any aspects of the environment that could disable a person? If so, what changes could be made to make the environment more enabling?

AC 2.4 State the approximate proportion of individuals with a learning disability for whom the cause is 'not known'

Reasons for finding out the cause

There are a number of reasons for finding out the cause of a person's learning disability. First, individuals and their families want to know and also have a right to know. There are also health factors, as some forms of learning disability or syndromes can increase the likelihood of certain health problems occurring. **Genetic counselling** may also be required both for the family and the person with the learning disability, especially where there is a wish to start a family.

We have identified some of the causes of learning disability in AC2.2; however, the British Institute of Learning Disabilities (BILD) states that for 50 per cent of people who have a mild learning disability, no cause has been identified. For people who have severe or profound learning disabilities, no cause has been identified for around 25 per cent of them.

Key term

Genetic counselling involves talking with people who are at risk of developing or transmitting conditions that are inherited.

Evidence activity

2.4 The cause of learning disability

Think about the individuals you support. Do any of them have a learning disability for which the cause has never been identified?

AC 2.5 Describe the possible impact on a family of having a member with a learning disability

More than 60 per cent of people with learning disabilities live with family carers who often sacrifice their own lives in order to support the person. Family members who provide care for those with a learning disability can suffer immense emotional and physical strain, but taking a rest from their role as a carer can be made difficult by the negative effects it can have on the person they are caring for.

While every family can have stresses and strains, these are often bigger in families where someone has a learning disability. Depending on the family members, the amount of support they receive and the person who has the learning disability, this can impact on every aspect of the family's needs, including financial, domestic, health care, relationship and self identity. It can also impact on other aspects of family life, leading to significant extra costs and complications.

A child who does not have a learning disability will usually mature and become more independent, eventually leaving the family home. A child with a learning disability, however, may not follow this pattern, and is more likely to remain within the family home into adulthood. This person may also require prolonged periods of intensive care. This could impact upon everyday occurrences such as family outings, which could become complicated or even impossible.

Evidence activity

2.5 Impacts

Choose two individuals for whom you provide support. While maintaining confidentiality, develop a case study for them. Identify the impact that their learning disability has had on other members of their family, taking into account the:

- financial impact – perhaps some members of the family cannot work because they provide a lot of care at home?
- relationship impact – how do you think the relationship between family members might be affected?
- domestic impact – how is home life affected?
- social impact – how are interactions with friends affected?
- self-identity impact
- health care implications.

LO3 Understand the historical context of learning disability

AC 3.1 Explain the types of services that have been provided for individuals with learning disabilities over time

Little has been written about the lives of people with learning disabilities before the 18th century. There are, however, references to 'village idiots'. It is thought that these people represent a small minority of those we would describe today as having a learning disability. Literacy skills were less in demand than labouring skills, so mild learning disabilities would easily go unnoticed.

The Poor Laws of 1834

The Poor Laws of 1834 led to the building of purpose built institutions called 'asylums' to house people described as 'mad' or 'mentally weak'. They had harsh and rigid regimes, and contained many people who had learning disabilities. These individuals had little choice and were not valued as people. The asylums became overcrowded and conditions worsened as attitudes changed and the people who were housed there began to be regarded as dangerous and a drain on society.

The Radner Commission

The development of such places continued into the early 20th century, though the purpose of moving people to them changed. Laws were passed that encouraged the building of schools for 'mentally disabled' children and in 1908 the Radner Commission stated: 'Feeble-mindedness is largely inherited.' It was suggested that such people were genetically inferior and needed to be segregated from the rest of society.

Mental Deficiency Act 1913

The 1913 Mental Deficiency Act stated that any person admitted to an institution had to be

Figure 11.4 Institutionalisation

certified as 'mentally defective'. The institutions were now renamed 'colonies' and their purpose was to separate their residents from society. In 1929, the Wood Committee suggested that such people were a threat to society.

Eugenics

During the periods between the two World Wars, the numbers of people admitted to institutions increased. Laws were passed to further segregate all people who had learning disabilities and their families from the rest of society. Proposals were introduced to round up and separate all families of 'feeble minded people', including 'insane, epileptics and drunks', to name but a few. It was suggested that such people would 'take over' and 'infect' others and that a 'racial disaster' would ensue.

Cyril Birt was a member of the Eugenics Society, a group that believed society was in decline and that there was a need to separate those with learning disabilities, keeping men and women apart so they would not procreate. History shows that the theories of eugenics have been used as a reason for many atrocities committed against people with a learning disability and the mentally ill, as well as the millions of victims of the Holocaust.

The IQ Test

Fortunately, the UK drew back from such unthinkable measures. However, this kind of mindset continued to affect the huge numbers of people admitted to institutions right up until the late 1980s. In the 1930s, the IQ test was introduced – people scoring low on the test were categorised as 'mentally defective' and unable to learn.

The NHS 1946

The introduction of the National Health Service in 1946 and the development of the medical model of disability had an impact. The term 'mentally handicapped' came into use and the institutions turned into hospitals, with the emphasis now on caring for their residents. Society had moved from seeing the 'mentally handicapped' as dangerous and degenerate to viewing them more sympathetically, as people in need of treatment, although still a drain on the public purse. People with a learning disability remained segregated and isolated, and the standard of care was extremely poor. This remained the case right up until the closure of the long-stay hospitals.

The Mental Health Act 1959

In 1959, the Mental Health Act began to think about the idea that some people might not need to be cared for in a hospital. It was also the first time that people with a 'mental illness' were distinguished from those described as having a 'mental handicap'.

'Better services for the Mentally Handicapped' 1971

In 1967, national newspapers started to draw attention to the bad conditions in 'mental handicap' hospitals. In 1971, the government published a paper, 'Better services for the mentally handicapped', in response to continued reports about appalling conditions in the hospitals. This paper laid the foundations for 'Care in the Community', with the expectation that half of the people in hospitals should be living in the local community by 1990.

Level 2 Health & Social Care Diploma

Normalisation, 1980s

During the 1980s, the concept of 'normalisation' began to influence the delivery of care for people who had a learning disability. Normalisation emphasises the 'value of the individual', their right to choice and opportunity, and the right to any extra support they need to fulfil their potential. At this time there was also recognition that the existence of institutions for people with learning difficulties and mental health issues was a major barrier to inclusion.

The idea that everyone in society has the right to a life with choice, opportunity and respect, and with extra support according to their needs, helped to change the way services were planned and delivered. The National Health Service and the Community Care Act 1990 recognised the right of disabled people to be an equal part of society, with access to the necessary support.

Today

We might like to believe that the task of de-institutionalising the care of people with a learning disability is now complete. Nearly all the long-stay hospitals are closed, and many rights are now law, as detailed in the Disability Discrimination Act 1995. However, the reality is that many people are still denied the things that most people take for granted, such as a decent income, somewhere appropriate to live, the chance to work, leisure opportunities and choices in education.

Attitudes and understanding

Today's services aim to enable people and promote equal treatment and inclusion. This brings with it new challenges and responsibilities, the greatest of which is to change public attitudes towards people with a learning disability and raise understanding.

Evidence activity

3.1 History

Find out about the history of the individuals you work with. Were any of them 'cared for' within an institution?

Make a note of the differences between the care that was provided within 'institutions' and the support provided by your organisation.

AC 3.2 Describe how past ways of working may affect present services

People who have worked in health and social care for some time may remember some of the institutions, and indeed may have worked in them. Some health and social care workers may therefore have adopted the medical model approach to disability. This will, affect the care and support that these health and social care workers are delivering.

Evidence activity

3.2 Past ways of working and present services

How do you think past ways of working may affect present ways of working?

AC 3.3 Identify some of the key changes in the following areas of the lives of individuals who have learning disabilities:

- where people live
- daytime activities
- employment
- sexual relationships and parenthood
- the provision of health care.

There have been major changes in the lives of individuals who have a learning disability. We have already discussed the institutionalised medical model approach to care and support. Person-centred planning has generally led

204

to positive changes for people who have learning disabilities. However, Mencap reports that people who have a learning disability are still treated differently.

Where people live

There have been major changes in the living arrangements of people who have a learning disability. With a move away from an institutionalised approach to care, more people are being empowered to maintain their independence for as long as possible. While over 60 per cent of people who have a learning disability live with their family, there are also a significant number of people who maintain their independence within their community through supported living.

Daytime activities

With the introduction of self-directed support, service users are able to make choices about where they go and what they want to do during the daytime. Self-directed support should enable service users to decide:

- how to live their lives
- where to live and who with
- what to do during the day
- how to spend their leisure time
- what to spend money on
- who they are friends with.

Employment

Mencap reports that only 1 in 10 people who have a learning disability are in employment. They are more excluded from the workplace than any other group of disabled people. Where they do work, it is often for low pay and part-time hours. Research shows that 65 per cent of people with a learning disability want to

> **Research and investigate**
>
> **3.3** Employment
>
> Using any information that is available to you, take a look at why people who have a learning disability find it difficult to get paid work.

work and that they make highly valued employees when given the right support.

Sexual relationships and parenthood

Discussions surrounding sexuality are uncomfortable for 'able bodied' people. This is a very private area of a person's life and one which we choose not to discuss openly. It is now recognised that people who have learning disabilities also have sexual feelings and may want to engage in close personal relationships. Some organisations run courses for people who have learning disabilities where they are taught about social and personal development. Because those with learning disabilities are a vulnerable group of people, there are many aspects that need to be considered to ensure any relationship remains safe and healthy.

All too often support services start out with the belief that people who have a learning disability will not make good parents and that their children should be taken away. Mencap identifies that this is backed up by research that shows that 40 per cent of parents who have a learning disability do not live with their children. Not all parents with a learning disability can look after their own children and the welfare of the child is essential. However, if parents who have a learning disability are given adequate support, they should be able to keep their children.

Case study

3.3 Frank

Frank is a young man who has learning disabilities. He confides in his support worker about the difficulties he is having with his girlfriend. Frank and his girlfriend (who also has learning disabilities) want to have sexual intercourse but they are unsure about 'safe sex'. The worker advises them of the different organisations that have up-to-date information in user-friendly format that would provide them with some knowledge of 'safe sex'. The worker also advises them that these organisations can provide support and help in talking over the issues.

What responsibility does the support worker have at this stage?

What responsibility does the person with learning disabilities have?

Who else has responsibilities and what are they?

Evidence activity

3.3 Key changes

Make a poster that identifies the key changes in the lives of people who have learning disabilities. The poster should take into account where people live, daytime activities, employment, sexual relationships, parenthood and the provision of health care.

Provision of health care

People who have a learning disability generally experience poorer health and poorer health care than other members of the public. However, as we are well aware, these people have just as much of a right to receive good health care. They will need health care in the same way that everyone else will, and some people with a learning disability will have additional health needs (for example, people with a learning disability are more likely to have epilepsy). Often, they need more support to understand information about their health, to communicate symptoms and concerns, and to manage their health.

LO4 Understand the basic principles and practice of advocacy, empowerment and active participation in relation to supporting individuals with learning disabilities and their families

AC 4.1 Explain the meaning of the term 'social inclusion'

The term 'social inclusion' has come to replace older terminology such as 'community development work'. In practical terms, social inclusion means working within the community to tackle and avoid circumstances and problems that lead to social exclusion, such as poverty, unemployment or low income, housing problems and becoming housebound and isolated due to illness.

Historically, people with learning disabilities have faced poor life chances, largely due to social exclusion. They have not been accepted by mainstream society, faced, prejudice and even fear, and this has led to these people becoming socially excluded within society.

Promoting social inclusion is closely linked to empowering the individual. This means giving people with learning disabilities a voice, allowing them to make choices for themselves about the direction of their life based on their wishes and aspirations.

Evidence activity

4.1 Social inclusion

Explain the steps you take to ensure social inclusion within your place of work.

AC 4.2 Explain the meaning of the term 'advocacy'

The term 'advocacy' is concerned with speaking up for, or acting on behalf of, yourself or another person. The other person

Evidence activity

4.2 **Advocacy**

Think about a time when you have advocated the wishes of service users for whom you provide support. Explain the circumstances surrounding the episode.

Why could the service user not speak out for themselves?

What did you need to take into consideration prior to advocating the person's wishes?

is often receiving a service from a statutory or voluntary organisation. Some people require an advocate to assist them because they are not clear about their rights as citizens, or have difficulty in fully understanding these rights. Other people may find it difficult to speak up for themselves. Advocacy can enable people to take more responsibility and control for the decisions that affect their lives.

Advocacy can help service users to:

- make their views and wishes known
- express and present their views
- obtain independent advice and accurate information
- negotiate and resolve conflict.

AC 4.3 Describe different types of advocacy

All people are very different from each other. Their needs for support are different and may also change at different stages throughout their life. All advocacy types are of equal value. Which type of advocacy is used, and when, should depend on what is best suited to the person who seeks it. A single person may ask for different types of advocacy support at different times in their life.

What is essential to all types of advocacy is that it is the person who has a learning disability who is always at the centre of the advocacy process. Advocacy can therefore be described as a process that is person-centred. It

is about the person's needs, what that person wants and finding the best way of getting that across to the people who need to know.

Advocacy can be likened to a box of tools. Different types of advocacy can be used together or they can be used separately depending on the job that needs to be done.

Professional advocacy

Professional advocacy is frequently described as the 'case work' model. It is used for short to medium term involvement, which often supports people in finding a solution to a problem. Professional advocacy may be required where an individual needs support with issues requiring specific expertise, for example child protection, education, housing, employment and financial matters.

Citizen advocacy

The advocate in this relationship is usually called the 'citizen advocate' and the person receiving the service is called the 'advocacy partner'. An advocacy partner is someone at risk of having choices, wishes and decisions ignored, and who needs help in making them known and making sure they are responded to. A citizen advocate is a person who volunteers to speak up for and support an advocacy partner. The citizen advocate is unpaid and independent of service providers and families and is a member of the local community. The advocacy relationship is based on trust and confidentiality.

Crisis advocacy

Crisis advocacy provides support that aims to give the person a voice in a situation that requires a quick response. It is usually short term and aimed at helping the individual solve a problem.

Peer advocacy

Peer advocacy is usually provided by a person who has experienced a similar situation. People who have experienced the same things feel they have a better understanding and can be more supportive. In the past, peer advocacy occurred when people with learning disabilities lived in isolated hospitals. They were often separated from others in their community and only had each other for company. There was no one else to speak up for them other than their peers. As people with learning disabilities began to learn more about their rights and the obligations of citizenship, more of them began to speak up for each other. Peer advocacy is often of great support to an individual but is not recognised as being independent or **unbiased**.

Self-advocacy

Self-advocacy is what most of us do most of the time. It is about speaking up for yourself. This type of advocacy should be encouraged wherever possible. Many people with learning disabilities are well able to speak up for themselves. However, they sometimes find it hard to get others to accept this or even to listen to them. Self-advocacy groups are a good way to encourage this. Self-advocacy groups are run by people who have learning disabilities. These are often groups of people who use services or have the same interests locally. They work together to make sure they have a say in how those services are run. Self-advocacy groups are a positive way for people to support each other and they can help to build confidence so that people feel more able to speak up for themselves.

Legal advocacy

As the name suggests, legal advocacy is concerned with using the services of a lawyer or ombudsman which is a public advocate appointed by the government or parliament to support an individual with specific legal issues.

AC 4.4 Describe ways to build empowerment and active participation into everyday support with individuals with learning disabilities

Empowerment is a word we hear a lot and has become an important aspect of delivering health and social care services. Empowerment for people with learning disabilities is the process by which individuals develop increased skills to make decisions and take control over their lives. This helps individuals to achieve their goals and aspirations, thus maximising their quality of life.

A key feature in empowering people is giving them a voice and actively listening to what they have to say. Empowerment is therefore closely linked to the concept of person-centred care and various forms of advocacy.

Person-centred planning places the individual at the centre of all processes and uses techniques to ensure meaningful participation is key to empowering individuals in this way.

For the person with a learning disability, the **subjective** experience of empowerment is about rights, choice and control, which can lead them to a more **autonomous** lifestyle. For the health and social care worker, it is about anti-oppressive practice, balancing rights and responsibilities and supporting choice and empowerment while maintaining safe and ethical practice.

Key terms

Autonomous means independent, not controlled by others.

Subjective means influenced by personal feeling or opinion.

Evidence activity

4.4 Empowerment and active participation

Explain the processes that are in place within your organisation to ensure the people you support are empowered and enabled to actively participate in decisions on a daily basis.

LO5 Understand how views and attitudes impact on the lives of individuals with learning disabilities and their family carers

AC 5.1 Explain how attitudes are changing in relation to individuals with learning disabilities

People who have a learning disability and their families have always been affected by the way they are viewed and treated by society. Sadly, the history of public and private attitudes to learning disability has been one of intolerance and lack of understanding.

In the past, people with learning disabilities were cared for in institutions and often stigmatised and kept apart from mainstream society. Over the years attitudes have changed and there is a growing understanding of their personhood, and the role they are entitled to have within society.

There is recognition that people with learning disabilities can live independently, gain an education and employment and contribute to society. This can be called 'normalisation'.

Stigma and hate crime is still apparent but there is greater public pressure to deal with this and

Evidence activity

5.1 Attitudes

Why do you think attitudes towards people who have a learning disability are changing?

national organisations like 'Mencap' work to reduce the discrimination that can still be experienced by people with learning disabilities.

AC 5.2 Give examples of positive and negative aspects of being labelled as having a learning disability

Negative aspects

The way people with learning disabilities have been portrayed has often been with a **'label'**. Terms like 'the mentally handicapped', 'the blind' and 'the mentally ill' place the person in a group, which risks a stereotypical view. Being labelled as 'disabled' and 'inadequate' or not good enough also creates barriers to things that 'able-bodied' people enjoy and take for granted, for example relationships, employment, education, housing, transport and many more. In addition, it continues the prejudice and discrimination. Anti-discriminatory legislation is helping to remove barriers and shake off negative attitudes and discrimination, but there is still a long way to go.

Positive aspects

In some respects, it is important to apply a 'label' to a certain condition as this will ensure the person who has a learning disability is given any support and care that they require to ensure they lead a good quality of life. It is the type of label that is applied that makes all the difference.

The most important aspect to remember with any label is that the person is an individual with individual needs. This tends to be

Key term

Label is a 'tag' that we use to describe someone and is usually based on their appearance and behaviour.

forgotten sometimes. Using the right positive language goes a long way to defining people with a learning disability as a person first.

AC 5.3 Describe steps that can be taken to promote positive attitudes towards individuals with learning disabilities and their family carers

The media: It is now accepted that the way people are portrayed within the media can greatly influence public perception and attitude.

The recognition of the social model of disability has gone a long way in changing the attitudes of health and social care workers towards people who have learning disabilities and recognising that the person comes first.

Some employers undertake disability awareness training as part of their general staff training programmes, and this can go a long way in changing attitudes towards people who have learning disabilities.

More people who have learning disabilities are now using **mainstream community facilities**, such as colleges, hospitals, libraries and leisure centres. This sends out a clear message that segregation is no longer acceptable, but more could be done to ensure that people are positively welcomed and included.

AC 5.4 Explain the roles of external agencies and others in changing attitudes, policy and practice

External agencies have an important role in facilitating and aiding changes in attitude, policy and practice. One support group is the Learning Disability Coalition, a group that represents 14 learning disability organisations and over 140 supporter organisations that have come together to form one group with one voice (**www.learningdisabilitycoalition. org.uk**). They believe that people with a learning disability have the right to live independent lives, with the support they need. Their aim is to make sure that the government provides enough money so that people with a learning disability have the same choices and chances as everyone else. They do this by:

- providing a unified voice to government and other key decision-makers
- gathering evidence on cuts to services at local level
- raising awareness of the financial pressures on services for people with learning disabilities and
- campaigning for better funding
- achieving an evidence-based assessment of the long term resource requirements for people with learning disabilities.

LO6 Know how to promote communication with individuals with learning disabilities

AC 6.1 Identify ways of adapting each of the following when communicating with individuals who have learning disabilities:

● verbal communication
● non-verbal communication.

Communication is a two-way process in which messages are sent, received and understood between people or groups of people. It is a basic human right upon which we build relationships, make friends and control our existence. It is the way we become independent and make choices. It is the way we learn and express our thoughts, feelings and emotions. The British Institute of Learning Disabilities (BILD) estimates that between 50 per cent and 90 per cent of people who have learning difficulties also experience difficulties with communication. People who have learning disabilities do not have one recognised tool to help them communicate and every person is different. It is therefore essential that an assessment is undertaken to ensure effective methods of communication are identified for each individual.

Generally, people in societies develop common languages so that they can live together with a shared method of communication. In fact, communication is fundamental to being a part of society. People who find it difficult to communicate, or are undervalued in their societies, will automatically feel excluded unless those around them are prepared to adapt their method of communication. Effective communication is therefore essential in order to promote the principles associated with independence, choice, rights and inclusion.

Figure 11.5 Accessible communication

Methods of communication vary and can be either verbal or non-verbal. A high percentage of communication is non-verbal.

● When communicating verbally it is important not to overestimate language skills. Equally it is important that the pace of communication (how slow/fast you speak) is consistent with the person's level of understanding.
● Objects, pictures, signs and symbols are all powerful ways of communicating meaning.
● British Sign Language (BSL) has long been established as a language used by people who have a hearing impairment.
● Braille enables people with a visual impairment to read.
● People with more complex learning disabilities may not be able to use any recognised means of communication and will therefore be dependent on others to interpret their needs and choices through observation and response to their communicative behaviour.

See SHC 21 for more information on communication.

Evidence activity

6.1 Adapting communication

Explain how the communication requirements of individuals are assessed within your organisation.

Think about the service users you support and identify ways in which the methods of verbal and non-verbal communication have been adapted to facilitate communication with these individuals.

AC 6.2 Explain why it is important to use language that is both 'age appropriate' and 'ability appropriate' when communicating with individuals with learning disabilities

When communicating with people who have a learning disability, it is essential that the communication takes place at a pace and in a manner that the individual can process. This means that the information should be both 'age appropriate' and 'ability appropriate'. Communication must also take into account the person as a whole and sensitive consideration should be given to the person's cultural and religious beliefs.

Evidence activity

6.2 Age and ability appropriate language

Explain why it is important to use language that is both 'age appropriate' and 'ability appropriate'.

How do you ensure you take these factors into account when communicating with service users?

What could be a consequence of not taking these factors into consideration?

AC 6.3 Describe ways of checking whether an individual has understood a communication, and how to address any misunderstandings

Within your role as a care worker you will want to help individuals communicate to the best of their ability and promote understanding of their needs and preferences whenever appropriate. When communicating with a person who has a learning disability it is essential that they understand what has been communicated. If the individual has understood, this may be immediately obvious; however, there will be times when you will be unsure whether they have understood. Hopefully you will know your service users well, but it is also important to seek advice from a senior member of staff.

Individuals who are unable to successfully communicate with you, or understand what you are communicating to them, may become distressed. The extent of the frustration and distress will vary from person to person but will be apparent through verbal communication, body language or facial expression.

Evidence activity

6.3 Ways of checking

How do you check understanding when you are communicating with service users?

How do you address any misunderstandings as they arise?

Legislation

The Human Rights Act 1998

The Disability Discrimination Act 1995

The Mental Capacity Act 2005

Mental Health Act 2007

The Equality Act 2010

Health and Social Care Act 2012

Useful resources

Websites

Office for Disability Issues
www.officefordisability.gov.uk

About Learning Disabilities
www.aboutlearningdisabilities.co.uk

Mencap
www.mencap.org.uk

Learning Disability Coalition
www.learningdisabilitycoalition.org.uk

The Foundation for People with Learning Difficulties
www.learningdisabilities.org.uk

Easyhealth
www.easyhealth.org.uk

Understand the factors affecting older people

This unit is worth 2 credits

What are you finding out?

Statistics taken from the Office for National Statistics 2011 census say that there are 9.2 million people over the age of 65, which is 16 per cent of the population of England and Wales. We also know that 31 per cent of people over 65 were living alone, and 50 per cent of people over 65 reported living in good health compared to 88 per cent of people under 65.

The ageing process affects people, and because we are unique it affects all individuals in different ways. There are positive and negative approaches in society towards older people and therefore we must look at the importance of challenging stereotypes and discrimination. We should, as a society, promote social inclusion, independence and control for older people.

This unit covers an understanding of older people, the impact of ageing, the range of factors that impacts on older people and the role played by society. The unit promotes a person-centred approach as an underpinning value in working with older people.

By the end of this unit you will:

1 Understand the impact of the ageing process on older people
2 Understand attitudes of society to older people
3 Understand the importance of using person-centred approaches with older people
4 Understand the importance of independence for older people.

LO1 Understand the impact of the ageing process on older people

AC 1.1 Describe changes that may come with ageing

Ageing is 'the process of growing old'. Older people are sometimes defined as over 50 but as we are now living longer this definition is open to debate. Most services in health and social care define 'older people's services' for people over the age of 65. Health and social care are also working towards ageless services – this means services not based on age as this is seen to be discriminatory. We will discover, although there are biological signs of ageing, being 'old' does not necessarily mean you feel old or act in a stereotypical way, i.e. the way society might assume an older person will act. We could argue that the concept of ageing is subjective, that is, it is a personal view. We will also discover that different cultures and sections of society have different attitudes to older people and this influences the ageing process.

Consider this question: how old do you have to be to be considered 'an older person'? The World Health Organisation (**WHO**) says:

'Most developed world countries have accepted the chronological age of 65 years as a definition of 'elderly' or older person …… it is many times associated with the age at which one can begin to receive pension benefits. At the moment, there is no United Nations standard numerical criterion, but the UN agreed cut-off is 60+ years to refer to the older population.

Although there are commonly used definitions of old age, there is no general agreement on the age at which a person becomes old. The common use of a calendar age to mark the threshold of old age assumes **equivalence** with biological age, yet at the same time, it is generally accepted that these two are not necessarily **synonymous**.'

Key terms

Equivalence means equal to.

Synonymous means to have the same meaning, i.e. two words that mean the same thing.

This means that we cannot assume that having your 65th birthday automatically means you are 'old'.

Changes that may come with ageing

Generally speaking, from what is commonly called 'middle age' there is a decline in physical and in some cases mental functioning. There is no consistent definition of 'middle age' but for the purposes of this unit we would consider a person aged under 60 to be in middle rather than old age.

Physical effects of ageing will include:

- hearing, taste, sight and smell are affected
- the proportion of fat to muscle may increase by as much as 30 per cent
- the amount of water in the body decreases – there is less saliva and other lubricating fluids, for example, fluids that stop your mouth or eyes drying out
- the liver and the kidneys cannot function as efficiently (See AC 1.3)
- digestion of food is affected, with a decrease in stomach acid production (see AC 1.3)
- a loss of muscle strength and co-ordination, affecting mobility and flexibility
- changes in the cardiovascular systems, leading to decreased oxygen and nutrients throughout the body
- a decrease in bone strength and density which can lead to an increased risk of fractures
- hormone levels, which gradually decline – thyroid and sexual hormones are affected
- shrinkage in muscle mass and decreased bone formation, possibly leading to osteoporosis.

Figure 12.1 The ageing process and its physical effects

Effects of age on cognitive/mental function

These can include:

- a 'slowing down' in thinking
- taking more time to process information
- some forgetfulness (this is not the same as dementia)
- not being able to learn new things as quickly
- decreased functioning of the nervous system so that reflexes are not as sharp, and memory and learning are affected.

See AC 1.3 for information on emotional, social, environmental and financial/economic impact related to ageing.

Evidence activity

1.1 Changes that come with ageing

Choose three of the physical effects of ageing above and investigate the impact they can have on the individual.

AC 1.2 Explain how the experience of the ageing process is unique to each individual

We are all the products of:

- inherited genes from our parents
- our environment
- the culture or society we live in, including social class
- education
- standard of living
- economic and political factors.

All these factors will affect our experience of the ageing process. As unique individuals we will not only experience different rates of physical decline, but our attitude to our ageing process will differ.

We may age physically in different ways. This can depend on how well we have looked after ourselves in earlier years. People who live in less wealthy areas with a lower standard of living may experience ageing differently. They may not have the same opportunities to enjoy retirement or maintain good health. The culture we live in may have different attitudes to older people. In many cultures older people are respected still as the head of the family; they may still work to a great age and are seen very much as contributing to the family and society.

Evidence activity

1.2 How ageing process is unique to individuals

Consider this situation.

Ellie is 56 years old and has taken early retirement. She spends her day watching TV and reading. She says she cannot walk very far because she gets too tired. She has diabetes and arthritis. Ellie says she deserves to retire because she is approaching 60 and it is time she had a rest.

Megan is 62 and has just been successful in gaining a very responsible managerial position. She says she loves being busy and after all, age is only a number!

- Why do you think Ellie and Megan's experience of the ageing process is so different? What factors could have affected this?
- Why do you think they view ageing in such different ways?
- Think about an older person you work with or know within your family. How is the ageing process affecting them? Are they more like Ellie or Megan?

AC 1.3 Analyse the potential impact of factors associated with ageing on older people to include

- **physical**
- **emotional**
- **social**
- **cognitive**
- **environmental**
- **financial/economic.**

Physical impact

You have already read about the potential physical effects of ageing in AC 1.1. Here we analyse the potential impact of factors that are related to ageing.

- Hearing, taste, sight and smell are affected.
  Poor hearing affects our ability to participate in conversations or we can misunderstand what is said. This can lead to feelings of isolation. It is very important that hearing problems are addressed to help prevent these problems arising.
  Loss of taste and smell can affect our appetite. Think how much we enjoy the sight and smell of food, which helps to stimulate our appetite.
  Reduced vision is obviously a risk to both the individual's safety and independence. Lack of sight can also stop people feeling confident about going out to see friends, go shopping and socialise generally. This can lead to social isolation.
- The liver and the kidneys cannot function as efficiently.
  This decreased functioning affects our ability to eliminate waste properly. This can lead to urine infections. As the liver gets rid of toxins and drugs in our bodies, an older person may become unwell because there is a build-up of these in their body.
- Digestion of food is affected, with a decrease in stomach acid production.
  Poor digestion leads to pain, constipation, nausea and weight loss. If this is the case, an older person can become weaker and

more frail and more likely to contract other illnesses, such as infections.

- A loss of muscle strength and co-ordination, affecting mobility and flexibility.
  If the muscles are not exercised and begin to lose strength, it becomes more difficult to support our own skeleton, as well as not being able to lift or carry loads. We cannot sustain activities and will tire more easily. We slow down and find bending and reaching more difficult. All this impacts on everyday activities and as the individual struggles with this lack of strength, so they will need to rely more on others and lose some of their independence. There may also be an increased risk of falls.
- Changes in the cardiovascular systems, leading to decreased oxygen and nutrients throughout the body.
  People can become breathless and tire easily. They may be more at risk of heart attacks. A lack of oxygen to the brain can also cause confusion.
- Decreased functioning of the nervous system so that reflexes are not as sharp, and memory and learning are affected.
  This decrease in functioning does not necessarily mean that the individual will develop dementia, but can experience mild **cognitive impairment** as a result.
- Shrinkage in muscle mass and decreased bone formation, possibly leading to **osteoporosis**.
  Both men and women can develop osteoporosis. Fractured bones take longer to heal in older people and can affect their ability to recover to the level of independence they enjoyed before the accident.

Key terms

Cognitive impairment means some alteration in memory and ability to reason or think.

Osteoporosis is a condition that affects the bones, causing them to become weak and fragile and more likely to break (fracture).

Emotional impact

Older people are often associated with loneliness and isolation. This is certainly the case for people in their 80s and 90s, whose family and friends may be dying and they are not able to get out and about and socialise any more.

Family life has changed in the last 50 years or so. Most people no longer tend to live in 'extended families'. Sons and daughters often move away to work and they are not able to see or support ageing parents as easily or as often. A third of older people live alone.

Growing older can be a frustrating time. Some people embrace it and enjoy their wisdom and experience, and are respected by family and friends. Others feel marginalised (left out) and ignored. There can be feelings of low self-esteem and helplessness.

Social impact

Having an active role in the community can become more problematic as people grow older and find it more difficult to go out. The older person may no longer be able to drive or use public transport easily. They may no longer be able to participate in social events, family occasions or social groups. This all contributes to feelings of isolation and often depression. The 2011 census tells us that 31 per cent of older people live alone. The amount of people over 65 with long term health conditions living at home has increased, and equally the number of older carers who look after a husband, wife or other family member has also increased.

Cognitive impact

This relates to the way we think and learn. As we get older this function may slow down. We may struggle more to learn and remember new things, our attention may not be as keen and we might not grasp new ideas as quickly.

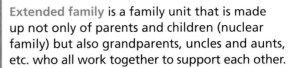

Key terms

Extended family is a family unit that is made up not only of parents and children (nuclear family) but also grandparents, uncles and aunts, etc. who all work together to support each other.

Financially dependency means relying on other people and/or the state for financial support.

Economically inactive means neither earning money/nor spending it on items other than essentials.

However, it is very important to remember this mild cognitive impairment is not the same as dementia and although some people may go on to develop dementia it is not automatic.

Environmental impact

Ageing affects our ability to remain in a familiar environment. Health and social care organisations now have a big commitment to enable older people to remain in their own home for as long as possible because we all thrive in a familiar place that holds all our memories and gives us emotional stability. However, for some older people, remaining in their own home can also have a negative impact. Familiar friends and neighbours may have moved away and young families are too busy with their own lives to feel they can provide any meaningful support.

Financial/economic impact

Generally speaking, most older people do not do paid work and they may have to rely on the state pension and/or a private pension. One view is that older people do not contribute to the national economy once they stop working and paying taxes. **Financial dependency** can lead to poverty, particularly fuel poverty. This is when people cannot afford to heat their home adequately. In 2011, 90 per cent of people

Evidence activity

1.3 Potential impact

Walter is 83 years old. He has osteoporosis and his eyesight is failing. He also has diabetes. He used to work as a farm labourer. Since he retired he has had to live in a small ground floor flat in the town. His only source of income is his state pension and benefits. Walter never married and his best friend lives in the next town.

What do you think are the factors impacting on Walter? Consider emotional, social and financial issues.

Time to think

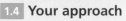

1.4 Your approach

Think about Walter from the evidence activity in AC 1.3. How could you enable him to adopt a positive outlook?

How can your approach help him with his current situation?

Evidence activity

1.4 A positive approach

Think about an individual that you have supported. Make a list of the ways in which you have worked with them in a positive way. Describe one other way in which you can work with them in a positive way.

over 65 were **economically inactive** (see page 217 for definition). However since 2001 the numbers who are economically active has doubled. This may be partly due a number of older people working past the usual age of retirement as companies expand opportunities for older people. Older people are also beginning to see themselves in a different light. Ageing is more about opportunities than giving up, for example, and so they are more engaged in activities related to spending – retirement homes, holidays or even investments.

AC 1.4 Describe how a positive approach to ageing can contribute to the health and well-being of an individual

So far we have primarily covered the negative aspects of the ageing process. Physical and mental decline can affect not only the health of the individual but also their overall well-being. A positive approach by both the individual and those around them can help them to manage their situation and actually enjoy life.

Positive approaches

In your role, you:

● Must always concentrate on what the individual can do rather than what they cannot do.

● You should use problem-solving to find alternative solutions to problems associated with ageing.

● You should not concentrate on the biological age of the individual, but rather talk to them about their hopes and dreams and fears.

● You should value the contribution they have made to society and the things they still have to offer.

Ageing does not stop us being the person we have always been. We may still have the same outlook on life, the same likes and dislikes and the same ambitions.

Adopting a positive view can give the older person a feeling of optimism, that there is something to look forward to. Working with them to set small achievable goals can give a sense of purpose and self-esteem when the goals are achieved. Compromise is also effective, so that although the older person is too frail to go to the supermarket alone, they can manage with support. This is better than 'taking over' and doing the shopping for them. Through your support they can maintain their independence and therefore their self-esteem.

Figure 12.2 We must not forget that people are still themselves, despite the ageing process

LO2 Understand attitudes of society to older people

AC 2.1 Describe the contributions to society made by older people

As a care worker, you should always place the individual at the centre of the support you give them. This means finding out as much about them, their needs, preferences and histories which we covered in unit HSC 026. You should therefore not make assumptions about the individual because of their age. Rather you should understand them as individuals with a history who have made a significant contrition to society.

Economic

The usual or stereotypical view of older people is that they no longer work and therefore do not pay taxes. However, we know that the number of older people who are economically active (earning, saving and paying taxes) has increased. The 2011 census indicated that the number of

unpaid older carers is increasing, which means that they are contributing their time free rather than using paid carers. Older people are still consumers – they buy goods, pay for services and support their local communities.

Social

Older people shaped our past. They have made history and formed the society we live in now. In 2014 we celebrated the 100th anniversary of the start of World War One, which highlighted the major contributions of people over the last 100 years and perhaps made us more aware of the respect we should show the older generation for their contribution to society.

Other contributions

There is a wealth of famous older people who have made contributions to society later on in their lives. For example, Nelson Mandela was still president of South Africa at 77 years of age; Pablo Picasso was still painting at 90; and Coco Chanel was still running her fashion house aged 85.

However, there are thousands of 'ordinary' older people who continue to contribute to society. They support churches, social groups, local communities and neighbourhoods. **Intergenerational work** brings younger and older people together to share knowledge, experience and skills.

In one area of research, people over 55 expressed frustration at the feeling of being sidelined. They had worked in many different industries but felt that their skills, knowledge and experience were not being acknowledged or used. They felt that given the opportunity, they could pass on those skills to the younger generation. A scheme was set up and now the older people support university students and school children in cooking and other skills.

> **Key term**
>
> **Intergenerational work** refers to different generations (children and older people) working on projects together.

Figure 12.3 Older people can pass on their skills

Research and investigate

2.1 Famous contributions

Research two famous contributions to society made by older people. Also think about the older people in your own community, and look at the local media. Describe a situation where an older person has made a contribution.

Evidence activity

2.1 Contributions to society

Go back to Walter's situation in AC 1.3. What skills do you think he could share? What has been his contribution to society?

Write a small case study about how you might engage Walter in intergenerational work.

AC 2.2 Explain what is meant by age discrimination

What is age discrimination?

Age discrimination is unfairly treating people differently because of their age, although some forms of differential treatment can be a good thing. This means that sometimes we treat people differently because it has a positive outcome for them. This is the case for older people when they do not have to pay for prescriptions, for example.

Key term

Age discrimination is treating people differently because of their age.

The legal definition of discrimination is when a person is treated less favourably than someone else and that the treatment is for a reason relating to the person's protected characteristic (e.g. disability), according to the Equality Act 2010.

There are different types of discrimination related to age:

- **Direct age discrimination** where someone is unfairly treated in comparison with another person – for example, where an older person is refused admission to a club when a younger person would be admitted, or where a job that an older person could do equally well is given to a younger person.
- **Indirect age discrimination** where a rule or practice applies to everyone but puts certain people at a disadvantage – for example, where a shop allows you to pay for an expensive item in instalments, but only if you are employed.
- **Harassment related to age**. Harassment is unwanted behaviour that has a negative effect on the person's dignity or well-being. Harassment often involves bullying or offensive behaviour. For example, a beautician might make fun of an older lady who asks for an appointment for a facial.
- **Victimisation** of someone who has made a complaint of discrimination.

The Equality Act 2010 makes it unlawful to discriminate against employees, job seekers and trainees because of their age.

Evidence activity

2.2 Age discrimination

How would you define age discrimination? Can you give an example of age discrimination that you have seen in practice?

Positive action can be taken to prevent or compensate (make up for) disadvantages older people might experience.

Think about the experiences of older people you know. What kind of positive action can be taken that demonstrates anti-discriminatory practice?

One example is intergenerational work.

AC 2.3 Explain how societal attitudes and beliefs impact on older people

In a recent report from Age UK, older people said they feel that they are a **burden** to society due to the way services are provided. They said that the traditional services such as care homes, **domiciliary care**, day centres contribute to feelings of dependence and stereotype older people. The 700 older people surveyed also thought that they were being seen as a burden by society and that their talents and abilities were being ignored.

Barriers

There are also barriers that impact on the life of older people, including:

- a lack of support for older people to increase or improve their skills: there are not always the right facilities to enable older people to access educational groups – for example they may need to travel a distance or the classes may be at night
- a lack of information available to older people: as a society we still tend to focus on education and leisure for younger people and older people have to seek their own solutions
- a lack of practical support: for example, older people may need access to transport, or a person to support them on outings, shopping trips etc.
- poor information between different organisations: older people are not always aware of what is available or who to turn to – they may not have access to the internet and have to rely on other people
- poor communication between professionals and between professionals and older

Key terms

Burden is a weight or an inconvenience that can cause problems for another person.

Domiciliary care is care and support delivered to the individual in their own home in the community.

people: we still assess people in relation to their mental, physical or social needs. It is important to look at these as a part of the whole person and think about how they all affect the person and how these issues might prevent older people being able to access services or support that would help meet their needs.

Ageing is a personal issue and as a care worker you will need to support the individual to make personal adjustments. It is also a social issue and therefore we need to make social changes (through health and social care policies and legislation).

One way this is being encouraged is the use of personal budgets. These are to encourage older people to make their own choices in how to meet their assessed needs by purchasing services to suit them.

Societal attitudes and changes

As a society we can have contradictory attitudes – we can view older people as 'national treasures', but we also assume they can no longer participate or contribute to society. We hear patronising language such as 'Bless her', 'What a shame', 'Old dear' but also refer to the bravery of older people who fought in the war or worked in industries as Britain began to develop after the war.

Recent government thinking is that older people need to have a voice. This means a political voice that can influence the services they need in health and social care.

As the generations move on, the older generation changes. Older people now use the internet and are more aware of their rights. Health and social care organisations have also recognised that the older person should be at the centre of their care and need to be consulted.

Portrayals in the media

We still have a long way to go. Media images of older people tend to keep the stereotype going – we see pictures of frail people shuffling in slippers or negative terminology like 'dementia sufferers'. Items in the news about older people often start with a picture of an older person using a Zimmer frame or a shot of feet in slippers. However, in contrast, some advertising campaigns show older people enjoying life and being active members of society. Recent Marks and Spencer advertising campaigns show older famous women modelling clothes. The underlying message is that it is possible to be both elegant and older – basically, that being old does not stop you being a woman.

Impacts on older people

Negative attitudes can impact on older people in various ways. There is still an assumption that as we get older we do not want to continue with activities we have always enjoyed. One example is dancing – in one nightclub for example 'special' evenings have been organised for older people – but perhaps this shows how we see older people as 'apart' from the rest of society. Consider whether it would be better if the nightclub was all inclusive, or do you think older people prefer mixing with their own generation?

Evidence activity

2.3 Societal attitudes and beliefs

Produce a poster for your workplace that challenges the negative attitudes and beliefs of society towards older people. Look at the examples mentioned in the paragraphs on pages 225 and 226. Can you What other ways can negative attitudes and beliefs impact older people? In contrast, how do positive attitudes impact older people?

AC 2.4 Describe strategies that can be used to challenge stereotypes and discriminatory attitudes towards older people

Before we consider the strategies that can be used to challenge stereotypes and discriminatory attitudes, we need to consider where these stereotypes and discriminatory attitudes towards older people come from.

Stereotypes of older people assume that ageing means the person must be more vulnerable, less able to cope and more likely to need help. Although this is true for some older people, it is incorrect to associate ageing with a lack of self-determination or the ability to contribute to society. Older people are active rather than passive members of society.

The effects of stereotypical and discriminatory attitudes

Stereotypical attitudes and discriminatory attitudes can affect older people in many ways:

- They may be subject to **hate crime**.
- They may not be employed due to age even though they are competent to do the job in question.
- They may be denied access to education.
- They may be denied access to certain social clubs, societies, etc.

Time to think

2.4 Strategies to challenge stereotypes and discrimination

Have a discussion with your colleagues. Think about people, organisations and sections of society that may stereotype and discriminate against older people. Compile a list of these.

Key term

Hate crime is crime motivated by racial, sexual or other prejudice, typically involving violence or anti-social behaviour.

What can we do?

There are a number of ways we can challenge stereotype and discrimination attitudes towards older people.

- **Education**. Attitudes are formed from an early age. We need to start young and ensure that we talk about age and the ageing process in schools to ensure greater understanding, perhaps by inviting older people into schools to help. This education should follow through into adulthood, particularly in health and social care training. Ageing is a natural process in our lives and we need to educate younger people to understand that older people are 'you and I', not a different species.
- **Positive role models**. Many older people are successful, or talented. They may simply be fit and well and are continuing to work or contributing to their local community. We should celebrate this and demonstrate that this is not 'abnormal' – that ageing is not the end of a productive and interesting life.
- **Social inclusion**. Older people need to be included more in society. Better access to transport and buildings, and affordable entertainment for example would help this. Intergenerational work is an example of social inclusion.
- **Incentives for businesses**. Financial incentives for businesses to employ older people could be considered. Some businesses already employ older people because of their experience and 'people skills'– Waitrose and Homebase are examples.

- **Consultation**. Older people should be consulted or asked more about the services they need. **Personalisation** is one initiative that does this.
- The Equality Act 2010 seeks to outlaw discrimination on grounds of age in the provision of goods and services, including social care and NHS services.

LO3 Understand the importance of using person-centred approaches with older people

The person-centred approach puts the person at the centre of the service you provide. It recognises that the individual is unique and it is this idea that forms the basis for planning and delivery of care and support. The approach promotes dignity for older people.

AC 3.1 Describe how the effects of ageing can affect the day-to-day life of older people

In LO1, you read about impacts of ageing such as physical, emotional and social, and here we look at how the effects of ageing can affect the day-to-day life of older people. The term 'day-to-day life' may include:

- relationships, family role, social status
- access to community, social and leisure facilities

- personal and health care
- independence
- lack of social support
- lack of material well-being
- education and employment opportunities
- housing
- sensory loss.

Relationships, family role and status

Older people who are isolated due to disability or lack of social outlets may not be able to form new relationships or sustain new ones. We have already discussed how families are changing and that as children move away to start their own lives, older parents may be left to act as carers for their partner, or are living alone with limited access to the outside world. As people age, they may lose their role in the family as being the 'head' as well as the status of being a wage earner.

By contrast, some families remain as an extended unit and the older person is still viewed as head of the family. It is not uncommon, for example, for grandparents to act as direct carers for their grandchildren while the parents are at work.

Access to community, social and leisure facilities

There are several reasons why older people may not be able to easily access their local community and social and leisure facilities. These may include:

- lack of accessible transport
- lack of a support network to help the person access local services
- attitudes of others (see LO2) – they may lack confidence or experience feelings of anxiety.

Facilities such as these are ways of forming new connections, and if older people are unable to access such facilities, they may be unable to form new relationships. It is therefore your role to ensure that older people are able to access these, or are able to access information telling them about the different community, social and leisure facilities available to them.

Personal and health care

It is likely that due to increasing personal and health care needs the older person relies more on primary care (GPs and community nurses) and care at home, whether for domestic or personal care tasks. Although our goal today is to maintain and encourage the independence of the individual, the fact that they have to rely on someone to arrive to support them with personal care or meals can be **disempowering** for the individual.

This is why it is so important to work truly within the principles of:

- person-centred care
- dignity and privacy
- partnership
- enabling the individual to be as independent as possible.

These are covered throughout the mandatory units.

Independence

Independence in every life is an important aspect of maintaining dignity. Reliance on others can affect our self-esteem and disempower us. It is therefore important to ensure that older people can maintain as much independence as possible.

Key term

Disempowering means taking away a person's independence and the power to make their own decisions.

Lack of social support

Without support to maintain links with their own community and society, older people become detached, isolated or lonely and this can affect their mental well-being.

Lack of material well-being

Although some older people are materially wealthy, many rely on state benefits. Although levels of poverty have reduced, there are still older people who struggle to pay bills and 'make ends meet' and who do not rely on a more modern concept of credit.

Relying on a limited income means that they may have to prioritise the essentials like food and heating. Social activities may not be possible if it means spending money that has to be saved to pay the bills. Hence, some older people may not be able to afford to go out and socialise, leading to isolation and loneliness.

Education and employment opportunities

There is still an assumption in society that older people do not want or indeed need to work or further their education. We talk about a 'youth culture' and there is a lot of emphasis in the media on being and looking youthful. To reverse this trend, older people are coming forward to show that being over 'retirement age' does not actually mean they have to

Research and investigate

3.1 'Living on a low income in later life'

Use a search engine to read Age UK's 'Living on a low income in later life', which describes how older people manage on low incomes and how this affects their well-being.

Investigate the state benefits an older person can claim. Compile an information leaflet for your colleagues.

withdraw from life and that in fact they are still capable of working and learning.

Out of work older people can find it more difficult to get a job and they are more likely than younger people to remain unemployed for longer. Of unemployed people aged over 50, 46 per cent have been unemployed for 12 months or more compared with around 30 per cent of Jobseeker's Allowance claimants aged 18 or over.

Working longer can have a positive impact on an individual's savings for retirement and also for the economy as a whole.

The Department of Work and Pensions is actively encouraging employers to take on older people in an initiative called 'Age Positive'.

Housing
The effects of ageing may mean that the older person can no longer live in their family home. Moving to new accommodation can be distressing. It often involves 'downsizing' or moving to a smaller property and having to make decisions about getting rid of well-loved pieces of furniture and mementos for example.

Moving into a care home is a large step and the individual must be well supported in this decision because they are giving up a large measure of their independence. This is why health and social care professionals should try to enable the individual to access more appropriate housing and services to prevent admission to care homes.

Sensory loss
Being unable to hear or see properly prevents the individual from fully participating in everyday life, unless we provide them with appropriate support.

Evidence activity

3.1 Ageing and day to day life
Summarise how the effects of ageing can affect day-to-day life.

AC 3.2 Describe ways of using a person-centred approach to support older people to maintain health and well-being in day-to-day life

A person-centred approach is one that fully recognises the uniqueness of the individual and establishes this as the basis for planning and delivery of care and support. This approach promotes dignity for older people.

Uniqueness
In order to maintain health and well-being we must recognise that the individual has their own needs and preferences. We must not make assumptions that because the person is 60 or 90 years old they will have a different view on the world or want different things. The support or care plan should therefore be based on the actual needs and preferences of the individual which are discussed in an assessment. By doing so we can maintain their well-being by paying attention to the things that matter to them.

Person-centred approach as basis for planning and delivery of care and support
The most reliable source of information for planning care and support is the individual. If they lack capacity, you may also need to consult the people closest to them. You should ask: 'What would the individual have wanted

Figure 12.4 We need to pay attention to the things that matter to the older individual

Case study

3.2 Walter (1)

Go back to Walter's situation. In conversation he tells you that he used to work with shire horses and that he really misses the countryside.

Is there anything you could do to help his well-being, bearing in mind that at the moment he lives an isolated life?

He has disclosed that he has a niece and would like to contact her, and that he has not been able to see his friend in a nearby town for the last few months.

Evidence activity

3.2 Person-centred approach

Look back at the second walter case study in AC 3.2. Explain why the second conversation is person-centred.

If you were Walter, how would the two approaches make you feel?

Summarise how a person-centred approach supports older people to maintain health and well-being in day-to-day life.

Think about your own role. Give an example of how you have used a person-centred approach to support an individual's well-being?

to happen?' Consider the situation they are in and ensure you work in partnership. There may have to be some compromises because of the person's disability or mental health. However, this does not mean that you impose your own ideas, but rather work with them to find a solution.

For example, Walter may be finding it difficult to keep to a strict diet for his diabetes. Rather than having a confrontational approach, use problem-solving skills. Ask advice from the diabetic nurse about suitable alternatives and take Walter shopping to look for them, or if you shop for him, talk about the items you may be able to bring back.

Promote dignity

By keeping the person at the centre we can empower them so that they feel they are at the centre, and not on the 'receiving end' of care and support. This also helps to support the overall well-being of the individual.

AC 3.3 Explain the importance of social inclusion for older people

Key terms

Ethical means morally good or correct.

National political agenda is a set of issues and policies laid out by the government to help shape the way we do things.

Influencing society

Social inclusion is an economic, political, social and **ethical** concept. To be included within a society or a group of people might mean that you are accepted whatever your financial situation or social status. The **national political agenda** realises that older people should have a voice. The term 'silver power' has been used to describe how older people are becoming a significant and more influential section of society.

Case study

3.2 Walter (2)

Think about Walter again. You are talking to him about his diabetes. He has requested some sweets. What would be a better approach when talking to him about this:

'Walter, you can't have anything sweet. You are being silly because it will make you ill.'

OR

'Walter, I know you are missing sweet things, it must be difficult. I tell you what, let's talk to the diabetic nurse and see what she can suggest. In the meantime, could you try to keep away from the sweet things as I am a bit worried they are making you feel poorly?'

How does the second approach help to promote Walter's dignity?

Since 2007, for the first time in British history, there have been more people over pension age than children. At every election there is an increase in the numbers of older voters compared to younger voters, which means they are in a stronger position to influence British politics.

Importance of social inclusion

It is particularly important for older people to feel included, accepted and valued within the family, community or neighbourhood. This is so that they can ensure they can maintain their social status, as well as prevent isolation and loneliness. Not only that, older people have a great deal to offer society, and their life experience and knowledge can enrich our own lives.

Strategies to promote social inclusion

Some of the strategies to promote social inclusion include group activities, making sure one to one social support advice and information is available and assessments on health needs of individuals. Home visiting and befriending schemes are also helpful. An example of this is a 'secretarial service' provided by Age UK, which offers support with writing to relatives, managing bills and other correspondence. Information technology (IT) is also being used more to enable older people to communicate with friends and family.

AC 3.4 Outline barriers to social inclusion for older people

Barriers to social inclusion might include:

- transport
- lack of income
- mental health issues
- disability
- environment.

Transport

Barriers to social inclusion are practical and emotional. Older people who cannot access public transport or who do not have a social network to support them to go out cannot be involved in activities outside their home. Schemes to 'bring 'activities to them are helpful, but our emotional well-being is enhanced when we change our environment. Think about how much we enjoy holidays and visiting other people.

Lack of income

Lack of income stops the individual prioritising social events as they are often seen as a 'luxury', when in fact socialising is crucial not only to feeling happy but also as a source of stimulation. Meeting other people, sharing experiences and seeing and hearing new things all keep us alert and interested. When older people are unable to do this, boredom and **apathy** can set in, leading to depression.

Mental health issues

Older people who are experiencing mental health problems, whether it is dementia or depression, may be less likely to be included in life outside their home. Others may find it difficult to interact with a person living with dementia or the individual may feel anxious about socialising with others because they feel vulnerable due to their mental health problems.

Disabilities

Older people who experience disabilities (poor mobility, sight or hearing) can struggle with maintaining their independence. They cannot necessarily go out on their own and rely on other people to support them.

Facilities and the environment

Social inclusion also depends on facilities, environments, and social groups – for example, being accepting of older people. The National Audit Office ('Older people – independence and well-being') commented:

'The challenge for communities and councils is to be inclusive, to help older people to stay healthy and active and to encourage their contribution to the community. Councils need to accept responsibility for investing in opportunities and services for older people; to see them as full citizens and a resource for society, rather than as dependent on it. Those whose health has begun to fail also deserve to enjoy life as fully as possible and we need to find new ways to support them.'

Evidence activity

3.4 **Barriers to social inclusion**

Think about the attitudes of society to older people. Why might these attitudes help or hinder social inclusion of older people?

Discuss one example of a positive attitude and one of a negative attitude.

AC 3.5 Describe ways of using a person-centred approach to enable older people to make positive contributions to their community

By understanding the history, experiences, interests and talents of older people we can use a person-centred approach to support them to make positive contributions to their **community** (see page for 230 definition).

Case study

3.5 **Walter**

Walter has talked about his love for shire horses, and his care worker has contacted a local school, who have said they would be pleased to have him go into the school to talk to the children about work on the farm after the war.

Explain why this scenario uses a person-centred approach.

What are the benefits for both Walter and the children?

Figure 12.5 Older people can make positive contributions to their local community

As a care worker you should empower the older person and not accept the stereotype that because an older person may require support from health and social care they are unable to make a positive contribution.

For example, they may still wish to attend their local place of worship, but need help to get there. This should not be a barrier and by talking your manager or the care coordinator, a key person from the place of worship as well as the older person it is possible to find a solution. Older people are respected members of such places and their attendance must be encouraged.

Barriers to making positive contributions

Physical illness or disability may prevent the older person being able to make a positive contribution. By adopting a person-centred approach and addressing their health needs it is possible to increase the individual's level of independence. If for example Walter's diabetes is managed properly, he is less likely to become unwell and more likely to feel able to go out and take part in his local community.

LO4 Understand the importance of independence for older people

AC 4.1 Explain how independence can contribute to the well-being of older people

Independence means different things to different people. As a baby develops into a toddler, their level of independence increases but we would still never leave them unsupervised. Levels of independence might be measured by the child learning to eat or walk without help and guidance. The same is true for all adults. An older person who is quite frail may rely on you as a care worker for support with everyday tasks, but they can be independent in spirit. They are still able to exercise choice and give an opinion. This level of independence should not be underestimated.

Being able to manage activities of daily living independently gives the older person **self-determination**. Mental well-being relies on the individual feeling that they have some control over their life, that their choices and opinions are respected and valued.

AC 4.2 Describe how to support older people to maintain independence

We exercise our independence in many ways. We move about freely, we eat and drink what we want, without assistance, we choose where we go, who we talk to and which activities we wish to engage in. We have the right to say yes or no and we learn new skills that increase our independence, such as driving or using a computer.

How can you support an older person to maintain their independence?

You should start by assessing what they are already able to do and what potential they may have. For example, you may be asked to support an older person recovering from a fall. They are able to walk but have lost their confidence. The assessment indicates that they will be able to walk independently once they have gained their confidence. Your role is to support them to achieve that level of independence.

You should consult the older person because they must be at the centre of the assessment. You need to understand how they view their own independence. What does it mean to them?

Maintaining independence may range from being able to get on the bus to visit friends, to being able to eat unassisted. It all depends on what the 'baseline' is. It would be unreasonable and unrealistic to expect a frail older person to walk to the shops, but they may wish to go with you in a wheelchair so that they can choose their own food. You are therefore working within the individual's assessed ability and should support them to make the most of their situation.

Evidence activity

4.2 Supporting older people to maintain independence

Look at some care plans at your place of work. Is it clear how the individual's independence is to be maintained?

Think about Walter. Write a care plan that helps to maintain his independence, using the information you have about him.

How could you support an older individual to be independent?

How will this contribute to their overall well-being? Discuss this with your manager.

AC 4.3 Describe how older people can be in control of decision-making about their care and support needs

Involving users in their own care decisions is essential to a sense of well-being for the individual and has benefits for everyone involved in social care provision, including health and care support staff, family and carers.

Organisations

On a national level there are a number of organisations that involve older people in helping to develop services, for example, the Joseph Rowntree Trust.

Shaping Our Lives networking website (**www.shapingourlives.org.uk**) is a website that provides help for organisations that support people and for the people who use those services. These organisations can voice their views and concerns. It also provides information and support about how people can be involved in these groups and how they can link up with each other.

How the assessment process enables individuals to control decision-making

On a personal level older people can control decisions about their care and support through the assessment process.

If they have difficulty expressing their preferences, they can use the support of advocacy services to ensure that their views are heard in an impartial way. This means the person acting as **advocate** explains the views of the individual and does not impose their own views.

We can help older people to control decision-making by ensuring they are able to communicate in a way that suits them. We must not assume they cannot make a decision because they cannot hear or speak, for example. The most important thing is that they are consulted and helped by using sign language or symbols, or an interpreter.

The **Personalisation Agenda** influences the way in which the individual is assessed. A person-centred approach and personal budgets should be explored to enable an outcomes-based care plan that meets the **outcomes** the older person thinks would meet their needs. This reduces the reliance on traditional care services such as 'meals on wheels' and enables the individual to access different community services such as luncheon clubs, or 'casserole clubs', provided by the independent and voluntary sectors.

Key terms

Advocacy services are services that help people who cannot speak up for themselves. An example is the Independent Mental Capacity Advocacy Scheme.

Outcomes are the results that the care worker and individual agree they would like to see at the end of the care plan.

The **use of life story and talking mats** is a way of supporting older people with dementia to take more control of their care and support. Life stories help to inform the assessor about the history, lifestyle and preferences of the individual, and talking mats enable the individual to express themselves through a series of pictures (**www.talkingmats.com**).

Evidence activity

4.3 Decision-making

Arrange to talk to a social worker/social care assessor. Discuss with them how they ensure that the older person is in control of the decisions about their care and support needs.

Write a short report based on your discussion.

AC 4.4 Explain how to encourage older people to take positive risks

Risk taking is not about being reckless. For many people taking risks is an accepted part of life and in fact can add to our quality of life as long as we have the skills to manage that risk. For example, Formula 1 drivers take enormous risks, but these risks are well managed by training, safety measures and a lot of support from their team.

Older people can take positive risks to enhance their quality of life if care workers ensure they understand the risk, have the skills to manage the risk, appropriate safety measures are put in place and they are well supported by their team of family and carers.

Older people are often discouraged or stopped from taking risks, either because people assume they are unable to or because of concerns that they or others might be harmed. However, changes in society's attitudes towards ageing, social care and health policy mean that older people are being actively encouraged to be more independent in their

Figure 12.6 Formula 1 driving, for example, is a balance of risks and managing those risks

daily activities and make decisions about the services they receive. The focus is now more on enhancing people's abilities rather than concentrating on their disabilities. It is important for all of us, including older people, to take risks because it can add to our quality of life. Imagine how would feel if you did not dare to cross a road or try a new activity.

Traditionally, health and social care services have been good at providing services that minimised risk. However, personalisation means that in the future health and social care services have to work towards providing choices rather than services. This means that they will try to enable people to use services that meet their needs better than relying on traditional types of services, like day care.

As a care worker, you can encourage older people to take positive risks by:

- undertaking a thorough assessment so that the older person has a clear understanding of their capabilities and strengths
- ensuring a good risk assessment is in place that everyone understands, so that any risks are minimised
- working in partnership with older people, their family and advocates
- developing trusting working relationships

- helping older people learn from their experiences – what has and has not worked in the past – and being positive about the problems and understanding why they arose.

Evidence activity

4.4 Positive risks

Consider some examples of positive risk taking to enhance Walter's independence. How would you manage these risks?

Legislation

The Equality Act 2010

The Care Act 2014

Useful resources

Joseph Rowntree Foundation
jrf.org.uk

SCIE (Social Care Institute for Excellence)
www.scie.org.uk

Age UK
www.Ageuk.org.uk

Causes and spread of infection

This unit is worth 2 credits

What are you finding out?

The prevention and control of infection are essential within any health or social care setting. In order to be able to prevent and control the spread of infection, it is useful to have some knowledge about the different types of infection, how they are caused and how they spread. This unit will help you to develop and demonstrate your knowledge

about the causes of infection and the ways in which infection spreads.

By the end of this unit you will:

1 Understand the causes of infection
2 Understand the transmission of infection.

LO1 Understand the causes of infection

AC 1.1 Identify the differences between bacteria, viruses, fungi and parasites

How infection is caused

Infection is caused by **micro-organisms**. These are tiny living **cells** that cannot be seen by the naked eye yet they are all around us. Micro-organisms can be found in water, food, soil and the air. They live in and around our homes and our pets and they even live on and within our body. They exist everywhere and can survive very high and very low temperatures. Because they are so small we are unaware of them and often go about our daily lives without giving them a second thought.

Many micro-organisms are helpful and are essential to our well-being. However, some micro-organisms are harmful and can cause disease and infections. The four most common types of micro-organisms that you will come across within a health or social care setting are:

- bacteria
- viruses
- parasites
- fungi.

Characteristics of these micro-organisms are outlined in the table on the next page.

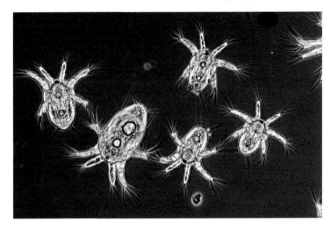

Figure 13.1 Micro-organisms

Key terms

Micro-organisms are tiny organisms or living cells which can be seen properly only with the aid of a microscope.

Cell is the basic unit of life. All living organisms are composed of one or more cells.

Antibiotics are medicines used to kill bacterial infections.

Contaminated means that something has become infected or polluted.

A **host cell** is a cell which has some other organism living inside of it. For example, viruses can only multiply once they are inside a host cell.

Immunisation is used to protect people against harmful infections before they come into contact with them. Immunisation is usually given as an injection but in the case of polio is given as drops in the mouth.

The **immune system** is the body's defence against harmful micro-organisms.

Corticosteroids are a group of medicines used in cancer treatment to reduce the growth of **tumours**.

A **tumour** is a lump or growth in a part of the body which is formed of abnormal cells.

(Some of these terms are covered in the table on page 236).

Table 13.1 Characteristics of micro-organisms

Bacteria	Viruses
<ul><li>Bacteria are found almost everywhere, including in and on the human body.</li><li>Most bacteria live in close contact with us and our environment without causing any harm. However, some bacteria can infect the body and cause disease.</li><li>Bacteria are made up of just one cell. They have the ability to divide and are capable of multiplying by themselves. They can reproduce very quickly given the right conditions and can double in number within minutes.</li><li>Bacteria need time, food, moisture and the correct temperature to get established and multiply.</li><li>Bacteria must multiply in large numbers to cause infection and illness.</li><li>Most bacteria can be eliminated with **antibiotics**.</li><li>The overuse of antibiotics has led to some bacteria becoming resistant to some antibiotics.</li></ul>	<ul><li>Viruses are much smaller than bacteria.</li><li>Viruses can only grow and reproduce inside other living cells; these are known as **host cells**. Once the virus enters, the virus will reproduce.</li><li>Viruses cannot survive long outside their host cell.</li><li>Only one or two viral cells are needed in order to cause illness.</li><li>When viruses enter our body, they then multiply to cause illness.</li><li>Viruses cannot be treated with antibiotics; however, there are some effective antiviral medications available.</li><li>The main means of control for viruses is through **immunisation**.</li></ul>
Parasites	**Fungi**
<ul><li>Parasites are organisms that must live in or on another person, animal or plant (host) to survive.</li><li>Parasites feed off the host, often causing harm in the process.</li><li>There are several parasites in the environment and when they get into a person's body, the person's health can be affected.</li><li>Some parasites enter the body by way of **contaminated** food or water and some live on the skin and hair.</li><li>Examples of parasites include scabies, head lice, crab lice, fleas, threadworms and tapeworms.</li></ul>	<ul><li>Fungi are a group of organisms that include yeasts and moulds.</li><li>Fungi prefer to live in damp, warm places.</li><li>Many fungi are not harmful, but some can cause disease such as athletes foot or ringworm.</li><li>People who have a weakened **immune system** and those who are taking certain medicines, for example antibiotics and **corticosteroids**, are at increased risk for fungal infections.</li><li>Fungal infections can be treated with antifungal medications.</li><li>Superficial fungal infections are found in the top layers of the skin and mucous membranes, the hair and the nails.</li><li>Examples of superficial fungal infections include athlete's foot, ringworm and thrush.</li><li>Deep fungal infections invade deeper layers of the skin and hair follicles and can spread to the blood or internal organs.</li></ul>

Evidence activity

1.1 Bacteria, viruses, parasites, fungi

Identify the differences between bacteria, viruses, parasites and fungi.

Give four facts for each of the following:

Bacteria	1
	2
	3
	4
Viruses	1
	2
	3
	4
Parasites	1
	2
	3
	4
Fungi	1
	2
	3
	4

AC 1.2 Identify common illnesses and infections caused by bacteria, viruses, fungi and parasites

If you work in a health or social care environment, the chances are that you will be required to support people who are experiencing illness. It is important to have some understanding of the common causes of illnesses within your workplace so that you can take appropriate steps to minimise the risk of spreading illnesses and infections. In general, illnesses and infections are caused by bacteria, viruses, fungi and parasites. The following table indicates some common infections and their causes.

The Evidence activity for this assessment criterion is on page 239).

Research and investigate

Research the meanings of the different common illnesses and infections mentioned in the table below, so you understand what each of these are. How many did you already know and how many did you have to research in more detail?

Bacteria	Viruses
• Acne	• Measles
• Bacterial meningitis	• Mumps
• Cellulitis	• Infectious hepatitis
• Chlamydia	• Chicken pox
• Cholera	• Shingles
• Conjunctivitis	• Influenza
• Diphtheria	• Common cold
• Tetanus	• Glandular fever
• Gangrene	• HIV
• Gastroenteritis	• Herpes
• Impetigo	• Viral meningitis
• Tuberculosis	
• MRSA	
• Clostridium difficile	
• E. coli	
• Salmonella	
• Lyme disease	
• Legionella	
• Syphilis	

Parasites	Fungi
• Threadworms	• Athlete's foot
• Tapeworms	• Ringworm
• Ticks	• Thrush
• Mosquitoes	
• Head lice	
• Fleas	
• Scabies	

Time to think

1.2 **Bacteria, virus, parasite, fungi**

There are a number of differences between bacteria, viruses, parasites and fungi. Take a look at the following statements and think about whether they relate to bacteria, viruses, parasites or fungi. An example has been given to help you (in bold).

One or two cells are enough to cause illness	Virus/Bacteria
Immunisation provides the main protection	
Examples of illnesses they cause include ringworm and thrush	
These cells cannot survive for long outside the body	
Most can be killed with antibiotics	
They can be seen only with a microscope	
These live in or on the body	
Examples of illnesses they cause include chicken pox and measles	
These must multiply in large numbers to cause illness	
These need time, food, moisture and the correct temperature to multiply	
These cannot survive for long outside the body	
Examples include scabies and head lice	
These prefer to live in dark, damp places	
Examples of illnesses they cause include MRSA, acne and salmonella	
Some can be killed with antiviral medication	

AC 1.3 Describe what is meant by 'infection' and 'colonisation'

Infection

An **infection** can be described as an invasion and multiplication of harmful micro-organisms such as bacteria, viruses, parasites or fungi that are not normally present within any organ or system of a **host**. If an infection can be passed from person to person then it is said to be infectious. However, not all infections can be passed from person to person. Infections can also:

- cause disease
- be treated
- cause an individual to experience symptoms and feel unwell
- vary from mild to severe and even lead to death.

Colonisation

It is important to be aware that potentially harmful micro-organisms can sometimes grow and multiply on a person without causing them any harm. This is known as **colonisation**. Colonising micro-organisms establish themselves in a particular place, for example on the body, but do not necessarily cause infection. For example, the bacteria that cause **MRSA** can live harmlessly on the surface of the skin of many people without causing a problem to the person at all. Colonising micro-organisms can:

● continue to colonise without causing harm
● clear naturally
● develop into an infection.

Key terms

Infection happens when harmful micro-organisms invade and multiply inside the body.

Host is a human, animal or plant on which another organism lives.

Colonisation happens when potentially harmful micro-organisms grow and multiply on a person without causing them any harm.

MRSA is a type of bacterial infection that is resistant to a number of antibiotics. This means that MRSA can be more difficult to treat. The full name of MRSA is meticillin-resistant staphylococcus aureus. This is sometimes referred to as a superbug.

AC 1.4 Explain what is meant by 'systemic infection' and 'localised infection'

When a person develops an infection, the body's immune system will be activated. The way in which the immune system responds will depend on the type of response needed, for example, whether the infection is localised or systemic. There are two types of infectious responses and these will depend on whether the infection is localised or systemic.

Localised infection

A **localised infection** is limited to a specific area or single organ. Therefore a localised infection will remain in and affect only one part of the body with symptoms such as **inflammation** – for example, redness, tenderness, pain and swelling. (See page 240 for definition).

A common example of a localised infection is an infected wound. The infection is localised to the wound and the symptoms may be present as pus, pain, redness, swelling and skin that is warm or hot to the touch. This type of localised infection does not usually make a person feel unwell, but without appropriate treatment it could develop into more serious problems and could eventually lead to a systemic infection.

Systemic infection

A **systemic infection** affects the whole of the body and can also affect the body's organs. One example of a systemic infection is tonsillitis. As well as making the person feel unwell, tonsillitis will cause pain in the tonsil area. The person will develop a temperature, the whole body will also ache and the person will probably feel lethargic. Some systemic infections can be life threatening if left untreated.

Key terms

A localised infection is one which is limited to a specific area or single organ.

Inflammation is part of the body's immune response. This leads to swelling, redness and pain because of an infection or injury.

A systemic infection is one which affects the whole of the body.

Evidence activity

1.4 Localised and systemic infections

Explain what is meant by the term 'systemic infection'.

Explain what is meant by the term 'localised infection'.

AC 1.5 Identify poor practices that may lead to the spread of infection

The prevention and control of infection are not just the responsibility of one person – it is everybody's responsibility to make sure they maintain good standards to prevent the spread of infection. Every person working within a health or social care environment has a duty of care to ensure they maintain good standards to ensure infections do not spread within their workplace.

Although there are effective methods for preventing and controlling the spread of infection, poor practices can still be observed in many health and social care settings. Some of the poor practices that may lead to the spread of infection include:

- poor personal hygiene and hand hygiene
- failure to wear personal protective equipment (PPE) when required
- failure to take adequate precautions when preparing, serving and eating food such as not washing hands
- failure to take adequate precautions when caring for people who have infections
- poor environmental hygiene such as not cleaning the environment
- poor ventilation
- overcrowding
- failure to dispose of waste
- failure to fully clean equipment
- failure to undertake risk assessments
- staff not following policies and procedures
- poor training.

Evidence activity

1.5 Poor practice and spread of infection

Identify five poor practices that could lead to the spread of infection.

Time to think

1.5 Poor practices

Take a look at the following picture and identify all the poor practices that could lead to the spread of infection.

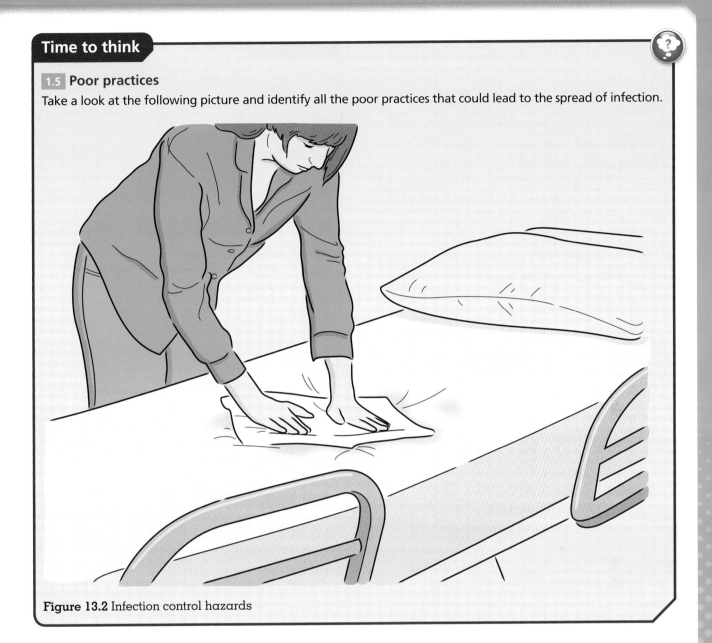

Figure 13.2 Infection control hazards

LO2 Understand the transmission of infection

AC 2.1 Explain the conditions needed for the growth of micro-organisms

Bacteria

Given the right conditions, bacteria will multiply rapidly. A single bacterial cell can become billions in a very short space of time.

In order for bacteria to grow and multiply, the following conditions are required:

- **Food.** Bacteria most easily multiply in foods containing protein and carbohydrates – for example, chicken, meat, fish, shellfish, cooked rice and pasta, milk products and eggs. Bacteria can also be found on and in the body, animals, plants and soil.
- **Time.** Given the ideal conditions, bacteria will grow and multiply by

dividing every 20 minutes. The bacteria grow slowly at first, then move into a rapid growth period.

- **Temperature.** Some bacteria grow at low temperatures and some at high temperatures, but most like warm temperatures between 5°C and 63°C. This is commonly referred to as the danger zone. The ideal temperature for growth and multiplication is 37°C (human body temperature). This is when bacteria will multiply most quickly.
- **Moisture.** Most foods contain enough moisture for bacteria to grow. Bacteria will not grow on dry foods such as dry soup mixes, but once water has been added they can grow. Bacteria thrive in moist, damp conditions.

Other factors that affect the growth of bacteria include:

- **Acidity or alkalinity of foods** – pH is a measure of how acidic or alkaline food is. **Acidic** foods, such as lemons, for example, have a pH of between 0 and 6.9. **Alkaline** foods, for example crackers, have a pH of 7.1 to 14. Most bacteria grow best in neutral environments.
- **Oxygen** – bacteria vary in their oxygen requirements; for example, **aerobic bacteria** require oxygen to grow, while **anaerobic bacteria** can grow only when oxygen is not present.

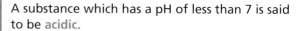

Key terms

A substance which has a pH of less than 7 is said to be acidic.

A substance which as a pH greater than 7 is said to be Alkaline.

Aerobic bacteria are bacteria that require oxygen to grow.

Anaerobic bacteria are bacteria that do not need oxygen to grow.

DNA is the chemical that carries genetic information.

RNA is ribonucleic acid and acts as a messenger, carrying instructions from DNA for controlling the synthesis of proteins.

Viruses

Viruses cannot multiply alone, so in order to do so they have to invade a 'host' cell. Viruses consist of genetic materials known as **DNA** or **RNA** and are surrounded by a protective coat of protein. They are capable of latching onto cells and getting inside them. Eventually, there are so many viruses in the cell that it bursts and the viruses are free to move on to other cells in the host and the process is repeated.

Parasites

Different parasites have different requirements for growth. Parasites can be internal or external and thrive on or inside a host where all of their needs can be met by feeding off the host body. Unlike viruses, they do not invade cells but they find a suitable habitat in places such as the intestines or hair. The needs of parasites are always met at the expense of the host, which is weakened as the parasites gain strength.

Fungi

Fungi exist naturally in our environment, as well as on and in our bodies. Fungi thrive in warm, moist areas of the body, such as the groin or in between our toes. Fungi can be passed on quite easily from one person to another, but this does not mean that the

Research and investigate

2.1 Acidic and alkaline foods

Do some research to find examples of acidic and alkaline foods.

Examples of acidic foods	Examples of alkaline foods

Evidence activity

2.1 Micro-organisms

Explain the conditions that are required for the growth of the following micro-organisms.

Bacteria	
Viruses	
Parasites	
Fungi	

fungus will necessarily infect the other person. Some people are more susceptible to fungal infections than others, for example people whose immune systems do not work as well as they should. In these people, the presence of fungi on the body will result in fungal infections.

AC 2.2 Explain the ways an infective agent might enter the body

An infective agent is a micro-organism that could lead to an infection. Micro-organisms that cause infection move from place to place by different methods. They can find their way into the body by a number of different routes. To establish themselves on or in a person, micro-organisms must either attach to the body's surfaces or enter the body. The site through which a micro-organism enters the host is called the route of entry. It is useful to think of our skin as a protective barrier. In order to cause infection, micro-organisms such as bacteria and viruses must break through the protective barrier. They can do this through either a natural opening or an unnatural break in the skin.

Natural openings include the mouth, nose, ears, eyes, **urethra**, anus and vagina.

Unnatural breaks in the surface of the skin can occur accidentally, for example scratches, bites, grazes and cuts. They can also occur because of a medical reason or an operation – for example, a surgical wound or the insertion of a drain or a needle or because of a condition such as psoriasis or eczema. Whenever there is a break in the skin this creates an opening by which micro-organisms can enter.

The routes by which micro-organisms can enter the body include the following:

Key term

Urethra is the tube that leads from the bladder to the outside of the body.

Digestive route	This is through eating food. Micro-organisms can be spread through poor hygiene, for example, failure to wash hands following high-risk tasks such as using the toilet, or through the ingestion of contaminated food or water.
Blood circulation route	Micro-organisms can enter the bloodstream through unnatural breaks in the skin such as scratches, cuts, grazes, the use of needles and through surgical wounds.
Respiratory route	Micro-organisms can be inhaled via droplets in the air from people who are coughing and sneezing.
Genital route	Micro-organisms can enter the genital route during sexual intercourse. Infection can also occur as a result of poor personal hygiene.
Body fluids route	Micro-organisms can be spread via all fluids and that circulate around or are let out from the body.
Placenta route	Micro-organisms can be spread from the mother to her unborn baby via the umbilical cord which connects a baby in the womb to its mother.
Touch	Although the hands are not a route into the body, they are one of the main ways by which micro-organisms can be transported to a route, for example, the digestive route.

Evidence activity

2.2 Ways infective agents may enter the body
Explain the ways that an infective agent/infectious micro-organisms might enter a person's body.

Evidence activity

2.3 Common sources of infection
Identify seven common sources of infection.

What would you identify as a common source of infection?

AC 2.3 Identify common sources of infection

Micro-organisms can be spread in a number of ways. It is important to fully understand the procedures that are needed to prevent their spread. Micro-organisms do not have the ability to move on their own – they require a means of transport in order to move from place to place, from place to person and from person to person. Common sources of infection include:

- water
- food and the food chain
- animals and insects
- air and dust
- droplets
- contaminated objects
- other infected people.

AC 2.4 Explain how infective agents can be transmitted to a person

Harmful micro-organisms can be spread from person to person in a number of ways. The process by which this happens is called cross infection or cross contamination. In order for infection to spread, there must be contact of some sort between people. This contact may be either direct or indirect (see the table on the next page).

Direct contact happens when physical contact takes place between a person who is infected and a person who is not. This results in a physical transfer of harmful micro-organisms from one person to another.

Water	There are a number of ways in which water can become polluted. Open waters such as the sea and rivers are vulnerable to pollution from things like sewerage, dead animals and chemicals. This sort of pollution can introduce disease causing micro-organisms into the water supply. In some countries water and sewerage systems are under-developed, and polluted water is a common cause of fatal disease. In the United Kingdom, however, we are fortunate enough to have good standards of water purity, protected by law.
Food and the food chain	Food can become contaminated by harmful micro-organisms at any stage in the food chain. Food that is contaminated with micro-organisms can infect people who eat it, leading to severe stomach upset.
Animals and insects	Animals and insects can carry micro-organisms. Animals and insects can pass on infections through their body fluids, especially through their faeces and through biting. In fact, some insects can transmit serious infections because when they bite us the infection is transmitted directly into the blood stream. One common example in some countries is malaria.
Air and dust	Some harmful micro-organisms can be carried along with dust in the air. These micro-organisms are so small that we breathe them in without realising. Some particles are so small that they remain in the air for a long time, giving them the opportunity to be inhaled or even settle on wounds.
Droplets	Infections that can be caught through coughing and sneezing are referred to as droplet infections. This is because the micro-organisms are transported in the tiny droplets that are expelled when a person coughs or sneezes.
Contaminated objects	Any object can become contaminated with harmful micro-organisms. For example, within a health care environment communal objects such as cutlery, moving and handling equipment, commodes, sinks and baths can all become contaminated with micro-organisms from bodily fluids. If not cleaned on a regular basis, this could lead to the spread of micro-organisms. Transfer of these micro-organisms can occur when a person unknowingly comes into contact with the contaminated object. Some micro-organisms have the ability to survive on objects for long periods of time, for example, MRSA and Clostridium difficile.
Other infected people	The transfer of micro-organisms from person to person can occur when infection is passed directly from one person to another. Direct transmission can occur through skin to skin contact. Contaminated hands that have not been washed are one example of how micro-organisms can be transferred from one person to another.

Figure 13.3 Infections can be passed on in many ways

Indirect contact occurs when infecting micro-organisms are transported via contaminated objects such as food, water, objects, animals or insects.

Evidence activity

2.4 Infective agents

Explain how infective agents can be transmitted to a person.

Explain how micro-organisms can be directly transferred between people.

Explain how micro-organisms can be indirectly transferred between people.

AC 2.5 Identify the key factors that will make it more likely that infection will occur

Remember that infections can be caused by bacteria, viruses, fungi and parasites. We have looked at the ways in which these micro-organisms can be passed from person to person, but we also know that not everyone will go on to develop an infection. However, there are a number of key factors that can increase the likelihood that an infection will occur and we will explore some of these factors below.

Proximity

First, it is important to remember that health care settings are ideal environments for harmful micro-organisms because these are places where people who carry harmful micro-organisms and people who are at increased risk of infection gather together. The risk of spreading infection further increases when these people are being cared for in close proximity to each other, or close to each other.

People who are hospitalised

People who are in hospital are at risk of developing **healthcare acquired infections** (HCAIs), but some people are at greater risk than others. Children and the elderly are two groups with the highest risk of developing an infection. This is because both of these groups have a weaker immune system, making infection much more likely. In addition to age, there are a number of key risk factors that can contribute to the likelihood of developing an HCAI. These include:

- failure of healthcare workers to wash their hands
- failure of visitors to wash their hands before and after visiting their loved ones
- prolonged hospital stay
- weakened immune system
- poor nutrition
- overuse of antibiotics.

There are certain medical procedures that will also increase the risk of infection. In most cases, these are procedures that involve some type of medical device being inserted into the body. Some common procedures that will increase an individual's risk of infection include:

- insertion of a tube into the bladder such as when a person is catheterised.
- operations such as when a person has had surgery and will have a wound
- respiratory procedures requiring the use of a breathing tube for example when a person is ventilated
- use of invasive procedures to give nutrition or administer medication. For example, if a person has a PEG tube.

Broken skin

People with broken or damaged skin are at higher risk of developing an infection. If the skin is damaged in any way, for example due to surgery, grazes, wounds or sores, it can no longer provide a protective barrier and micro-organisms are able to enter the body.

Vulnerable groups

We have already mentioned that children and the elderly are at increased risk of developing an infection. Vulnerability usually occurs because the immune system is weakened in some way. Some people will be more vulnerable than others and may include:

- pregnant ladies
- people who have a learning disability such as Down's syndrome – these people are particularly prone to chest infections because their immune system has not developed properly
- people who live in poor conditions
- individuals receiving treatment to weaken their immune system, for example following organ transplants
- individuals receiving chemotherapy
- people who already have a health condition such as diabetes, asthma, heart disease or poor circulation.

Key factors in everyday life

There are typical situations in everyday life that can increase the risk of catching and spreading infections. These are usually in communal or shared public places. For example when:

- eating in restaurants
- using public toilets
- taking holidays abroad
- visiting a healthcare environment such as the doctor's surgery or a hospital
- using a public swimming pool
- using public transport.

Evidence activity

2.5 Key factors

Identify the key factors that will make it more likely that infection will occur.

Identify five key factors that could increase a person's risk of getting an infection.

Legislation

Health and Safety Act 2012

Substances Hazardous to Health Regulations 2002

Public Health (Control of Disease) Act 1984

Health Protection (Notification) Regulations 2010

Useful resources

NICE Guidelines
www.nice.org.uk/guidance

NICE Quality Standard 61 Infection Prevention and Control April 2014

Royal College of Nursing (RCN)

RCN Infection Prevention and Control Information and Learning Resources for Health Care Staff 2014

Department of Health
www.gov.uk/government/organisations/department-of-health

Department of Health Prevention and Control of Infection in Care Homes – An information Resource 2013

Optional
Group C Units

Understand and implement a person-centred approach to the care and support of individuals with dementia

This unit is worth 3 credits

What are you finding out?

In this unit you will find out about the most appropriate ways to support individual living with dementia, using person-centred approaches which recognise the specific needs of people living with dementia.

You we will consider why and how we involve the person in their own care and support and look at the issues surrounding the role of care workers and others who support the person with dementia. We will think about how we work with others to ensure both person-centred and relationship-centred approaches. We will also think about the

importance of considering well-being in a person centred approach.

By the end of this unit, you will:

1 Understand the importance of a person-centred approach to dementia care and support
2 Be able to involve the individual with dementia in planning and implementing their care and support using a person-centred approach
3 Be able to involve carers and others in the care and support of individuals with dementia.

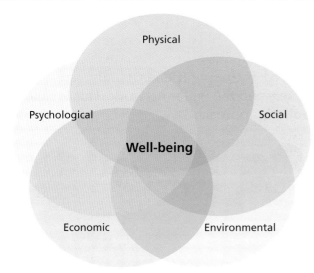

Figure 14.1 There are various aspects to an individual's well-being

The diagram above explains how different factors contribute to both mental and physical well-being. It is important to consider these aspects of a person's life when you are implementing a person-centred approach.

LO1 Understand the importance of a person-centred approach to dementia care and support

AC 1.1 Describe what is meant by a person-centred approach

What is a person-centred approach?
A person-centred approach to care and support is a basic principle in health and social care.

A recent government document 'Independence, Well-being and Choice 2005' says that person-centred care planning should be part of the way in which we support people. This means that when we offer and deliver care to any adult, whatever their illness or disability, we should keep them as the focus and make sure we:

- help them be as independent as possible
- support their **well-being**
- enable them to make as many choices about their lives as possible (including the care they receive).

A person-centred approach values people in a way that reduces **stigma** and sees the individual for who they are, not who we think they might be because of the way they look or behave.

People with dementia have the same rights as all citizens in society. This includes the right to be treated with dignity and respect.

Tom Kitwood talks about 'personhood' as the recognition, respect and trust given to one individual by others. It is what makes us individuals, unique and with the right to make decisions for ourselves.

Support and reassurance
When a person with dementia begins to struggle with everyday tasks, they often feel vulnerable and can lose confidence and feel a 'failure'. It is important that we offer reassurance and support. The people closest to them – their carers, support staff, friends and family – must help the person with dementia to keep their sense of identity and feelings of self-worth. We must value their sense of reality, which may be very different to ours, as well as respect their **life story** (see page 252 for definition) and history because these are some of the things which make us unique.

Avoid stereotypes

Person-centred approaches mean that we cannot view people with dementia in a stereotypical way. As a society we often view older people as 'sweet', difficult, odd or eccentric, for example. This can be seen in the media or in attitudes among the general public. Instead, it is important to understand the person as an individual with their own personality which does not necessarily fit into a 'category'.

Key terms

Life stories are used extensively in the support of people with dementia. They focus on the individual' past life and the interests and achievements of the person – what is significant for them. Life story work is used to help people remember their past, and helps them to feel positive about themselves. It can also help us to understand them more.

Holistic is a way of ensuring we see the person as a whole, taking into account all sides of a situation, and see all the sides of an individual's personality. For example, it is important to see a person with dementia as an individual, with their own needs, preferences and history rather than define them through their illness.

Time to think

1.1 **Person-centred approaches**

Think about those things which make us unique as individuals. How do you think we can incorporate them into a person-centred approach when working with a person with dementia?

Research and investigate

1.1 **Society's views of older people**

Look in a media source (TV or newspaper, for example) for a story about the care of older people. What does it tell you about society's view of older people? Does it describe a person-centred view? How would you change the way in which the article is written?

The National Care Forum describes standards that meet a person-centred approach. It explains that this is important to everyone involved, including friends, family, care workers and the wider network. This is called a **holistic** approach.

Figure 14.2 A person-centred approach involves a wider circle in the individual's care

Evidence activity

1.1 **Person-centred approaches**

Describe what you would include in a care plan for a person with dementia, using person-centred approaches.

AC 1.2 Describe how a person-centred approach enables individuals with dementia to be involved in their own care and support

What do we mean by care and support? We all have a different view of care and support depending on our own circumstances and needs. It is because care and support mean different things to different people that we must put the person at the centre of our approach. This includes the way we assess people and the way we deliver care through their care plans.

The government has understood that much needs to be done to improve things and they have changed the law to do this.

The Care Act 2014

This Act of Parliament has reformed (improved) the law relating to care and support for adults and the law relating to support for carers.

The Act gives local authorities a responsibility to assess a carer's needs for support, where the carer appears to have such needs. This replaces the existing law, which says that the carer must be providing 'a substantial amount of care on a regular basis' in order to qualify for an assessment. This will mean more carers are able to have an assessment, comparable to the right of the people they care for.

The local authority will assess whether the carer has needs and what those needs may be. This assessment will consider the impact of caring on the carer. It will also consider the things that a carer wants to achieve in their own day-to-day life. It must also consider other important issues, such as whether the carer is able or willing to carry on caring, whether they work or want to work, and whether they want to study or do more socially.

If both the carer and the person they care for agree, a combined assessment of both their needs can be done.

Maintaining dignity and privacy

This is core to all our values when working in a person-centred way. It is a basic human right to be treated with dignity and to have our privacy respected. The Social Care Institute for Excellence (SCIE) describes in this way:

'Dignity consists of many overlapping aspects, involving respect, privacy, autonomy.'

www.scie.org.uk

The standard dictionary definition is 'a state, quality or manner worthy of esteem or respect; and ... self-respect'. Dignity in (person-centred) care, therefore, means the kind of care, in any setting, that supports and promotes, and does not undermine, a person's self-respect regardless of any difference.

We have already thought about people with dementia having a weaker sense of self-worth because they realise that they are not as independent as before, and perhaps not able to contribute to society or their family as they used to.

They see their skills and knowledge fading as their memory begins to deteriorate and this leads to feelings of frustration, helplessness and anxiety. They may feel worthless and inadequate. It is therefore important to respect and if appropriate acknowledge those feelings and treat the person with dignity and respect, whatever the situation. We should offer reassurance and support but be careful not to 'talk down' to the person.

Person-centred care means that we take into account the feelings of the person. They may need you to acknowledge their sadness or frustration and if so it is important to show that you have empathy.

Figure 14.3 People with empathy consider the individual's feelings

Personalisation

The Personalisation Agenda makes us think about services in a different way. It starts with the person rather than the service and means that we shape support to suit people's individual needs.

Accessible services

Personalisation is about making services accessible (easily available) to all. We should no longer rely on traditional kinds of services and expect a person with dementia to fit into them. For example, not everyone will want to go to a day centre. Instead everyone, regardless of their need or disability, should have an equal right to use services available to all, for example, health clubs, golf clubs, the local café or even bingo!

Access information

We should make sure that individuals are given as much information as possible about services like housing, care support, voluntary organisations who can offer help. and are helped to make informed decisions about their care and support.

Personal budgets

In many areas people who have been assessed as needing services are awarded **personal budgets**. This helps them to get the support they need in other ways rather than relying on traditional services.

A person-centred approach means that when you **assess** the person you should:

- Enable individuals with dementia to be involved in their own care and support.
- Make sure that you support individuals earlier in their illness or disability through early **intervention**, re-ablement and prevention

- Recognise and support the role of carers.so that they are able to cope with their caring role and that we recognise that they have needs of their own, and may need support with their caring role at times.
- Respect the fact that the person with dementia is an adult and never assume they do not realise what is happening. By doing this, you are able to acknowledge their right to dignity.

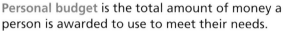

Key terms

Personal budget is the total amount of money a person is awarded to use to meet their needs.

Assess is to spend time with the person, understanding their personal circumstances and their problems and how they impact (affect) their day-to-day life. This also allows you to think about what would help the person the most.

Intervention is when a social care worker works with the person to support and enable them. This includes assessment and one-to-one support.

Time to think

1.2 Person-centred approaches
Think about the service you work in or one that you have some experience of. What evidence is there to show the service is person-centred? How can you contribute to improving that person-centred approach?

Research and investigate

1.2 'Dignity in Care'
The National 'Dignity in Care' Campaign (**dignityincare.org.uk**) is a national campaign led by the Department of Health. Go onto the website and look at the leaflets. Produce your own leaflet for your place of work which explains the principles of keeping the person at the centre by respecting their dignity.

1.2 A person-centred approach

Have a look at a recent care plan. How much do you think it reflects (shows) the support the person needs? Are the needs of the person at the centre being met in a way they prefer? Has thought been given to different ways of meeting the person's needs? How does this enable them to be involved in their own care and support?

How could you improve the care plan? Discuss this idea with your line manager or supervisor.

LO2 Be able to involve the individual with dementia in planning and implementing their care and support using a person-centred approach

AC 2.1 Explain how information about personality and life history can be used to support an individual to live well with dementia

The more we understand the person with dementia, the more we can help. We can see that, generally speaking, the more we know about anyone (not only a person with dementia) the more we understand them and can, if necessary, support them and communicate with them in a meaningful way.

Time to think

2.1 The person with dementia

Talk to a close friend or colleague. Tell them one fact about yourself that they will not know. What is their reaction? They may be surprised or impressed. They may now have a slightly different view of you. That new piece of information has added to the jigsaw picture of you, and your friend or colleague can use it to help them have a clearer understanding of you. Think about the person with dementia. What would you like to find out that would help you understand them better?

There are a variety of ways in which we can learn more and get to know the person with dementia. We can talk to:

- the individual
- their family
- their friends and neighbours
- previous colleagues
- other professionals.

They are all part of the individual's social network and will, depending on their role, probably see the person in a slightly different way. They will describe them as a parent or sibling or friend or colleague and in doing so you will be able to picture the different qualities of the person.

It may be helpful to look at:

- photo albums
- photographs on display in the person's home (they are usually of great significance to the person)
- 'treasures' kept by the person such as photos – but remember this must be done with the person's permission, or if they are unable to give permission, ask the person who acts on their behalf.

These mementoes give us a real 'feel' for the person and an understanding for the things and

Figure 14.4 Looking at keepsakes and photographs gives us an insight into the individual

people that are important to them. This helps us to relate to the person, it gives us opportunities to find things in common, and things to discuss – to make a connection with the person. This in turn allows you to tailor your support to the individual and builds trust, and a therapeutic relationship with the individual.

Life stories

Life history or 'Life story' is very popular as a way of getting to know the person with dementia. It has several benefits. Life story work is organic. This means it can grow and change as you gather more information and consequently more insight into the person with dementia. It is therefore not only about remembering the past (reminiscence) but is also a way of finding out about the person's likes and dislikes, their fears and hopes.

You can share a life story in different ways, not just in a book, because stories can be told in different ways – through music, pictures or objects.

A life story belongs to that person, not to you or the care home or the service. It does not serve its purpose if it is kept in an office. It should be a well-used possession.

Case study

2.1 Jenny

Jenny works as a domestic assistant in a care home. She cleans Emily's room every day. Emily has dementia and finds difficulty in accepting people in her room. Emily likes to stay in her room while it is being cleaned and Jenny is not sure how to help Emily feel comfortable with her being in there with her. Jenny thinks that Emily is being awkward because she has dementia. She talks to her manager who suggests she looks at the photos on the bedroom wall – and sees the real Emily, the person.

Jenny sees that there are pictures of Emily as a young woman, riding motor bikes, and Emily working as a waitress.

How do you think this will help Jenny to understand Emily better? What can she now do to support Emily? How can she involve Emily?

Patient stories

Other ways of finding out about the person include 'patient stories'. These are accounts of someone's personal experience of their illness and the support they received. In them they might describe how they felt about their care and the people who helped them. Patient stories can be used in '**reflective practice**'.

Are we being truly person-centred? That is a question we should ask ourselves. The way *we* think we are giving support and the way it *actually* feels for the person on the receiving end can be very different!

Remember, when helping someone in their life story the facts may not seem so important. Memories can be about feelings, so a person may remember how they felt when they first went to the seaside, but might not remember the actual place.

Ideas and tips

Communicating with a person living with dementia is a real skill because you need to be able to relate to their feelings and experiences. To do so it is helpful to think about the topics that may interest and engage the individual as well as understanding the most effective and sensitive ways to communicate.

Ideas for things to talk about include:

- likes and dislikes – food, colours, activities, books, places
- parents – what did they do, what were they like?
- school – teachers they liked, favourite subjects, school life
- holidays – did they go on holiday, outings, places visited

Key term

Reflective practice is a way of understanding and learning from our working practices by talking to colleagues or mentors or supervisors.

- pets – what were they, names, funny stories
- what makes them laugh/feel sad/cross, etc.?
- what have they done that makes them proud?

Tips when communicating with individuals with dementia

- Never talk over the person but include them in the conversation.
- Do not over-correct but rather concentrate on what the person *can* do rather than what they cannot do.
- Help the person to have positive feelings about themselves by acknowledging achievements or respecting their feelings.
- Respect privacy – there may be times when the person may prefer to talk to you in private.
- Remember, there may be some aspects to their life that the person does not want to share. You must respect this and work with the person on the memories and feelings that they feel comfortable with. This is person-centred care.

For more information you can go to the website **www.lifestorynetwork.org.uk/**

Understanding anyone's life history, likes and dislikes, hopes and fears helps us to build a relationship with them. Reminiscing (talking about at memories) also helps the individual remember past experiences and can give you some further understanding of them as a person. This adds to their mental well-being, helping their confidence and self-esteem.

Research and investigate

2.1 Lifestory network

Go to **www.lifestorynetwork.org.uk/** for more information.

How can this information be used to support an individual to live well with dementia?

Evidence activity

2.1 Putting ideas into practice

In your workplace, how could you introduce life story work, or improve it if you have started to use it? Who could help you with this?

Think about how finding out more about someone's personality and life history can help you to support an individual to live well with dementia?

Discuss one way in which you have done this in your role with your manager, and the ways you could improve this.

AC 2.2 Communicate with an individual with dementia using a range of methods that meets individual abilities and needs

If we are to ensure that we include the person with dementia in planning and implementing their care, we must communicate with them using a range of methods that meets their individual needs and abilities.

Communication takes several forms

It is not just about speaking and listening. It involves sounds, body language, music, pictures and stories. We use the environment or our surroundings to communicate too.

Think about walking into a sacred place like a church or a mosque – or a shop or a library. What do these environments convey? They all have different 'messages' and we behave in different ways according to that message.

We must think about different ways of communication when we help the person with dementia and when we plan and implement their care.

Although we may be required to write a care plan to ensure that we are all aware of the required outcomes for the person with dementia, we can also think more imaginatively about how we express that for the person themselves.

Understand communication needs of the individual.

Before we support the person, we need to understand their communication needs. We should not make assumptions about them and we must instead find out as much as possible to help them interact in a meaningful way for them.

Different methods of communication

Remember, some of the 'rules' of communication include:

- look for clues in the person's behaviour
- maintain good eye contact
- mirror body language – respond to the person's emotions
- follow up comments rather than ask questions all the time
- go at their pace
- do not over stimulate and upset the person by bombarding them with questions
- do not persist if the person tires or seems to lose concentration or interest – it is more helpful to try again another time
- when asking a question, give them an option – say 'do you like the seaside?' rather than 'what holidays do you like?' – or use pictures of seaside resorts and take your cues from the body language of the person as you point to different pictures.
- People may respond to a variety of methods. Memories are strong when a person is introduced to music or scents. The smell of cooking can remind someone of their mother, or a particular song of their wedding day.

Pictures and symbols can be helpful. **Talking mats** are an example of this. The person may not be able to explain a preference to you but they may be able to point to the relevant picture.

Case study

2.2 Mrs Brown

Mrs Brown lives alone. She has dementia and the care staff visit her four times a day to help her with personal care and meals. They notice that she is not drinking the tea they are leaving for her. They decide to ask her daughter if she has any ideas, because they are worried Mrs Brown is not drinking enough in the hot weather.

Her daughter explains that Mrs Brown has always drunk from a cup and saucer and hates mugs. The care staff have been giving her tea in mugs because they thought it was safer. They start using a cup and saucer. Mrs Brown drinks her tea – she is used to managing a cup and saucer and is safe to use them because they are so familiar to her.

How do you think this situation could have been avoided? Can you think of similar examples in your work setting?

When we and a person with dementia plan their care, we must always take into account their previously held views and preferences. They may no longer be able to explain to you how they like to drink their tea or where they prefer to live, but both these things, whether seemingly unimportant or major to you, are important for that person.

Personal profiles

A personal profile should be used in addition to a care plan. This can give more detail about the person. Personal profiles can be used in different settings. They are invaluable in care homes but are also a very good way of sharing important information when a person with dementia transfers from one place to another – on admission to hospital, for example.

The Alzheimer's Society produces a profile specifically for this purpose called 'This is me'.

Research and investigate

2.2 A personal profile

Find out if there is similar documentation used in your local hospital or your care setting. If not, perhaps you could talk to your manager about implementing something similar.

Some areas that should be covered by a personal profile include:

- likes and dislikes
- favourite pastimes
- personal care needs
- things that make the person anxious
- people and things that are important to them
- particular routines.

Evidence activity

2.2 Communication

How do you think you could 'translate' these ideas into a more person-centred approach? For example, 'I am afraid of loud noises' or 'I like to hold something to help me feel safe'. If the person is afraid of loud noises, using a person-centred approach, what could you do to reassure and support them?

Think about how you could encourage the individual to hold objects that comforted them and made them feel safe. What might you suggest?

For someone with dementia, changes such as moving to an unfamiliar place or meeting new people who contribute to their care can be unsettling or distressing. **This is me** provides information about the person at the time the document is completed. It can help health and social care professionals build a better understanding of who the person really is.

This is me should be completed by the individual(s) who know the person best and, wherever possible, with the person with dementia. It should be updated as necessary. It is not a medical document.

On the back page you will find more detailed guidance notes to help you complete **This is me**, including examples of the kind of information to include. You might find it helpful to read through these notes before you begin to fill in the form.

photo

Name I like to be called

Where I live (list your area, not your full address)

Carer/the person who knows me best

I would like you to know

My life so far (family, home, background and treasured possessions)

Current and past interests, jobs and places I have lived

The following routines are important to me

Things that may worry or upset me

What makes me feel better if I am anxious or upset

Figure 14.5 The Alzheimer's Society's 'This is me' profile

AC 2.3 Involve an individual with dementia in identifying and managing risks for their care and support plan

What is a risk?

A risk assessment is a thorough examination of what could cause harm, so you can weigh up whether you have taken enough precautions or should do more to prevent harm.

In the Department of Health's guidance 'Nothing ventured nothing gained' (2010) outlines that:

'We all face risk in our everyday lives and regularly make judgements, sometimes unconsciously, about risks and benefits for everyday actions. It is a challenge to tread the line between being overprotective (in an attempt to eliminate risk altogether) while respecting individual freedoms. The trick is giving people the opportunity to live life to the full.'

This is what we mean by 'living well with dementia' – that as support workers we must enable people to manage risks as safely as possible and by doing so they can live a fulfilled life.

For example, put yourself in the place of Mrs Brown from Case study 2.2. Can you imagine being told that it was not safe for you to use a cup and saucer when you hated using a mug – or that you could not go for a walk in case you got lost, even though you had walked the same route each day for 20 years?

Risk management

'Nothing ventured nothing gained' says that risk enablement is based on the idea that measuring risk involves balancing the positive benefits from taking risks against the negative effects of attempting to avoid risk altogether. For example, the risk of getting lost if a person with dementia goes out by themselves needs to be set against the possible risks of boredom and frustration from remaining inside.

To support people with dementia manage these risks we should do risk assessments, but we must also ensure that we think about the principles of **positive risk** taking.

We must use the evidence from several sources. The idea of risk can be very **subjective**. This means that people see risks very differently. Mrs Brown did not think she was at risk of burning herself using a cup but the care staff did. However, they had not completed a risk assessment to weigh up the positive and negative aspects – they had just assumed it was a problem.

We must weigh up the risk because, although it may seem risky to us, getting rid of the risk may be of no benefit to the person. So we must always be person centred and consider what is in the person's **best interests**.

Figure 14.6 Even crossing the road can bring risks

> **Key terms**
>
> **Positive risk** means taking risks that are taken that add value to a person's life.
>
> **Subjective** means giving a personal view rather than being objective – not giving a personal opinion.
>
> **Best interests** means ensuring we work for the benefit of the individual not others.

2.3 Care and support plan

Look at care support plans for individuals you support. Is it clear that the individual has been involved in thinking about their risks? Are there activities that involve risks that they would be able to manage if they had more support? Discuss this with your line manager or the care coordinator.

AC 2.4 Involve an individual with dementia in opportunities that meet their agreed abilities, needs and preferences

Let's look back at some of the key principles we have talked about in person-centred dementia care. By understanding the principles of person-centred care we can support the person with dementia in **opportunities** to meet their needs and preferences.

Needs

We can define a need as something that as an individual we require to help us be fulfilled. This could be a physical need like warmth or food, or a spiritual need, like love.

Key terms

Opportunities to be able to have the choice to do things means that when we work with the individual we think about the things they can do rather than the things they cannot do, and we support them with tasks that may be difficult for them, but we do not 'take over'. For example, the individual can choose what they want to wear and may be able to dress themselves with just a little support with buttons or zips.

Research and investigate

2.4 Maslow

Research 'Maslow's Hierarchy of Human Needs'. This explains how people have different types of need. All are important to make us 'complete'.

When we are working with a person living with dementia we should be aware of their needs – dementia does not diminish these needs but the person may not be able to express them in the same way as before. It is therefore important that we work with the person to understand how they express their needs. For example, Mrs Brown may want her cup of tea but cannot verbalise or tell you this, but she can, by her body language, make you aware. So we need to get to know the person and 'tune in' to their own form of language. This is why assessment is so important because as we begin to understand the person we can communicate more effectively.

Well-being is a physical and emotional condition. To promote this sense of well-being we must enable the person to participate in the types of activities that are fulfilling for them. People living with dementia often struggle to carry on with favourite hobbies and pastimes. They may be reluctant to go out to social events because they find it difficult to follow conversations or remember their friends' names. Going to the pub, or out to lunch with friends, can become an ordeal. We can help the person by engaging with their friends and family and helping them understand the person's needs, and encouraging them to see the person first.

Personhood defines who we are. We identify ourselves in many ways – we may describe ourselves through our career … 'I am a nurse' or 'I have been a farmer all my life'. We may refer to ourselves as someone's mother or son. The way the person sees themselves, even if they are no longer a teacher or farmer, should be acknowledged or **validated** (see page 262 for definition). This means that we enter the person's reality and maintain their dignity and self-esteem.

Agreed abilities means that we have assessed the person and in doing so have liaised with other significant people. The assessment describes the actual abilities of the person which have been agreed between them, their families and relevant professionals. The person with dementia may lack capacity and actually think they still have the abilities they possessed in their younger years. In this situation we still must validate those feelings and, rather than dismiss them, work with the person to help them to be involved in opportunities.

They may not be safe to go out alone but they could go out with support. The care plan can indicate the least restrictive way of supporting the person. For example, rather than preventing the person from going on the long walks they used to enjoy they can be supported by being accompanied. This also balances the risks against benefits, and the decision to enable the person to continue to go for walks is described as 'positive risk taking'.

Tailored care plans to meet individual abilities, needs and preferences

The Personalisation Agenda helps people tailor services to meet their needs. Care plans should reflect what people want to happen. We look at outcomes – not just 'needs'. The person may 'need' support with personal care, but the outcome should describe how that personal care should be delivered. The care is therefore 'personalised'.

A care plan should be based on an assessment of the person's needs and preferences. All care plans should be **outcomes-based** and needs-led.

A care plan should be detailed enough for it to be meaningful to the person with dementia and their carer. It should be written in a way that reflects an understanding of the perspective and experiences of the person with dementia. By including the person as much as possible, the process will be more helpful and they are more likely to 'own' the care plan. They may be able to write their own plan with you. Language should be in 'plain English' and technical terms and abbreviations avoided. A care plan should

also be responsive – a document where day to day outcomes and preferences for care and support are recorded. We need to provide an individualised care plan that is in tune with people's changing needs.

In a care plan you may be aiming to achieve such outcomes as:

- the person with dementia being enabled to maintain the relationships with significant others as they choose
- develop a positive relationship and gain trust and confidence
- encourage social inclusion
- promote self-care when possible, including independence and control over support and care.

As we read about in AC 2.1, Life stories assist us in having a clear picture of the person's preferences and interests. There are many resources available and a 'life story' can be anything from a collection of photographs to a favourite memory that the person frequently recalls and from which you can help them enjoy the moment. If for example, the care workers got to know Mrs Brown better by talking to her about her life, or

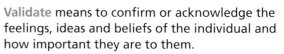

Key terms

Validate means to confirm or acknowledge the feelings, ideas and beliefs of the individual and how important they are to them.

Outcomes based refers to a care plan that concentrates on what the individual wants to achieve.

Research and investigate

2.4 Dementia Friends

Look on the Alzheimer's Society website for the Dementia Friends initiative.

What is the aim of Dementia Friends? How can this scheme help people living with dementia fulfil their abilities, needs and preferences?

to her daughter about her preferences, she would have been offered tea in a cup instead of a mug.

'This is me' is a way of capturing the most important information about the person if they are being admitted to hospital. It helps the nursing staff to meet the person's needs in a timely way. See AC 2.1 for an example of this.

Evidence activity

2.4 Agreed abilities, needs and preferences

Investigate in your local area – are there similar forms that can be used to communicate the person's needs?

Design your own format. How would you capture the needs, preferences and agreed abilities of the person? How would you start the process? Discuss this with your manager. Think about a person you currently support.

LO3 Be able to involve carers and others in the care and support of individuals with dementia

AC 3.1 Explain how to increase a carer's understanding of dementia and a person-centred approach and AC 3.2 Demonstrate how to involve carers and others in the support of an individual with dementia

Family members, partners, friends and neighbours often have to play a significant role in the support of a person with dementia. It is important that we treat them as partners in care and support by acknowledging the advice and knowledge they have about the person. We must also recognise that carers have rights and issues of their own.

Carers' assessments have an important role to play because they aim to help carers think about their own needs. In this way we can identify any unmet needs for both the carer

Figure 14.7 It is important that the carer is given support and is not forgotten

and the person living with dementia. It is crucial that we try to support the carer who often is the key person co-ordinating and providing care.

Traditionally, carers were often seen as working at the edge of care planning – their views may have been taken into account, but there was still a view that the 'professional' carers 'knew best'. The move towards person and relationship centred care as well as the personalisation agenda has not only put the person with dementia at the centre, it has also acknowledged that carers must be treated as true partners. It is often the carer who knows the person with dementia best, and who can give us that vital information that helps us understand the person better.

We can support the carer in their understanding of dementia as well as involve them in care planning and consultation. There is much information and advice available for carers today. The local mental health service usually provides leaflets explaining dementia and memory loss and the types of services and support available. The Alzheimer's Society website has a wide selection of information leaflets which are free and can be printed off. There are also carer groups and Admiral Nurses who specialise in the support of carers of people with dementia.

Health and social care organisations have recognised the importance of including carers as well as people with dementia in the design of services and the kind of information they receive. Many services now have service user and carer forums (meetings) as a means of exchanging views and consulting people about current and future services. This encourages both a person centred approach and a greater understanding of the issues surrounding dementia.

It is also understood that people with dementia need to socialise with their carers and more opportunities are being created, particularly by local charities. These social events can 'normalise' experiences. This means that there is no stigma attached and the emphasis is on the social event, not the dementia. People meet to go bowling, hiking or to have a tea party, and are simply a group of people sharing experiences. We are therefore not making 'special arrangements' because the individual lives with dementia, but instead we are including them in the normal activities that we can all enjoy.

Legislation

The Care Act 2014

Useful resources

Websites

Alzheimer's society

www.alzheimers.org.uk has a lot of information about dementia and the care of people living with dementia.

SCIE

Independence Wellbeing and Choice 2005

Coping with Dementia – a practical handbook. NHS Scotland 2008

Becoming a carer Mental Health Foundation

Evidence activities

3.1 A carer's understanding

Find through different sources the type of information available for carers and compile an information pack or folder that could be used easily by carers. Ask colleagues and or carers for feedback on your information pack – do they find it helpful? Would they add anything to it?

3.2 Involving carers and others

Investigate local groups in your area. Dementia charities often provide social groups for carers and also activities for both carers and the person living with dementia. One popular idea is 'dementia cafés'.

What do you think the principle of dementia cafes is?

Look for examples of organisations or events that include people living with dementia and their carers. There is a lot in the media now about 'Dementia Friends'. Use a search engine to look for examples of Dementia Friends in your community.

Support person-centred thinking and planning

This unit is worth 5 credits

What are you finding out?

We are going to explore what person-centred planning and thinking means to you as the carer, to the individual, to their relatives and to outside agencies. We will identify the different tools available for implementation, their effectiveness and how they empower individuals.

To explore person-centred thinking and planning we need to know its origins, the legislation and the tools that enable us to implement the process effectively. We need to understand the importance of person-centred planning and identify how useful this tool is in helping us care for/assist the individual.

By the end of this unit you will:

1 Understand the principles and practice of person-centred thinking, planning and reviews
2 Understand the context within which person-centred thinking and planning takes place
3 Understand own role in person-centred planning, thinking and reviews
4 Be able to apply person-centred thinking in relation to own life
5 Be able to implement person-centred thinking and person-centred reviews.

LO1 Understand the principles and practice of person-centred thinking, planning and reviews

AC 1.1 Identify the beliefs and values on which person-centred thinking and planning is based

The history of care

We are all aware of the concept individuals have of care, due to experience or media information. Try to recall your understanding of care before you started working in the sector. The role of the carer was seen as practical assistance, the need to help the individual with personal care and dietary needs. When we had this view, how much thought went into how this was to be achieved?

The history of care for those with any form of learning disability prior to the 1970s was unacceptable; the aim was to keep them out of sight and treat them as a lower class citizen. The development of community care and legislation has dramatically changed the way individuals are cared for.

The importance of the individual receiving the right care and being empowered to have their choices heard is a human right (Human Rights Act 1998). With person-centred thinking and planning we are addressing their individual choices, needs and rights.

In the past care plans were used to identify what care was needed to support the individual. The care planning approach made assumptions. It did not ask or involve the individual, or if it did it was only to inform them of what the carers were going to do.

The need for individuals to have control and become empowered is of the highest importance in achieving a good outcome. To do this we need to be clear on what they want to achieve. By doing this we **value** and

reinforce their **beliefs** and include them in our society as equal members. Person-centred thinking derives from the concept of the individual being at the centre of decisions and in control. Previously, care planning was often carried out without the individual being involved in the process. Professionals decided what was needed and the views of the individual or others involved in their care were not encouraged. Many care plans were templates and only slight adjustments were made for each individual. The care plans were often not communicated to the carers or support workers, leading to failure. Care plans were not individualised or agreed by the majority of people involved in caring for an individual and so frequently had little or no effect.

It was recognised that changes were needed. Person-centred planning was developed on the basis of empowering individuals with learning disabilities.

As individuals we can explain the difference between the old way of care planning by thinking of how we react to situations ourselves. If we are told to do something with no explanation as to why, we may be less likely to do it. If we are involved in the process of the task, and understand why we are being asked to do it, we are more likely to follow the instructions.

Person-centred caring is about identifying who the person really is, where we as carers fit into their lives, and what we are able to do together to improve their lives now and in the future.

Key terms

Value can be defined as worth. In person-centred planning it is to demonstrate the importance of the individual.

Beliefs are ideas or principles that we hold to be true.

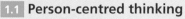

Time to think

1.1 Person-centred thinking

Think about how you like to be treated in your everyday life. Imagine if it was your day off from work and you had decided to relax all day. Your parents or friends decide that you are going to do an extra shift. They have not discussed this with you and the first thing you know about it is when they enter your room at 6am and start pulling you out of bed and preparing you for work. You would not be happy.

Think how they could have done this in a manner that would be agreeable for you, as in person-centred thinking. Explain why this approach would be better.

Evidence activity

1.1 Person-centred thinking

List beliefs and values that person-centred thinking is based on?

AC 1.2 Define person-centred thinking, person-centred planning and person-centred reviews

As we have seen, person-centred thinking, planning and reviewing aims to empower the individual, increase the involvement of the individual and those they wish to help them in their journey. The **medical model of care planning** involved only professionals who were asked to prescribe the best way of assisting an individual. We all prefer to make our own decisions and be in control of our lives, to do as much as possible for ourselves and make our own dreams and ambitions. We will require support at times on this journey and as an adult we know who we could ask to support us.

People with learning disabilities have the same visions and aspirations, and have the right to be treated as an equal. With learning disabilities there may be many more obstacles than we would face to achieve our goals, which is why planning is required and support needs to be obtained. This still should be the individual's choice. As support workers we are the advocates for the people we support and we need to ensure their rights are met. Person-centred thinking, reviewing and planning put individuals in the centre of their care and enables them to take charge of the direction they wish for their care to be delivered.

Evidence activities

1.2 Thinking, planning and reviews

Explain what 'person-centred planning', person-centred reviews and 'person-centred thinking' are and what beliefs and values they are based on.

In the table below, in each column list words that describe person-centred planning, person-centred thinking and person-centred reviews (see AC 1.6).

Person-centred thinking	Person-centred planning	Person-centred reviews

AC 1.3 Describe the difference that person-centred thinking can make to individuals and their families

The need for the individual to be at the centre of their own planning appears obvious to us now, and the more person-centred thinking and planning is used, the more the culture in how individuals are treated will change. The medical model of planning care and the lack of involvement for families and carers left the individual's family detached from the process and feelings of helplessness must have occurred. With person-centred thinking and planning the family and carers are seen as vital to ensuring that the goals and ambitions of the individual can be achieved.

By taking this approach to care, other benefits can occur. An example of this would be when an individual has requested to go to church on Sunday; unfortunately a member of staff has phoned in sick and the home has reduced resources and cannot help the individual with their wishes. The individual becomes cross and frustrated and you as the support worker have a more difficult shift. By involving family and friends in their care, extra resources are available to the individual, and this can reduce frustrations individuals may come across.

Time to think

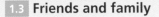

1.3 Friends and family

Recall a situation when family and friends have assisted in the individual's care. What went well? What did not go so well? What could have been done differently? How did person-centred thinking and planning benefit the situation?

Evidence activity

1.3 Difference that person-centred thinking makes

What difference do you think person-centred thinking can make to people and their families?

AC 1.4 Describe examples of person-centred thinking tools

To aid the process of person-centred thinking, planning and reviewing, tools have been developed to enable this process and record the information in a format that all can understand. These tools put the individual at the centre of the process and in the driving seat to progress the plan. There are four basic types of tools for person-centred thinking, planning and reviewing:

- Essential Life Planning
- PATH (planning alternative tomorrows with hope)
- MAPS (making action plans)
- Personal Futures Planning.

Essential Life Planning

This approach identifies seven tools to plan person-centred thinking:

- **Sorting importance to/for**. This tool asks the individual what is important to them, to make them both happy and socially included. Contrasted against the environment they live in, restrictions, health and safety. From this guide and identifying any obstacles, you have a basis to clarify information you need to find out, or support you need to gain, for the individual to achieve their wants.
- **The doughnut sort**. This tool identifies roles and responsibilities for the individual and identifies different people involved in their care.
- **Matching staff**. This identifies skills in performing care, identifies any extra staff/carers/family members that may be needed and the role they will perform.
- **Relationship circle.** This identifies all the people involved with the individual, the support needed and the level of involvement from people that the individual requires.
- **Communication charts**. These identify the individual's preferred means of

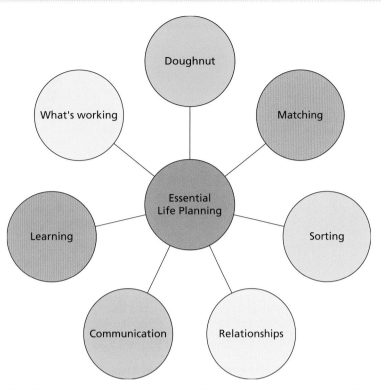

Figure 15.1 Tools have been developed to assist person-centred planning

communicating and identify any frustrations or communication problems.
- **Learning log**. The learning log identifies the development process, what has worked well for the individual, who has supported/visited and the impact that this has had, and also identifies things that have not gone so well.
- **Sorting what's working/not working**. This tool clearly identifies what is working, to allow enhancement/ maintenance of these aspects, and what is not working for the individual. It gives a clear picture of how things are for the individual at that moment in time.

PATH (planning alternative tomorrows with hope)
The aim of this tool is to identify what the individual's goals are and steps to achieve them. This is broken into the following steps:

1 **What are the goals/dreams?** This can be a long term or short term goal/dream.
2 **First steps**. What small changes are needed to help the individual achieve their goal/ dream?
3 **Now**. Where are they now in relation to their goal/dream?
4 **Enrol**. Who can help them achieve their goal/dream? The circle of support of family /friends/carers.
5 **Keeping strong**. How are they being supported/responsibilities?
6 **Action plan**. The full plan on how to achieve these goals and dreams.
7 **Next steps**. The long term changes that need to be implemented.

MAPS (making action plans)

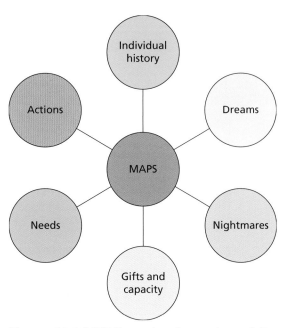

Figure 15.2 MAPS can be drawn from different areas of an individual's life

Maps are pictures and are drawn from different areas of the individual's life:

- **What is the individual's history?** The need to listen to past experiences, events that have occurred that have been a positive or negative influence on the individual.
- **The dream**. What the individual would like to happen/occur.
- **The nightmare**. Identifying the anxieties and obstacles in the way of achieving the dream.
- **Gifts and capacity**. Recognising their abilities, their strengths and achievements; this will then be a tool to help them achieve their goal.
- **Needs**. The need to identify what support and help the individual requires from others. Paid or unpaid support.
- **Action**. Action plan to achieve their individual care needs, a very simple plan clearly stating what, how, when and where.

Personal futures planning

Figure 15.3 Personal futures planning

This approach aims to identify those that wish to be involved in helping the individual towards the future they want. This includes their family, friends, and social contacts. Meetings are arranged at a suitable time for all who want to be involved and at a location suitable for all those attending. There are five steps to planning:

1 All the people that are involved recognise and share the individual's gifts and strengths.
2 All that are involved develop a common understanding of the future/dream for the individual.
3 The group agrees to meet and share ideas on how to achieve the dream.
4 This group identifies a champion who will advocate and organise.
5 At least one care deliverer is committed to supplying and implementing the dream.

This is not an exhaustive list of the tools available, just the main ones. With these tools it is easy to identify patterns and the need for person-centred thinking.

1.4 Person-centred tools

From the list above, identify a person-centred tool that is in use in your workplace and write a brief explanation of why you use this tool.

AC 1.5 Explain what a 'one page profile' is

A one page profile should consist of all the things that are important to the individual. The one page profile should include details of how the individual likes to be supported, what other people like about them and what makes the individual really happy.

One page profile

Photo
Each one page profile has a current photo of the person.

Appreciations
This section lists the positive qualities, strengths and talents of the person. It can also be called 'like and admire'.

What's important to the person
This is a bullet list of what really matters to the person from their perspective (even if others do not agree). It is detailed and specific. This section need to have enough detail so that someone who does not know the person can understand what matters to them. It could include:

- Who the important people are in the person's life, and when and how they spend time together.
- Important activities and hobbies, and when, where and how often these take place.
- Any routines that are important to the person.

How to support the person
This is a list of how to support the person, and what is helpful and what is not.

The information in this section includes what people need to know, and what people need to do.

Figure 15.4 An example of a one page profile

AC 1.6 Describe the person-centred review process

We have looked at person-centred planning tools and their application. Any planning will require reviewing on a regular basis to ensure it will achieve the goals set or whether the goals have changed and therefore the plan may need to be altered. An effective tool for reviewing is the learning log; this should be completed on a regular basis with the individual involved. The learning log will then become the focus point for the review process. An example is included below.

The review process will be assisted if you have a structured format. Some useful questions to consider are:

- Who contributed to the review?
- What do we like and admire about the person?

- What is important to the person now?
- What is important for the person in the future?
- What support and help does the person need to stay healthy and safe?
- Which questions and issues are we struggling with now?
- What is working and what is not?

You can then create an action plan from this. (Smull and Sanderson 2001).

LO2 Understand the context within which person-centred thinking and planning takes place

The need for planning to involve the individual and for the individual to feel in control has been highlighted in LO1. We now need to look at the practicalities of where person-centred planning takes place.

The easiest answer to this is where the individual would like this process to take place. The individual needs an environment where they feel comfortable and safe to do

Table 15.1 An example of review questions

Date	Activity (what, where, when, how long, etc.)	Who was there (staff, individual, others)	What worked well about the activity? What should continue? What did you learn?	What didn't work well? What must be different? What did you learn?

this. It is vital that to ensure that the everyone involved in their care can attend and support the process is there in the planning. You must support the individual prior to this process so they remain in control. You must also think ahead and forward plan as ensuring all those involved in the care are able to attend can be quite difficult and a major task.

AC 2.1 Outline current legislation, policy and guidance underpinning person-centred thinking and planning

Valuing People: A New Strategy for Learning Disability for the 21st Century (January 2002)

This was a strategy introduced to ensure that those needing help had a say in the way their care was going to be delivered, with the emphasis on how the individual could achieve their goals and how they were to be included in society. Care plans and reviews used to be built on the medical model: you have an infection, here is a prescription, and the nurse will give you your tablets four times a day for seven days.

Person-centred thinking addresses this differently by clarifying what you are feeling, how you would like treatment to be achieved and who you would like to support you. It is a very simple concept, but by using person-centred thinking we give choices and encouragement to the individual to enable them to achieve the outcome they wish. The role for a person-centred thinker is to assist with looking at the support the person needs, involving them, carers/family/friends and health professionals if needed. As with any plan, it needs to be reviewed. Again, with person-centred thinking the review mostly involves the person who is receiving the care, and the people who are assisting them with their care (who are not always paid professionals; the majority of care delivered is by unpaid carers and family members).

Valuing People was updated; *Valuing People Now* in 2009 was a three-year strategy based on similar themes. However, since then a change of government has meant that the exact status of the *Valuing People* programme is somewhat unclear. Its ideas, however, are very helpful when considering person-centred thinking and planning.

Health and Social Care Act (2012)

The Health and Social Care Act (2012) was a major piece of legislation covering all aspects of health and social care provision. Within it there is a legal requirement that people are involved in the decisions about their care. However, many implications of this Act are still being worked through.

The Mental Capacity Act 2005

The Mental Capacity Act says that every adult has the right to make their own decisions and it should be assumed that they can, unless it is proved that they cannot. Any decisions that are made on their behalf must be with their best interests at heart. There are clear implications for person-centred thinking and planning within this legislation.

Evidence activity

2.1 Legislation

Read through your workplace's policies and local procedures on person-centred thinking and planning and review them against legislation.

AC 2.2 Describe the relationship between person-centred planning and personalised services

Person-centred thinking is about asking questions and listening to the individual's responses, how much help they require and how they would like their personal needs delivered. This is the beginning of planning their care and ensuring inclusion for the individual.

Key term

Partnership boards consist of persons with disabilities, friends, carers, support workers and adult social services and PCT (Primary Care Trust) staff.

Evidence activity

2.2 Person-centred planning and personalised

Think of someone you support, whether they live independently or in a support house, and describe how person-centred planning and personalised budgets work together.

Time to think

2.3 Person-centred thinking

Imagine you have walked into a shop and have been told you have to buy an article; you don't want the article but you still have to buy it. How would this make you feel? If the scenario was different, people were using person-centred thinking, and family and friends had identified places where you like to shop and taken you there, how different would you feel?

We are all aware that some people are 'morning people' and enjoy getting up and being active first thing, while others are late risers and are more active later on in the day. We may be aware of this in our own family and circle of friends but are we aware of this with the individuals we care for? Imagine if you needed care how you would like to be cared for. If you are a late riser, how would you feel about being woken at 6am and assisted with your personal needs? This is a small example but clearly illustrates attitudes we have all seen in the past when delivering any personal care.

Part of this process looks at what resources we need to ensure are available to support the individual. By completing these plans we can ensure the resources are there. After completing the planning, details of the resources needed are forwarded via the care manager to specialist boards, known as **partnership boards**, which influence budgets and ultimately governments on needs for the local person.

AC 2.3 Identify ways that person-centred thinking can be used:

- with individuals
- in teams.

With individuals

Person-centred thinking is focused on listening to and understanding the individual's needs and wishes. With person-centred planning the emphasis is put on everyone being involved in their care. There is a big emphasis on families' and carers' knowledge and skills when identifying all persons to be involved in an individual's care.

When individuals are listening or know you well enough to identify your likes and dislikes, this demonstrates that they care and understand you; the same principle applies to person-centred thinking and planning. As the name says the thinking and planning is about the person.

Involving families and friends (later this will be classed as the relationship circle) actually reduces the amount of input/work you need to do, as they can identify areas they wish to be involved in, with the agreement of the individual.

In teams

A person-centred team uses person-centred thinking within the team context, to clarify the purpose of the team, what is important to the team and what support team members need. Teams can work through seven questions to explore becoming a person-centred team. Each question uses a range of person-centred thinking tools to answer it. Information about purpose, what is important to the team, action and reflection is recorded and updated in a person-centred team plan.

LO3 Understand own role in person-centred planning, thinking and reviews

Person-centred thinking, planning and reviewing are now established as necessary to enable individuals to live as they wish to live and to have the right to choose the level of support they require. Your role or job description in your workplace will determine the amount of input and responsibility you have in planning and reviewing. All staff have a duty to use person-centred thinking.

AC 3.1 Describe own role in person-centred thinking, planning and reviews when supporting individuals

As a support worker, your role is to advocate for the individual you are supporting and ensure their voice can be heard. Person-centred caring is about identifying who the person really is, where we as support workers fit into their lives, and what we are able to do together to improve their lives now and in the future.

The person at the centre

It is vital that we think about how the person can be central throughout the process,

from gathering information about their life, preparing for meetings, monitoring actions and on-going learning, to reflection and further action. There is a danger that efforts to develop person-centred planning simply focus on having better meetings. Any planning without implementation leaves people feeling frustrated and cynical, which is often worse than not planning at all.

Very often you will only be caring for and supporting people when they are in a vulnerable position. The quality of care that you can provide will be improved if you have knowledge of the whole person, not just the current circumstances: for example, knowledge can help us to understand better why people behave in the way they do. A care plan, based on a person-centred approach, will help in understanding some of this, but what else might help? Person-centred planning, then, demands that you see the person whom you are supporting as the central concern. You need to find ways to care and support individuals, not 'one size fits all'. The relationship should move from being one of carer and cared for towards one based on a partnership: you become a resource to the person who needs support.

AC 3.2 Identify challenges that may be faced in implementing person-centred thinking, planning and reviews in own work

Sometimes, especially when we are facing a new process, obstacles and challenges

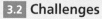

Time to think

3.2 Challenges

Identify a time when you have come across a challenge in implementing person-centred thinking, planning or reviews. Write about what went well, what did not go so well and what you would do differently next time.

can occur. An example of this may be that everyone in the supported house would like to get up at the same time and each individual needs individual support with their daily living skills. This is when we need to pool our resources and look at what compromises can be made so that we can achieve the desired outcome.

One way may be to discuss shift changes to ensure more staff are available in the morning when needed. It may be that family members would like to be involved. The other option might be an agreement of slightly later times for individuals to get up.

Challenges might include:

- The attitude of others, who may not share the view that the person with a learning disability has the right to make certain choices or take particular risks
- Lack of appropriate resources that can meet their needs, for example, inclusive employment, or appropriate accommodation.

AC 3.3 Describe how these challenges might be overcome

The challenges can be overcome to some extent by education, public awareness campaigns, and lobbying (pressure) from organisations who promote the rights of people with learning disabilities.

Case study

3.3 Alex(1)

Alex is 30 years old and has lived in care for several years. He has severe developmental dysphasia due to brain injury from an accident when he was three years old. His father has died and his mother visits frequently, although she is not physically well herself and has recently been diagnosed with terminal cancer. Alex has a great interest in modern music and enjoys interacting with others. However, sometimes social interaction causes him frustration due to his communication problems caused by his developmental dysphasia. Alex has been used to care delivery and supervision with his mother assisting. Alex has limited social contacts and has never been employed.

Using person-centred thinking and planning, describe how you could overcome some of the obstacles Alex is facing. List the obstacles and make sure you identify how you could overcome each one.

Evidence activity

3.2 and **3.3** Challenges and overcoming them

List challenges that you have faced in your setting when implementing person-centred thinking, planning and reviews. How have you overcome these challenges?

LO4 Be able to apply person-centred thinking in relation to own life

To fully understand person-centred thinking and planning it is important to identify where you may use it in your own life. To some extent we all use person-centred planning every day; for example, when planning a holiday you would contact a travel agent, go to the bank to change currency, ensure that transport is booked for example. When using person-centred planning in our own lives we may not necessarily write it down or think of this as planning in the same way.

AC 4.1 Demonstrate how to use a person-centred thinking tool in relation to own life to identify what is working and not working

To fully understand the process and how an individual may feel using person-centred thinking and planning it is sometimes useful to apply the principles to yourself. We have all been in a position when someone has told us what to do. Think about how that felt, and having no say in the matter. Imagine wanting to go shopping, with an idea of an item you want to purchase and the store you would be able to get this from, and someone stopping you by taking you to the wrong store and making you spend your money on something they feel is more suitable. How would this make you feel? Remember this feeling when supporting others with their choices.

Evidence activity

4.1 Person-centred tools
Use a person-centred tool to plan a shopping trip, identifying the key things needed and support required from others. Explain how the process made you feel.

AC 4.2 Describe own relationship circle

We all need support to achieve positive outcomes. Recall from Evidence activity 4.1 who you selected to go with you on the shopping trip. You may have chosen someone whose judgement you respect or it may have been someone who could help you with the finance. In everyday life we all rely on others to support us in our goals. As children the support comes from our parents and family to guide us on what is right and what is

Evidence activity

4.2 Relationship circle
Using the Essential Life Planning tool in AC 1.4, use the relationship circle and identify who you would include in your circle.

wrong. Encouragement from them to achieve our goals will help to build self-confidence and self-esteem. As children we need the support to learn and develop into adults.

Individuals with learning disabilities also require that support. The level needed will depend on each individual's abilities. This does not make the individual with learning disabilities weak; this enables them to learn and develop, and increases their confidence and self-esteem.

To understand your own relationship and network support, complete the following activity.

AC 4.3 Describe how helpful using a person-centred thinking tool was to identify actions in relation to own life

From the activities in this section, you should have gained some concept of the process of person-centred thinking and identified areas that are more difficult to plan and those that were easier to plan. It is important to think of these activities when assisting an individual to complete them. It is also important to note how empowering this was for you and hopefully will be for the individual.

Evidence activity

4.3 How helpful is a person-centred thinking tool?
Complete the 'what's working and what's not working' tool in relation to your personal development. How helpful was using a person-centred thinking tool in identifying actions in relation to your own life?

AC 4.4 Describe how to prepare for own person-centred review

When assisting individuals in person-centred reviews, we need to ensure they understand the process and are clear on what outcomes they want and that someone they trust is there to be an advocate for them. All of the people the individual wishes to be involved should be present. The venue and time should be agreed on by everyone involved.

- Prepare the environment so it is user friendly and non-confrontational – informal layout and chairs of the same height, for example.
- Ensure all significant people including an advocate (if appropriate) have been invited.
- Ensure the person who is at the centre of the review remains so – listen carefully to their views and preferences during the meeting and ensure they understand what the meeting is about and what form it will take before the meeting begins.
- Plan a follow up – do not leave things 'open ended' – you may have agreed to a particular plan but will need to check if it is effective.

Evidence activity

4.4 Review

Write an account of the type of support you would require for your review. Who would you want to be present and where would you like it to be held?

LO5 Be able to implement person-centred thinking and person-centred reviews

This section looks at ways of ensuring the person-centred planning process is implemented process. As a support worker your role as the individual's advocate is vital. You should also be aware of outside advocates such as family members, who the individual may choose as their advocate. Your role will be to support them in the process.

AC 5.1 Use person-centred thinking to know and act on what is important to the individual

As the support worker, you may have worked closely with the individual and be aware of their communication skills and preference of how they are treated. Use the information you have learnt so for in this unit to use person-centered thinking to know and act on what is important to the individual.

Examples of person-centered thinking include an understanding of their:

- history (life story)
- relationships with family and friends
- preferences
- hopes and fears.

Case study

5.1 Jane

Jane is unable to communicate her needs clearly by verbal means. If Jane is unhappy she will make a short murmur; if she is happy she will make a very sharp high-pitched noise. Jane is due to go clothes shopping. Generally her sister takes her and Jane comes back with dated clothes. You have noted that Jane does not wear the clothes she has bought. Her sister feels she is helping and that this is a task she can support Jane with. The relationship is very strained and Jane's sister attends once a month to take her shopping.

Write down what actions you should take to support Jane and her sister using person-centred thinking.

AC 5.2 Establish with the individual how they want to be supported

When supporting an individual it is important to be clear what their ambitions or goals are. Sometimes this can be difficult if they have limited life experiences.

Sometimes this can be difficult if they have limited life experiences or communication difficulties. In these circumstances it is important you use the communication skills as outlined in SHC 21. Consider their skills –

what they can rather than cannot do. Be realistic, but encourage small goals or steps to encourage a sense of achievement.

AC 5.3 Use person-centred thinking to know and respond to how the individual communicates

Person-centred planning is an effective tool if used correctly and frequently. The person-centred plan must be in a format for the individual to understand. It is important to start a communication chart as soon as possible so that this can be shared with all involved.

Through listening we find out what is important to the individual and what would make them happy and content. We also need to be aware of the limitations that the service has and find agreeable compromises.

AC 5.4 Be responsive to how an individual makes decisions to support them to have maximum choice and control in their life

Person-centred thinking allows us to deliver care in a manner that the individual chooses.

AC 5.5 Support the individual in their relationships and in being part of their community using person-centred thinking

Community person-centred planning uses the same tools but with different slants on the questions. This is called the community connecting approach. It begins with learning about the person and identifying their networks, and includes a passion audit about likes and dislikes. The next step looks at community mapping, the main focus being on exploring the gifts and capabilities of the individual, allowing identification of areas in the community that are accessible and where the individual will be able to participate and feel happy.

Time to think

5.5 Community

Think of an individual you support and describe the actions and planning you have done in including the individual in the community. Write about what went well, what did not go so well and what you would do differently next time.

AC 5.6 Ensure that the individual is central to the person-centred review process

To ensure the individual remains at the centre of the process, they need to be fully supported in the review process. As their support worker you will be aware of any difficulties they may have. You will need to ensure that someone attending their review will advocate for them.

Time to think

5.6 Person-centred planning process

Think of an individual you have supported in the person-centred planning process. State what you did to support the individual, what went well, what did not go so well and what you would do differently next time.

AC 5.7 Explain how to ensure that actions from a review happen

The review process is there to kick start the outcomes the individual has stated they want to achieve. While reviewing we can identify any obstacles, problems and hopefully solutions to these obstacles. This is only one part of the review process. As with any tool, the review process is only effective if it is used. At a review, actions to move the programme forward are made with responsibilities outlined to ensure those actions are followed. These action plans should be recorded and checked off when completed.

Evidence activity

5.3 , 5.4 , 5.5 , 5.6 and, 5.7

Look over a recent review plan of someone you support. Identify the actions made and the persons responsible for completing them. Look for any actions not followed up and describe what actions you can take to support the individual in this process. If all of the actions have been completed, reflect on what you could do if they were not completed.

Legislation

Human Rights Act 1998

The Mental Capacity Act 2005

The Care Act 2014

The Equality Act 2010

The Health and Social Care Act 2012

Useful resources

Office for Disability Issues
www.officefordisability.gov.uk

About Learning Disabilities
www.aboutlearningdisabilities.co.uk

Mencap
www.mencap.org.uk

Learning Disability Coalition
www.learningdisabilitycoalition.org.uk

The Foundation for People with Learning Difficulties
www.learningdisabilities.org.uk

Easyhealth
www.easyhealth.org.uk

Provide support for mobility

This unit
is worth
2 credits

What are you finding out?

This unit will help you to develop and demonstrate your knowledge and ability to provide support for people with their mobility. Throughout this unit you will learn about the importance of mobility and the impact this can have on a person's well-being. You will also learn about the risks associated with reduced mobility.

Being mobile helps people to remain independent and some people rely on the use of mobility aids. You therefore learn about your role in

supporting people to use their mobility equipment and appliances. Finally, you will learn about the importance of observing, recording and reporting mobility activities within your organisation.

By the end of this unit you will:

1 Understand the importance of mobility
2 Be able to prepare for mobility activities
3 Be able to support individuals to keep mobile
4 Be able to observe, record and report on activities to support mobility.

LO1 Understand the importance of mobility

AC 1.1 Define mobility

Being mobile will mean different things to different people. For some people being mobile will mean they are able to get around their home. For others being mobile will mean they are able to get in their car and go wherever they want to. Very simply, **mobility** can be defined as being able to move or be moved freely and easily. It may involve the movement of an individual from a particular place or position to another while ensuring their independence is maintained as much as possible. In a care setting, this could involve moving from a bed to a chair, or walking from the kitchen to the dining room, or it could mean moving from one bed position to another.

Key term

Mobility is the ability to move freely, either aided or unaided.

Time to think

1.1 Mobility

What does being mobile mean to you?

Ask some of your colleagues the same question and make a note of their responses. Are their responses the same?

Evidence activity

1.1 Mobility

In your own words, define what is meant by the term 'mobility'.

AC 1.2 Explain how different health conditions may affect and be affected by mobility

There are a number of conditions that can impact on a person's mobility and on the support they need to move and reposition. For this reason, moving and handling procedures must be adapted and agreed ways of working put in place that meet each person's needs. Specifically tailored moving and repositioning activities must be devised for people who:

- have bone and joint conditions, such as rheumatoid arthritis, in which the joints become inflamed and painful; osteoarthritis, in which the cartilage of the joints becomes worn, stiff and painful; and osteoporosis, in which the density of the bones is much reduced, increasing the risk of fracture
- have a physical disability that affects movement and mobility, such as amputation, muscular dystrophy, multiple sclerosis, stroke, Parkinson's disease, Huntington's disease, cerebral palsy and epilepsy
- have a sensory impairment, such as impaired sight or hearing, which may affect a person's ability to hear how to help in a manoeuvre or see where to move
- have attachments, such as a feeding tube, urinary catheter or oxygen therapy
- have variations in capabilities during the day and night – for example, an individual may be able to move themselves during the day but may not be able to move at all at night
- have issues with tissue viability, which is to do with the ability of the skin to remain intact and healthy. Reduced tissue viability manifests as skin breakdown and pressure ulcers. Skin breakdown is caused by failure to care for skin exposed to moisture from urine, sweat and **exudate** (see page 283 for definition), while pressure ulcers are due to pressure (of the body on

Key terms

Exudate is fluid that seeps out of injured tissues.

Comatose means that a person is in a coma and is therefore unable to move voluntarily and is unable to understand what is happening.

Case study

1.2 Mr Cassidy

Mr Cassidy is a 72-year-old gentleman. He has a condition known as chronic obstructive pulmonary disease, or COPD for short. This is a condition that has affected his lungs and he gets short of breath very easily, especially if he is walking and undertaking activities such as getting dressed. He sometimes requires oxygen therapy.

What effect do you think this condition has on Mr Cassidy's mobility?

What effect do you think that mobilising has on Mr Cassidy's condition?

Evidence activity

1.2 Health conditions and mobility

Choose three service users from your place of work and explain how their health conditions affect and may be affected by their mobility.

the bed or chair), shear (pressure created by pushing and pulling in a lateral direction) and friction (created by two surfaces moving over each other)
- are paralysed and unable to move
- are unconscious – someone who is **comatose** is unable to change their own position.

AC 1.3 Outline the effects that reduced mobility may have on an individual's well-being

Keeping mobile is very important for health and for maintaining a sense of well-being. However, as we have just discussed, some people may have difficulty in mobilising for various reasons. Reduced mobility can lead to other problems and could have a profound impact on a person's physical, emotional and social well-being:

- Physically, reduced mobility can increase the risk of a person developing blood clots. Reduced mobility will also lead to stiffness of the joints, swelling of the feet and ankles, and ultimately pressure ulcers. All of these could be very painful for the individual.
- Emotionally, reduced mobility could lead to frustrations because the individual cannot do the things they used to be able to do. This could also manifest itself as depression and the person may feel very negative and low in mood.
- Socially, reduced mobility could mean the person is unable to maintain friendships and may find it difficult to go to places they used to go as they will be dependent on others to get them there.

As a health or social care worker you will work as part of a wider multidisciplinary team to help to prevent these problems from occurring. People who have restricted mobility should have a care plan or a support plan that identifies the risks

Figure 16.1 What do you think are some of the effects that reduced mobility can have on an individual's well-being?

Evidence activity

1.3 Effects of reduced mobility

Outline how reduced mobility can affect an individual's well-being.

associated with their reduced mobility. These risks could include:

- **deep vein thrombosis**
- **pressure ulcers**
- **pulmonary embolism**
- loss of independence
- chest infections
- constipation
- swollen feet and ankles.

AC 1.4 Describe the benefits of maintaining and improving mobility

There are many benefits to maintaining and improving mobility. **Mobility activities** can have psychological, social and physical benefits for people using services and ultimately this will encourage independence. The benefits of maintaining and improving mobility include:

- more flexible joints, improved muscular strength and physical health fitness
- greater independence as the person will not need to rely on others for their health and support needs
- a better quality social life as there will be more opportunities to do different things

Evidence activity

1.4 Benefits

Explain to someone the benefits an individual may experience as a result of maintaining and improving their mobility.

and to take part in more activities with different people, which will also help to boost self-esteem.

Supporting a person to maintain their mobility will also have great benefits to health and social care staff as service users will be empowered to maintain their independence and ultimately this will mean that service users are not as dependent on staff when they need to mobilise.

LO2 Be able to prepare for mobility activities

AC 2.1 Agree mobility activities with the individual and others

Mobility activities may include activities such as:

- exercises
- physiotherapy
- occupational therapies
- household activities
- group activities.

Physiotherapists, in conjunction with **Occupational Therapists**, would take the lead in agreeing a programme of support with people using health and social care services. It is therefore essential that mobility activities are carried out as they were prescribed. It is crucial that you:

- detail the mobility activity in the person's care plan

- encourage and support the person to undertake the prescribed mobility activities
- report any problems associated with the mobility activity to your manager and to the person who prescribed the mobility activities
- carefully record any progress the person is making.

Your role in supporting a person to follow their mobility activity programme should be well defined within your job description.

Key terms

Physiotherapists help people affected by injury, illness or disability through movement and exercise, manual therapy, education and advice.

Occupational Therapist is a professional who supports individuals to engage in daily activities.

Research and investigate

2.1 Mobility activities

Find out how mobility activities are agreed within your workplace.

Who would you refer a person to if they were having problems with their mobility?

Evidence activity

2.1 Agree mobility activities

Spend some time with a Physiotherapist or an Occupational Therapist within your organisation and ask to be involved in agreeing mobility activities with the individual.

Make a record of the discussion and how the agreement was reached. Remember to include any other people who were involved in the discussion, for example the service user's family.

AC 2.2 Remove or minimise hazards in the environment before beginning a mobility activity

Mobility activities must be carried out in a safe environment, so it is important that the environment is included in any mobility risk assessment. The risk assessment should include checking:

- that floor surfaces are safe for mobility exercises
- that there is nothing the individual could trip over or that could lead to injury
- that the lighting is good to enable the person to see clearly
- there is sufficient space for the person to mobilise
- that the support required to facilitate the mobility activity is available
- the actions that should be taken in an emergency, for example if the person falls.

If the exercise is being carried out by a person sitting in a wheelchair, it is important to ensure that:

- the wheelchair is well maintained
- the brakes are on where necessary.

If the exercise is being carried out by someone in bed, it is important to ensure:

- the bed is stable and steady
- the bed brakes are firmly on.

If the individual is using a mobility aid, such as a walking stick, it is important to ensure:

- it is being used properly and has been measured correctly to make sure it is the correct size for the user.

Time to think

2.2 Removing minimising hazards

How do you ensure the immediate environment is safe before you begin to support people with their mobility activities?

What action do you take if there is a problem?

AC 2.3 Check the suitability of an individual's clothing and footwear for safety and mobility

It is important to check that the clothing and footwear an individual is wearing will enable them to mobilise safely. Loose fitting clothes such as a tracksuit would be ideal as they are comfortable, practical and easy to wear. It is important to ensure clothing maintains the individual's dignity so that they can concentrate on the task without having to worry about exposing parts that they would rather keep covered.

Shoes should be well fitting and offer support, with non-slip soles. It is important that individuals do not undertake mobility exercises with ill-fitting shoes or slippers as this will increase the risk of slipping and tripping and ultimately falling.

Figure 16.2 It is important that you check the suitability of an individual's clothing and footwear for safety and mobility

AC 2.4 Check the safety and cleanliness of mobility equipment and appliances

Mobility equipment and appliances must be safe and clean for the person using them. People also need to use them in the correct way, to avoid injury or discomfort. The use of mobility aids and appliances should be built into the person's mobility support plan.

Checking for safety may include visual checks to ensure the equipment is in good working order – for example, if a person is using a walking frame, check to ensure no screws have come loose and that the rubber feet on the frame are intact. Also make sure the legs on the frame are the same height and that it is the correct size frame for the individual. If there is more than one person frames it is easy for them to get mixed up.

It is also important to ensure mobility equipment is clean. Pieces of equipment such as walking sticks and frames frequently come into contact with people's hands, and hands are the main way in which micro-organisms are spread. It is therefore essential to ensure

equipment is cleaned with an appropriate cleansing agent in order to minimise the risks associated with cross infection. Your organisation should have a cleaning schedule, which should include the cleaning of mobility aids such as wheelchairs, walking frames and walking sticks.

A mobility appliance that fails when a person is using it can be extremely dangerous. It is therefore important to check the condition of mobility equipment on a regular basis. If you notice any signs of damage, it is important that the person does not use the equipment. The piece of equipment should be taken out of action so that others don't 'accidentally' use it. The fault should then be reported and arrangements made to replace the piece of equipment.

Case study

2.4 Check safety

Elm Tree House is a care home for elderly people. Some people need to be hoisted, as their mobility care plan indicates this. The hoist is shared between three service users; however, each service user is issued their own individual sling. One day you are assisting one of the service users with the hoist and you notice a split in their sling. You use it anyway because you are busy and you put it back on the hook. You see other members of staff continue to use the sling so you think it must be OK.

Explain what could happen as a consequence of these actions.

What should you have done when you noticed the split in the sling?

Research and investigate

2.4 Check cleanliness

Check out the cleaning schedule within your organisation. How often is mobility equipment cleaned and what is the procedure for cleaning this equipment?

What is the procedure if a piece of equipment is found to be faulty?

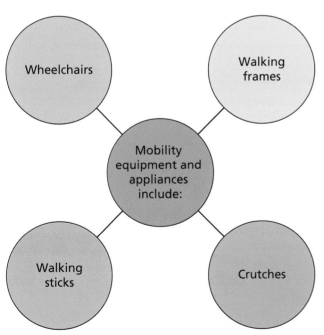

Figure 16.3 Mobility equipment and appliances

LO3 Be able to support individuals to keep mobile

AC 3.1 Promote the active participation of the individual during a mobility activity

Active participation is a way of working that recognises each person as an active partner in their own care or support, rather than a passive recipient of care. It recognises the right of each person to participate in the activities and relationships of everyday life as independently as possible. Active participation is an approach that puts the person at the centre of their care and involves them in decisions being made about them. It thus enables people to be included in their care and have a greater say in how they live their life in a way that matters to them.

As a health or social care worker, it is important to promote active participation through everything you do. People should be empowered to make decisions about their care throughout mobility activities. You can promote active participation by listening to service users and responding to what is important to them. In addition, you can offer people a choice about the type of mobility activities they would like to do, where they want to do them and at what time.

The benefits of active participation are many, some of which include:

- physical benefits, including greater activity levels

- increased levels of independence and autonomy in what people do
- increased opportunities for social contact and interpersonal relationships
- increased involvement and self-awareness
- enhanced well-being, self-confidence, self-esteem and self-belief
- decreased likelihood of abuse – as the individual engages positively by actively participating in areas of their life, such as personal care, the scope for abuse by others is reduced
- decreased vulnerability – as individuals gain in their self-confidence and self-esteem, they are less prone to exploitation and harm from others.

AC 3.2 Assist an individual to use mobility appliances correctly and safely

Mobility appliances help an individual with walking and getting around, and can make a major difference to a person's quality of life. These appliances will usually be prescribed by a trained professional such as a physiotherapist or an occupational therapist. This professional will have explained how the appliance should be used, and there would have been a period of assessment to ensure the appliance was right for the person and that the person was using it correctly and safely. However, as a health or social care worker you will have an ongoing responsibility to ensure the person continues to use the appliance correctly and in a safe manner.

There are many mobility appliances and there are particular ways of using them to get the maximum benefit from them. It is therefore important to ensure people using these appliances are using them correctly. It is also important to take into account the way in which different floor surfaces and coverings affect the safe use of appliances. We will look at just a few mobility appliances here.

Using a wheelchair

If a person has been assessed as requiring a wheelchair, they should be entitled to have their own wheelchair, which will be specifically tailored to them. There are many styles of wheelchair, with different functionalities. Some have to be pushed, some can be self propelled, and some are electric. When supporting someone to use a wheelchair, it is important that you encourage them to self propel the wheelchair whenever possible. This promotes independence and allows the person to go where they choose.

Wheelchairs should be fitted with appropriate cushions to minimise the risk of pressure ulcers for people who are in a wheelchair for long periods of time.

Using a walking stick

People may need differing amounts of support when using a walking stick. Some

Figure 16.4 How do you assist individuals to use mobility appliances correctly and safely?

individuals use a walking stick because they lack confidence or because they are a little unsteady on their feet. These people will require minimum support and will probably be fairly independent. If you are required to steady someone, you should position yourself to their side and slightly behind them, reaching one arm around their pelvis, just below their waist. Never stand directly behind a person – if they fall, they are more likely to fall on top of you.

Using a walking frame

Individuals using a walking frame should be given instructions on the recommended pattern of walking, otherwise the risk of falling will be greatly increased. The recommended sequence for walking with a walking frame is as follows:

● The frame should be placed in front of the person so they can lean on it with arms almost at full stretch. They should then take a step forward. If they have a weakness on one side, they should step with that leg first.
● The next step should be taken with the other leg walking past the first leg.

- The person will step into the walking frame, which should have all four feet on the ground.
- The person then moves the walking frame forward and repeats the process.

It is particularly important that the walking frame should have all four feet on the ground at any point when the user is taking a step, take note of this.

AC 3.3 Give feedback and encouragement to the individual during mobility activities

Service users need to feel confident about mobility activities, and supportive **feedback** and encouragement are essential in helping to build their confidence.

Encouragement should be on-going and feedback should be given to the individual throughout and after the mobility activity.

Feedback should always be constructive and should emphasise how well the person has done. However, in order to encourage the person to progress, it is also important to feedback on ways in which they could improve during the mobility activity.

It is important to be aware of the boundaries of your role in supporting people with mobility activities and you must never advise that the mobility activity is carried out in a different way as this would be unsafe. If a person is having difficulty following the mobility activities that have been prescribed, this should be reported back to the prescriber, for example the Physiotherapist or the Occupational Therapist.

LO4 Be able to observe, record and report on activities to support mobility

AC 4.1 Observe an individual to monitor changes and responses during a mobility activity

It is important to monitor individuals for any changes or responses during mobility activities. This is because you may observe changes in the person's ability to mobilise, there may be an improvement or you may see deterioration. The individual may find it more difficult to get around at different times of the day – for example, they may find it easy to walk to the bathroom in the morning but more of a struggle to mobilise to the bathroom in the evening. You might observe that the individual is struggling to get in and out of bed, or they may be finding the stairs more difficult to climb. You may observe the person to be in pain when undertaking mobility activities.

All of these observations are an important part of care planning and evaluating the care of the individual. This will also enable you to report any concerns that you have about the person's mobility.

AC 4.2 Record observations of mobility activity

Recording is an important aspect of providing all aspects of care and the recording of mobility activities is no exception. Recording a person's progress will enable other members of the team to monitor the progress the person is making. The individual should have a mobility care plan and this should be evaluated and updated regularly.

The recording of mobility activities should detail the progress the person is making towards their prescribed mobility plan – for example, how many times an activity has been carried out or whether there have been any signs of improved flexibility or strength. Equally, any discomfort the person feels should also be recorded. It is also important to record the progress being made for people who are using mobility aids.

AC 4.3 Report on progress and/or problems relating to the mobility activity including:

- **choice of activities**
- **equipment**
- **appliances**
- **the support provided.**

Having observed a person's progress with their mobility activities and recorded your observations, it is important to ensure you report on the person's progress to an appropriate person, such as the individual's Physiotherapist, Occupational Therapist or your manager.

It is also important to be aware of the importance of reporting faulty equipment, such as slings or slide sheets that have become torn. Your organisation should have a policy for dealing with this.

Legislation

The Health and Safety at Work etc. Act 1974

Useful resources

Websites

Disabled Living Foundation

www.dlf.org.uk

Research and investigate

4.3 Reporting

Access your organisation's policy relating to the reporting of faulty equipment. Make a note of the main points of the policy.

Who should the fault be reported to? How is faulty equipment dealt with in your organisation?

Evidence activities

4.3 Report on progress and/or problems

Report on the progress and/or problems relating to the mobility activity to the appropriate person within your organisation. Remember to report on the:

- choice of activities
- equipment and appliances
- level of support you have provided.

Unit HSC 2014

Support individuals to eat and drink

This unit is worth 2 credits

What are you finding out?

This unit is aimed at those care support workers working in a wide range of settings who provide support for one or more individuals to eat and drink, where substantial support is needed.

Some important facts:

- At any point in time more than 3 million people in the UK are either malnourished or at risk of malnutrition.
- Regular weight loss is one of the key physical measures of malnutrition.
- Monitoring weight is a valuable quantifiable measure by which carers can keep a proper record to check whether an individual is at risk of malnutrition.
- Malnutrition is a general term that refers to both under-nutrition and over-nutrition.

- Under-nutrition is due to inadequate food intake, dietary imbalances and deficiencies of specific nutrients.
- Over-nutrition is due to excess food consumption.

Source: NHS Choices

- Good hydration can help prevent falls, constipation, pressure ulcers, kidney stones, blood pressure problems and headaches.

By the end of this unit you will:

1 Be able to support individuals to make choices about food and drink
2 Be able to prepare to provide support for eating and drinking
3 Be able to provide support for eating and drinking
4 Be able to clear away after food and drink
5 Be able to monitor eating and drinking and the support provided.

Key terms

Hydration is the process of providing an adequate amount of liquid to bodily tissues to prevent the build-up of toxins in the body.

Brittle bones are bones that lack calcium and lose their strength and are more fragile and more likely to break.

Poor nutrition and/or **hydration** can lead to:

- increased risk of infection
- reduced wound healing
- skin problems (like pressure ulcers, from poor condition of skin and lack of mobility)
- constipation
- disturbed sleeping patterns
- weight loss/gain
- reduced brain function
- anaemia.

As we get older, or have a disability that prevents a lot of movement, we do not move around quite so much or use the same amount as energy as a younger or more healthy body. We therefore do not need to take in as much 'fuel' or food. However, if we do not eat enough our bodies do not have access to proteins, carbohydrates, fats and sugars and then we can face other risks such as muscle wastage and **brittle bones.**

Food also plays a significant role in mood and the ability to function cognitively. Food and drink contain vitamins and minerals, which are vital to the parts of the brain that send messages.

The NHS Essence of Care benchmarks for food and drink include attention to nutritional assessment, the environment, presentation of food and appropriate assistance (Department of Health, 2010, **www.gov.uk**). These can be used by care homes, as well as healthcare providers, to benchmark (get to the right level) services.

Eating and drinking is both a physical and a social human need.

LO1 Be able to support individuals to make choices about food and drink

AC 1.1 Establish with an individual the food and drink they wish to consume

In this section we will look at the skills required to ensure that we are able to help the individual make choices about their food and drink.

What should we consider?

- **Personal preference**. We should explain the food and drink options available. This might be from a menu in a care home, or the food available in the fridge and store cupboard if you work in the person's home. You may need to make some adjustments to suit individual needs and tactfully direct the person from choices that are difficult for them, for example discourage certain foods if the person finds difficulty chewing. It may be helpful to make a note of the food the individual dislikes or finds difficulty eating.
- **Give visual clues** if necessary, by showing the person the different choices on prepared plates of food and if possible photographs on

Research and investigate

1.1 Menus, choice and diets

1 Look at the menus in your care home. Are they clear and written in appropriate language and in clear text? Could you add pictures? Discuss with the cook and your manager how you might improve the menus. Get a group of residents together and seek their opinion and try to act on it.
If you work in the community, discuss with your colleagues and manager how you might improve the way in which the individual can exercise choice. For example, do they write a shopping list, do they go shopping with you, do they devise their own menus?

2 Research the different types of diets and restrictions individuals in your setting may have. This should include vegetarian and other diets and preferences based on religion.

a menu. Do not make assumptions about the individual's preferences on the basis of their cultural background, but ensure that preferences due to culture, religious beliefs, etc. are taken into account when required as it may affect the way food (e.g. meat) is prepared.

- **Appropriate portion sizes**. Appetites vary from person to person. To tempt the individual with a small appetite, give them a smaller portion on a smaller plate, then ensure you check if they would like more. If someone is on a weight reducing diet (this should be recorded on their care plan) it can also help to use a smaller plate. Although people may eat less as they get older and use less energy, this is not always the case, so do not make assumptions. Some older people remain very active and enjoy a good

appetite. The main principle is to encourage people to eat a healthy, balanced diet.

- **Dietary requirements or restrictions**. Ensure you are aware of any dietary requirements. Some people require enriched diets, low sugar or fat or salt, or may have a wheat intolerance. You should consider vegetarian and vegan diets as well as requirements and restrictions due to religious reasons as we have discussed. Food allergies should also be considered.
- **The individual's cognitive ability** may impact on them being able to explain their choice. This may also mean a loss of taste, smell or touch. They may prefer to eat with their fingers. They may have difficulty communicating hunger or thirst and it is important in these circumstances to be able to read body language.
- **Individual's level of independence**. Ensure that you are aware of any requirements for plate guards, adapted cutlery, etc.
- **Physical or functional issues**:
  - *Swallowing*: this will require a specialist assessment.
  - *Loss of sense of smell*: smell stimulates the appetite so show the person the food as we also 'eat with our eyes'.
  - *Dental or mouth problems:* sore gums or ill-fitting dentures may stop the person choosing particular food, so this problem must be tackled in order to promote the right choice of food.
- **Emotional or psychological factors**:
  - *Embarrassment*: the individual may have problems eating independently – they may spill and therefore will choose 'easier' food to eat, or 'finger food'. These are good options as long as they provide adequate nutrition.
  - The individual may be suspicious or have ideas about their food being poisoned (this is a common fear for someone who has delusional behaviour). We have to work with the person to ensure they make the right choices and help to allay their fears.

Figure 17.1 Body language can give us clues about what an individual wants

Key term

Cognitive refers to the ability to take in and understand information.

Case study

1.1 Gladys (1)

You are helping Gladys with her lunch. Gladys has Alzheimer's disease. She prefers tea after her meal, and you know she needs to drink plenty of fluids. You give her the tea in a mug. It is just as she likes it because you checked first – strong with a little milk. Gladys will not drink the tea.

What have you missed? What are the implications of Gladys not drinking her tea?

AC 1.2 Encourage the individual to select suitable options for food and drink

We all have personal preferences: tea or coffee, sweet or savoury. It is important to balance these preferences though. For example, you may have a sweet tooth and love doughnuts, but it would be very unhealthy to live on a diet of doughnuts. When we work with the individual we must work in a person-centred way to ensure we understand their preferences, but we can also work in partnership with them to enable them to select suitable options in their diet.

Suitable options will take account of:

- **Expressed wishes and preferences** – this might be a vegetarian diet, or a preference to eat more savoury than sweet food

- **General nutrition principles** – this means that the individual should be encouraged to eat the appropriate amounts of protein, carbohydrates and fat, for example

- **Specific dietary requirements** – it is vital that those individuals on specific diets are supported to eat the correct food and are offered interesting alternatives. For example, the individual on a diabetic diet should not eat a lot of sugary food, but offering fruit as an alternative to a dessert,

can become boring and may discourage the individual from keeping to the diet

- **Religious, cultural and personal beliefs** – people who are Jewish or of the Muslim faith will require meat prepared in a way that is acceptable to them. However, it is better not to assume that you are 'doing the right thing' without actually discussing the individual's dietary needs with them

- **Resources available** – this may depend on food the available (as some might be seasonal). If you are supporting people in the community, they may have a limited budget and it is necessary to help them budget wisely so they can afford to eat a healthy diet.

There are several things we must be aware of when encouraging the individual to choose:

- Have a good knowledge of any dietary restrictions – always check their care plan to see if anything has changed.
- Check that an assessment was undertaken when the individual was referred into your service.
- Record their dietary needs and preferences and any assistance they need at mealtimes.

Evidence activity

1.1 Establishing the food individuals wish to consume

Make a list of all the things you should consider when working out with an individual the types of food they prefer in their diet.

1.2 Suitable options wish to consume for food and drink

Encourage the individual to select suitable options for food and drink.

Investigate the different types of dietary requirements that the individual may have (e.g. diabetes).

Design a table as a memory aid for staff:

Type of diet	Restricted food/requirement

How can you encourage the individual to select suitable food and drink options for them?

Compromise is helpful. The individual may have to keep to a particularly restrictive diet, but with support from the dietician you will be able to find suitable alternatives to foods they may really like but cannot eat in any quantity.

People tend to have different habits related to mealtimes. They may, for example, be used to having a light lunch and a main meal in the evening. The routine of a care home may be different and the individual may have difficulty selecting suitable options. Remembering that you are working in a person-centred way, so it will be important to communicate with the cook to look at solutions.

AC 1.3 Describe ways to resolve any difficulties or dilemmas about the choice of food and drink

Eating and drinking is a very personal activity and the ways in which the individual may be accustomed to eating and drinking could cause difficulties and dilemmas about choice of food if they are not addressed or acknowledged.

The individual may find cooking difficult, may be used to a poor diet through lack of money, may be unaware of the importance of a healthy balanced diet or may just prefer to eat the same things. Although it is part of your role to encourage the individual

to modify their poorer eating habits, you must remember that this is their choice and may even be something they have done for many years. Frail, older people may prefer to eat the same thing because it is easier and gives them comfort (for example scrambled eggs, biscuits, bread and butter). If this is the case, you should respect their wishes as much as possible. Discuss this with your manager or supervisor as it is likely that it is better for their mental wellbeing to support them in these choices at this stage in their life.

The individual may or may not be used to eating with particular utensils and they have been faced with a choice of knives, forks and spoons they do not understand, or they may be used to eating with a spoon and are too embarrassed or do not have the communication skills to explain that to you.

Ensuring cultural preference to food and drink can make people feel that they are respected and included. As well as encouraging people to eat and drink it can increase their emotional and physical well-being.

Remember that people with sensory impairment may have difficulty making choices. Show the individual the prepared food – by doing this they are able to smell or even touch the food. Take cues from their body language – are they still hungry, would they like an alternative, for example fruit instead of cake?

If you are serving slightly different food to some individuals because of dietary requirements, ensure that they are not 'stigmatised' by serving them all at one table, or before or after the other service users. In these circumstances it is very important that you communicate such dilemmas to the kitchen staff and your manager to ensure individual preferences are taken into account. Working as a team you are able more easily to meet the needs of the individual.

Evidence activity

1.3 Resolving difficulties and dilemmas

Develop a survey to get feedback about the meals in the care home you work in. If you work with individuals in their own home, have a discussion with them about the food they are eating and the difficulties they have – for example, they may feel that their choice is restricted, or the portions are the wrong size.

Summarise the ways you can resolve difficulties or dilemmas about the choice of food and drinks.

Figure 17.2 It is important to give individuals a choice

AC 1.4 Describe how and when to seek additional guidance about an individual's choice of food and drink

Some individuals may experience difficulty with various aspects of eating and drinking. For example:

- The individual may have trouble swallowing.
- The individual may have problems chewing.
- The individual may have lost their appetite.
- They may appear not to want to eat, and consistently refuse food.
- In the latter case, it is vital you alert the rest of your team and your manager or supervisor. If the individual lacks the capacity to understand the problems they

will have if they do not eat, it is advisable to involve their care coordinator, social worker etc. Families are a good resource – they may be able to tell you what foods the individual preferred to eat and you can try tempting them with that. You must NEVER force a person to eat – this is assault. Rather work with others to think of ways to tempt them – little and often may help. Some people prefer warm to cold food or particular textures. You may have to be a bit of a detective to work out what may suit the individual.

In these circumstances it is crucial to seek the expert advice of the speech and language therapist or the **dietician**. The speech and language therapist can assess swallowing difficulties and recommend safe alternatives.

People are more likely to **aspirate** on fluids and so 'thickened fluids' may be recommended. The dietician will recommend and give diet plans for individuals who are under- or over-nourished, or who may need food prepared in a particular way.

The food still needs to look and taste appetising and you will need to work with the cook to think of ways to present pureed food, etc. in an attractive and well flavoured way.

Case study

1.4 Gladys (2)

Gladys has been assessed by the dietician as requiring a mechanical soft diet. Investigate what this means. Then produce a suitable menu for one day for Gladys, bearing in mind she is very fond of milky coffee and has a sweet tooth. Think about who you would involve in this.

Evidence activity

1.4 Additional guidance

Describe how and when you would seek additional guidance about an individual's choice of food and drink.

Describe how you would encourage an individual who was reluctant to eat- what might you need to consider and who would you consult?

LO2 Be able to prepare to provide support for eating and drinking

AC 2.1 Identify the level and type of support an individual requires when eating and drinking

We should never make assumptions about the level of support an individual requires in any activity. Always read and act on the individual's care plan and check nothing has changed. We all feel different each day and it is therefore important to check again with the individual or with colleagues if the individual is unable to communicate their needs to you.

Support can vary a great deal and some people may require a different level of support depending on whether they are eating or drinking, the type of food and drink and the time of day (some people struggle more when they are tired). Individuals with conditions that affect their muscles or joints may struggle to hold a knife and fork or a person living with dementia may not recognise the food on their plate. In each of these situations it is important to assess what the person needs to help them, and to offer support in a tactful way. This might include providing more appropriate cutlery, or sitting with the person and explaining what is on their plate.

The individual's dignity should be maintained at all times. If they are at risk of spilling, ensure that childish bibs or 'pinnies' are not used – large serviettes are more 'normal' and dignified.

Before the meal

It is important to let people know that a meal will be served to give them enough time to go to the toilet and mobilise safely or with assistance to the dining room. Never leave people seated at a dining table for long periods unless they are occupied in an activity. They should not be seated early at a set table for the convenience of the staff. Think how you have felt when you have sat in a restaurant but had to wait a long time to be served. You have the option to walk out – the resident does not.

Most of us prefer to sit with the same people at mealtimes, and although this may be true in a collective setting, be aware of the dynamics at the table and whether there are any issues. Some people may find it difficult to sit at a table for any length of time and may prefer either to sit on their own or walk away and come back later. You should discuss these issues with your manager to avoid an institutionalised approach where everyone is expected to conform to the same dining routine.

At the table
You should have already checked that the table is set appropriately and attractively, with the correct eating utensils in place. If the individual is independent, ensure they do not require anything further and that they are aware of the choices.

The individual
Be aware of the specific diets required and that they are served correctly. If the individual needs their food cut up, do this in a discreet way, sat at their side if possible, rather than leaning over them – this is not just a task but an opportunity to have a conversation about the food. Always personalise your explanation to help make the meal a more interesting and pleasurable experience for the person. For example:

If the individual has a visual impairment, explain where the food is by using a clock face. This helps them to maintain their independence and eat with dignity. They are also aware of what food they are putting in their mouth.

'Bill, your lunch looks lovely. Roast potatoes are at 12, roast chicken is at 3 and vegetables are at 6 and 9 – you have carrots and cabbage. Where would you prefer the gravy?'

Ensure napkins are to hand and that the individual knows where they are, so that they can manage to wipe their mouths and maintain their dignity.

If you are required to support an individual with eating, you must ensure you have been given appropriate training as it is very easy for the individual to choke when another person is placing food in their mouth. Dignity should be your first thought – avoid negative language like 'I am just going to feed Gladys'. This is not person centred and dehumanises the individual. You should sit at the same level as the individual, talk about the food they are eating and go at *their* pace. Observe carefully that they are chewing enough and are swallowing before offering another piece of food. Make sure you offer them fluids throughout the meal.

Remember to help the individual to maintain as much independence as possible so if they are able to manage some of the meal themselves, support them in doing so, but be vigilant.

Evidence activity

2.1 Level and type of support

Try eating a meal blindfolded and wearing gloves in order to replicate some of the difficulties individuals may have with poor sight and arthritis. Describe your experience and feelings to your colleagues and tell them what would have helped you.

How does this experience help you to identify the level and type of support an individual may require when eating and drinking?

AC 2.2 Demonstrate effective hand-washing and use of protective clothing when handling food and drink

- Always wash and dry hands thoroughly before touching food and then put on your apron as well. This is to avoid contaminating any food you may have to touch.
- Never touch your hair or face before touching food or supporting an individual to eat. Ensure hair is tied back. You should wear a hat in the kitchen area.
- Avoid wearing costume jewellery, place blue plasters on any cuts or abrasions on your hands and do not wear nail varnish.

- Discreetly check that the individual has washed their hands – if they are unable or reluctant to do so, have anti-bacterial hand wipes available – this may be more acceptable to them.
- Wash your hands before and after supporting each service user with eating.
- Change your apron.
- Wash your hands after serving food.

Source: Some of the above context and advice is sourced from the Food Safety and Hygiene Regulations 2013 and Food Standards Agency

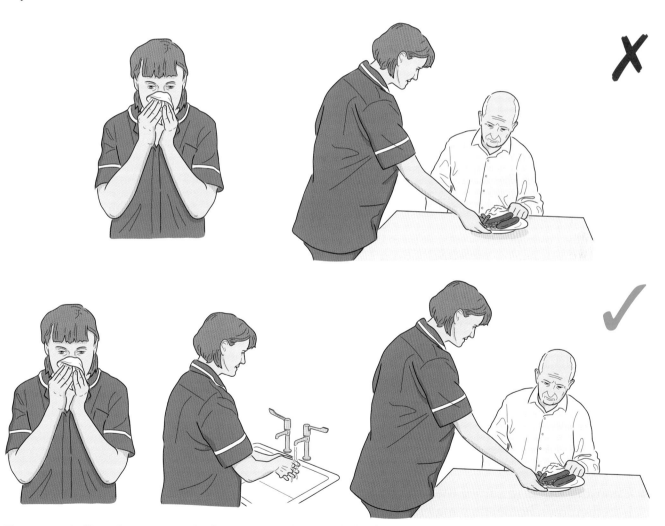

Figure 17.3 Cleanliness is vital when serving food and drink

Standard and effective hand-washing technique

- Ensuring hands are lathered well – avoid highly perfumed soap; your organisation should provide appropriate soap.
- With soap, wash thoroughly the front and back of hands, interlocking your fingers and washing round the thumbs, and then rinse off any soap.
- Dry hands thoroughly with disposable towels.

Case study

2.2 Hygiene policy

Investigate in your organisation. Is there a written policy or instructions about effective hand hygiene and protective clothing? If so, discuss it with colleagues. Could it be improved? Do they adhere (obey) to it?

If there is not a written instruction, discuss with your manager and colleagues and agree one together.

Evidence activity

2.2 Handwashing

Show another colleague how you can wash your hands effectively and use protective clothing when handling food and drink.

Your supervisor must observe you demonstrating this.

AC 2.3 Support the individual to prepare to eat and drink, in a way that meets their personal needs and preferences

Ways to prepare to eat and drink might include:

- Choosing where to eat – if the person is in their own home, they may have a preference for a particular room – this will be something they have done out of habit and should be respected. If the individual lives in a care setting, there will probably be an expectation that they eat in a communal dining area. However, where the individual eats should be based on an assessment and in fact it may be more appropriate for them to eat in their room, or in the lounge or with a member of staff. 'One size does not fit all' and the individual needs and preferences must be taken into consideration
- Choosing with whom to eat –we do not all want to eat with others and it is important that in a communal dining situation, the people around the table are compatible and able to tolerate each other.
- Protecting clothes from potential spills – this must be provided to ensure dignity, and it is important not to 'infantilise' the individual (treat them like a child) by using bibs or inappropriate items like tea towels tied round their neck. Discuss the most appropriate and dignified methods of protective clothes – this might be disposable napkins, for example.
- Taking up a comfortable position – it is important that the individual is comfortable and upright, and if necessary supported by cushions.

Once the individual is sitting comfortably at the table and is within easy reach of their place setting and in a place of their choosing, it is important to make sure they have everything they need to hand. Having read their care plan you will be aware of their level of independence as well as their individual preferences.

- Prior to and following eating and drinking, you should support individuals to meet their hygiene needs, according to their personal beliefs and preferences.

- You should respond appropriately to questions and issues raised about the food and drink, and any dietary requirements.
- You should take appropriate action when you feel unable to answer these questions and issues – this may be because you do not have the necessary skills and training. Discuss this with your manager or supervisor.

The dining experience

- Does the individual prefer a napkin? Where do they want it placed? Would they like one at the side of their plate?
- Are they left or right handed, as this will affect the layout on the dining table?
- Do they have particular cutlery, or a plate guard? Do they have a two handled cup, or a favourite cup and saucer?
- Are they able to recognise the food? People with dementia struggle sometimes to differentiate between textures and colours. A good example of this is placing mashed potato on a white plate or water in a clear glass – it is very likely that they will see neither the water or the potato.

Figure 17.4 Make sure the individual can recognise what is on their plate

- Consider the environment. Does it set the right 'tone' for the person? Is it too noisy and making communication difficult?
- Does the individual understand the choices of food available?
- Is there flexibility in dining arrangements? For example, if an individual has been unwell and does not want a heavy meal, can something lighter be offered?
- If it is a significant event or feast day, is this being acknowledged?

AC 2.4 Provide suitable utensils to assist the individual to eat and drink

Utensils to assist the individual to eat and drink must be provided with the aim of both promoting independence and maintaining dignity.

It is not person-centred to '**infantilise**' the individual by using bibs or leaving 'feeder' cups unattended; rather, this emphasises their disability.

Key term

Infantilise is a term used by psychologist Tom Kitwood in the field of dementia to mean that we treat the person as an infant and as such take their personhood away – we stop seeing them as an adult.

Used sensitively and appropriately and after a thorough assessment and checking with the individual at the level of assistance they need, suitable utensils can be of great help. Examples include:

- straws
- drinking cups with easy grip handles
- bowls with suction pads so they cannot be tipped over
- angled cutlery (this can help people who have arthritis)
- lighter cutlery
- tubing to fit over normal cutlery
- plate guards
- fluid level indicators (for people who are visually impaired).

LO3 Be able to provide support for eating and drinking

AC 3.1 Describe factors that help promote an individual's dignity, comfort and enjoyment while eating and drinking

Research has shown that mealtime **cultures** and environments can be a barrier or a positive factor in meeting the nutritional needs of an individual.

Factors

Barriers can include both the physical and social environment. For example, a dining room that is not sensitive to the needs of

Key term

Culture in a care home is the way things are done and tasks are performed.

individuals with particular needs can cause a negative social atmosphere, which discourages people from eating and drinking adequately. Issues such as staff talking over each other can create a negative feeling for the dining experience. Instead, the dining space should be light and airy, warm and clean with a feeling of a café or restaurant. Appropriate pictures and tableware should be used and staff should ensure they are interacting with the service users rather than merely 'serving' a meal.

Top tips for promoting dignity, comfort and enjoyment while eating and drinking

1 Provide assistance discreetly to people who have difficulty eating. You can support and chat with the person at the same time.
2 Offer finger food to those who find it difficult to use cutlery. This can preserve their dignity.
3 Provide adapted crockery and cutlery to enable people to eat independently where appropriate.
4 Socialising during mealtimes should be encouraged, but also offer privacy to those who have difficulties with eating, if they wish, to avoid embarrassment or loss of dignity.
5 Make sure food is available and accessible between mealtimes – not everyone is used to 'three square meals a day'.
6 Give people time to eat – they should not be rushed.
7 Use a 'secret signal' for people who need assistance with meals.
8 Encourage the use of protected mealtimes – it is both insensitive and unhelpful to expect the individual to stop eating because they have a visitor (unless they are happy to do so) and staff should give their undivided attention to service users at mealtimes.
9 Celebrate occasions – these are opportunities to have special food, entertainment and to be able to enjoy the dining experience together.

3.1 Special meals

Organise a special meal in consultation with the service users. This could be either in a care home or in the individual's home.

What is the focus of the occasion? How will it help promote an individual's dignity, comfort and enjoyment while eating and drinking?

3.2 Consuming manageable amounts

Consider how you might support an individual you observe to be eating too quickly and who is beginning to cough. The other service users at the table are beginning to tell them off. How and why would you intervene? Who could you ask for advice?

10 Be imaginative – fish and chips in paper, or afternoon tea: we all like 'treats'. Feeling that you have had a treat can help your mental well-being.

AC 3.2 Support the individual to consume manageable amounts of food and drink at their own pace

The individual may not be able to always control how much or how often they put food in their mouth or how much they drink during a meal. In these circumstances we should offer support in a sensitive, person centred way. On most occasions you may be aware of the needs of the individual and of any associated risks like choking or spilling hot food on themselves. However, it is best not to be complacent and assume problems will not occur for other people. Be vigilant (and discreet, so that you can intervene as necessary).

- Place plate and cup on the table in front and within easy reach.
- Cut up the food into sizeable pieces as agreed with the individual and as indicated on the care plan.
- Explain tactfully if the individual is eating too fast and is beginning to cough, other service users are looking alarmed and cup or fork is too full.
- Remind the individual to try to eat more slowly if necessary. Explain you are concerned they might choke and that there is plenty of time.
- Do not rush people.

- If the individual is hesitant about eating it may be necessary to sit with them to encourage them to enjoy their meal. Try to find out if they do not like the meal or if it is too hot or cold for them. Sometimes people do not like the textures of particular foods or certain food combinations.
- Modelling can work well with a person with dementia who may be struggling to remember how to use cutlery. Seat them next to a more able person or a member of staff and they may be able to follow their example.
- Do not start clearing the table until everyone has finished – it gives a negative signal that you want everyone to hurry up so that you can do something else. Everyone will go at their own pace and this should be respected.

AC 3.3 Provide encouragement to the individual to eat and drink

Reasons

People may not want to eat and drink for a variety of reasons:

- illness and loss of appetite
- dementia – they do not recognise the food or drink set before them
- lack of energy
- emotional problems or illness such as depression
- embarrassment about ill fitting dentures or spilling food.

Encouragement and ways to overcome reluctance

Always talk sensitively to the individual about likes and dislikes and reluctance to eat. They may need more practical help or reassurance, for example.

If people are reluctant to drink water, think of other ways of increasing their fluid intake, for example with alternative drinks and foods that have a higher fluid content (e.g. breakfast cereals with milk, soup, and fruit and vegetables).

Sometimes 'little and often 'is preferable, especially if the individual has a small appetite. Ensure you know what they have eaten in the past – favourite food, things they dislike.

If the individual is reluctant to eat, provide support with members of staff, or volunteers or other peers. We are more likely to eat if we feel there is a purpose. However, do not crowd the person or nag them. Be very encouraging if they manage a little.

Try different approaches – are they using the right utensils, are the portions the right size, do they need an assessment from a dietician, etc.

Eating and drinking is also a social activity, and part of our role is to support the individual to eat in a socially acceptable manner – this is to maintain their dignity and improve their self-esteem.

Case study

3.3 Gladys (3)

Gladys has been ill and she has lost her appetite. She is refusing anything but fluids. How do you think you can help her?

Walter has failing eyesight. He is beginning to struggle to eat independently and is getting frustrated and upset. Today he refused to come into the dining room. How could you help him?

Evidence activity

3.3 Encouragement

List the ways you can or have provided encouragement to individuals to eat and drink in your setting.

AC 3.4 Support the individual to clean themselves if food or drink is spilt

Prevention is better than cure. If you are aware through the care plan that the individual is likely to spill food or drink, ensure they:

- have a serviette that can be used to cover their clothes but does not take away their dignity. If they are able to clean up themselves, then make sure they have the opportunity to do so;
- have the correct utensils to minimise spills.

If food is being spilt, think about the way it is being served. Is it proving too difficult for the individual to deal with? Do not draw attention to the individual. This may make them feel embarrassed so make sure you are sensitive towards their feelings and that your reaction does not lower their self-esteem in any way. Sit next to them and clean the spill discreetly. If they tend to have food round their mouth or on their face, encourage them to wipe the food away themselves. If it continues to be an issue, reassess the situation.

Figure 17.5 It is important to deal with spills in a considerate manner

Evidence activity

3.4 **Good practice**
Observe a typical mealtime and make a note of the good practice you see. Also consider the things that could be improved. Discuss this with your supervisor or line manager first and think about how improvements can be implemented.

AC 3.5 Adapt support in response to an individual's feedback or observed reactions while eating and drinking

We should actively support individuals to do as much for themselves as possible to maintain their independence and physical ability. This means encouraging people with disabilities and older people to make the most of their potential and independence.

Feedback
Feedback from the individual can be individual or collective.

Individual feedback
The service user may be able to communicate their likes and dislikes clearly; they may be able to indicate what they would like to eat and where and with whom they would prefer to eat. You should respect their feedback and reassure them that it will be acted upon. It is helpful, for example, to ask the cook to talk to residents about their food preferences. Any major changes should also be reflected in their care plan.

For those individuals who cannot easily communicate their feedback, it is important to check with significant others (family, friends, carers and advocates) whether they are enjoying the dining experience. Are they being served the food and drink they prefer? What could be improved? What does their body language tell us?

Sometimes it is obvious that the individual is giving negative feedback – they may spit out the food or refuse to eat. This should not be termed 'difficult' behaviour. Look for the reasons behind the behaviour. Ask yourself the question: is the individual telling me they do not like this food or drink? Is it the taste, texture, or is it too hot or too cold? Look at the individual's facial expression and ask simple questions clearly and observe for their reaction: do they like the food? Would they like it changed? You can also use pictorial clues – smiley and sad faces – to indicate their reaction.

Collective feedback
In a residential care setting this can be achieved by discussing meals in smaller groups – people are more likely to give feedback in a less daunting setting. Questionnaires and feedback forms are helpful for individuals and their families who are able to use them. The cook and their team should be involved in individual and collective discussions and supervisors and managers should be available to hear and act on feedback.

Figure 17.6 Pictures can be used to give clues to what the individual wants

LO4 Be able to clear away after food and drink

AC 4.1 Explain why it is important to be sure that an individual has chosen to finish eating and drinking before clearing away

We all eat and drink at different paces and the individual may be a slower eater for a variety of reasons:

- ill-fitting dentures
- a sore mouth
- poor vision
- difficulty in managing utensils
- distraction
- personal preference or habit.

There are obvious clues that indicate the individual has finished their meal – an empty plate or the person placing their utensils on the plate and engaging in another activity or merely sitting inactively. However, you should not assume they have finished, especially if there is still food on their plate – they may be resting or have been distracted by something. If you clear away uneaten food you are depriving the individual of the opportunity of eating a full meal. This may be acceptable if the person says they have finished, but to do so routinely suggests that there is another issue. They may be struggling with the portion size, or finding it difficult to eat – possibly due to the reasons described already.

Clearing away before checking the individual has finished also demonstrates a lack of person-centred care – you are concentrating on the task rather than the individual. Mealtimes are a social occasion and the emphasis should be on the individual both enjoying and completing the meal, not on tidying away as soon as possible.

AC 4.2 Confirm that the individual has finished eating and drinking

Before clearing away, we must confirm with the individual that they have finished. Stand back for a moment and observe – they may just be pausing for a rest or to join in a conversation. Once you are satisfied they have finished, approach them and ask if they have enjoyed their meal and would they like a little more time before you take their plate. You should assure them that it is okay if they would like some more time. If you feel that they have not finished because of cognitive difficulties or other issues, suggest they may like to eat a little more. You may need to offer assistance. Ask if the individual would like your company for a little while. It is very important to report any changes in eating habits as this can have a negative effect on the individual's health. If you assume that the individual has finished their food and take their plate away, they may not eat a full meal each time and this could, if unchecked, lead to a gradual weight loss and other problems, like lack of energy or not having enough protein, carbohydrates etc.

Evidence activity

4.2 Confirm that the individual has finished eating and drinking

Describe the different ways you can confirm that an individual has finished their meal. Consider your observation and communication skills.

AC 4.3 Clear away used crockery and utensils in a way that promotes active participation

Active participation

Active participation means that the individual takes part in activities, but also is able to give their views and have a role in making decisions.

Rather than taking control and acting as a 'waitress service', remember that your role is to support the individual to maximise their independence. It is helpful to try to establish a routine, identifying and encouraging a particular individual to have a role, dependent on their abilities. This might range from passing items to the member of staff to stacking plates.

Equally, individuals should be encouraged to set the table. This participation encourages social activity, enables the individual to 'engage' in the mealtime activity and acts as a gentle reminder that a meal is about to be served. It is also a way of avoiding an **institutionalised approach**. Utensils could be left on the table for the individuals to arrange to their own satisfaction. Remember, it is the activity and the satisfaction the individual gets from it rather than how well the table is set or how efficiently the table is cleared.

Key term

An **institutionalised approach** is when people are treated not as individuals, but are expected to conform to a particular way of living in a care environment. Institutionalisation is the opposite of person-centred care – when the individual is not at the centre of the care they need.

Evidence activity

4.3 Active participation

Look at your current mealtime routine – this can be in a care home or in the person's own home.

- Who sets and clears the table?
- When is this done?
- How could you involve the individual more?
- How could you encourage a change in routine?

Explain how you can promote active participation when supporting the individual at mealtime.

AC 4.4 Support the individual to make themselves clean and tidy after eating or drinking

The individual can be supported in this way only if they have the correct equipment to hand. A 'one size fits all' approach must be discouraged – if certain individuals tend to spill their food, you should investigate the reasons and implement a person centred plan to support them.

Assess the individual's level of independence and their cognitive ability. Some individuals will only require napkins and will be aware they need to wipe their mouth, others may need gentle prompting. More dependent individuals could require a suitable cover for their clothing and one to one attention from care workers. Maintaining their dignity and independence should remain your priority. Encourage the person to wipe their own face if possible. If they are unable to do so, assist them discreetly and pay attention to any soreness or reddening of the skin.

We all find ourselves with food on our face and are embarrassed if it is left unattended. If you notice an individual with food on their face, draw attention to it discreetly. You may need to have a secret 'signal' that you can use.

For example – if you passed the person a napkin they might recognise that this means they need to wipe their mouth. This will not work with everyone, but it is a helpful way of maintaining

dignity. It might be appropriate to encourage the individual to use the bathroom after a meal, to 'freshen up', particularly as it is quite common for people to need to use the toilet after a meal.

LO5 Be able to monitor eating and drinking and the support provided

AC 5.1 Explain the importance of monitoring the food and drink an individual consumes and any difficulties they encounter

The amount of food and drink we have and the frequency with which we eat and drink are vital to our health and well-being. For example, we need to drink a certain amount of fluid each day to prevent dehydration and problems with our kidneys, urine infections, etc. Not eating breakfast or having only one meal a day also affects our blood sugar and energy levels. Constant 'grazing' can affect us because we are unaware of the amount of food we are actually consuming. It is important to record or pass on information about changes in eating habits as this could affect the individual's health.

We must be vigilant in monitoring the food and drink an individual consumes:

- They may be eating too much or too little. Are they bored and using eating as a distraction, or are they forgetting they have already eaten? Are they unwell and losing their appetite, or is their appetite changing due to other issues? This should be carefully monitored and reported back to your manager or supervisor and colleagues, including the cook.
- They may have difficulty eating certain things. Are they finding it difficult to chew, or to hold utensils?
- They may be reluctant to eat because they are worried about something or do not like the food they are being offered. Our appetite is affected by our mood – for example, anxiety can make us feel nauseous. Reluctance to eat should be investigated.
- They may be reluctant to drink because they are worried about incontinence. Reassure them that they will be given help with going to the toilet. It may benefit some people to avoid drinking just before bedtime.

AC 5.2 Carry out and record agreed monitoring processes

Agreed monitoring processes may include the use of a care plan, which gives staff an overview of how much food and drink the individual has consumed. This would be used in circumstances where there is no significant risk of malnutrition.

When the individual is causing concern, you may need to seek the assistance of more specialist staff. It is understandable that an individual may have a poor appetite if they are unwell, but continued reluctance to drink is alarming and advice should be sought if this continues.

Food record charts can provide the essential information in a nutritional assessment and help the treatment or care plan. They are therefore a valuable resource for dieticians and nurses and will help improve the individual's situation.

Why we use food screening charts

A food screening chart records the amount of all food and drinks consumed as accurately as possible and links to the individual's care plan. There are many screening tools and you should be guided by your own organisation and/or the dietician. You must also ensure that you have been trained and feel confident in using the chart capably. Food screening charts might be used alongside weight record charts. A food record chart will be started in all situations where there is any concern that a person's intake may be insufficient or poor.

If the information contained in the food record chart is in sufficient detail, it can be used to:

- assess nutritional intake
- assess adequacy of intake
- quantify (measure) nutritional deficits (if any)
- decide a diet plan and goals.

A fluid chart can be used in a similar way to assess how much a person is drinking. If there is thought to be a risk, the amount the person eliminates in their urine should also be measured. This would be done in a hospital or a care home with nursing, under the supervision of a qualified nurse who is trained to 'read' the charts.

AC 5.3 Report on the support provided for eating and drinking in accordance with agreed ways of working

Agreed ways of working include procedures and guidance within your own organisation. They will cover not only how to manage the nutritional and fluid intake of the individual but also the type and level of training you should undertake.

Methods of reporting in accordance with agreed ways of working might include:

- **Handovers** – verbal reports about the progress and problems of service users – usually take place in care homes and hospitals. Staff use these as a way of passing important information to each other to ensure care is provided in a consistent way and important changes to the individual are not missed
- **Team meetings** – when more general issues and ideas can be discussed – in terms of nutrition and food, for example, this might be a way of discussing ways to mark social occasions, anniversaries, etc. with particular meals. Such events are a good way of encouraging people to eat and drink and to give focus to a meal

- **Care plans** – individualised plans for each person which explain if they have particular dietary requirements or if there are risks associated with their nutrition or hydration
- **Individual daily records** – written records for each individual that will reflect issues discussed at handover, including any observations or actions to be taken
- **Food and fluid charts** – mainly used in hospitals and care homes with nursing when it is important for the individual's health that the amount they eat and drink is recorded – fluid output might also be recorded to check whether the individual is passing urine adequately.

Effective communication is vital. You must take responsibility for alerting your manager, supervisor and colleagues about any changes and developments in the support required for the individual.

Legislation

Health and Safety at Work Act 1974

The Food Safety Act 1990

The Food Safety and Hygiene (England) Regulations 2013

Useful resources

Websites

British Dietetic Association

www.mindthehungergap.com

NHS Healthy Eating

www.nhs.uk/livewell/healthy-eating

Support individuals to meet personal care needs

This unit
is worth
2 credits

What are you finding out?

This unit is aimed at those care support workers working in a wide range of settings. It provides the knowledge and skills needed to support individuals to meet personal care needs. It covers how to support the individual to maintain personal hygiene and manage their personal appearance in a way that will encourage them to actively participate and which respects their privacy, dignity and individual preferences. This is part of the person-centred approach to supporting people to meet their personal care needs.

By the end of the unit, you will:

1 Be able to work with individuals to identify their needs and preferences in relation to personal care
2 Be able to provide support for personal care safely
3 Be able to support individuals to use the toilet
4 Be able to support individuals to maintain personal hygiene
5 Be able to support individuals to manage their personal appearance
6 Be able to monitor and report on support for personal care.

LO1 Be able to work with individuals to identify their needs and preferences in relation to personal care

AC 1.1 Encourage an individual to communicate their needs, preferences and personal beliefs affecting their personal care

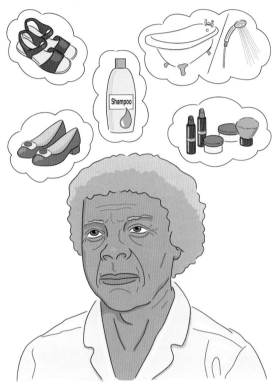

Figure 18.1 We all make choices in our daily personal care

> **Key term**
>
> **Personal care** in this unit this refers to using toilet facilities, maintaining personal hygiene and attending to personal appearance

The way we present ourselves tells us something about our personality and the way we are feeling on any particular day. When we are working with an individual it is important that we encourage them to communicate their needs, preferences and personal beliefs affecting their **personal care**.

Needs

The individual's personal care needs will have been assessed and described in the care plan, but remember that we all feel different each day, and although the care plan is a guide we must remain person centred and consult with the individual every step of the way. Helping the individual with personal care is not a task but an opportunity to spend time with them to support them in a very personal way. Work in partnership and discuss the process as you go along.

Preferences

This is about how and where to wash and dress, what to wear, how we style our hair. Choice must be considered at every stage. This may be simply giving the individual a choice between a shower or a wash, but the opportunity for the individual to exercise choice is the important factor.

Personal beliefs

These might influence what we wear, and our interactions. The individual may for example, due to a religious or cultural issue only be able to accept another female to support them. In fact this is an important aspect of all personal care interventions – you must consider if the individual is comfortable with you supporting them and if not consider how to provide an alternative. You should also consider the different personal beliefs of individuals in regards to personal care, such as different washing practices and ensure that you provide the facilities and equipment to meet such needs. You can check with your manager about the different ways you can support individuals in this.

Ways of encouraging individuals to communicate their needs, preferences, and personal beliefs

See SHC 21 for more information on effective communication.

You must encourage individuals to communicate their needs because when we support the person we should do so in partnership with them. We would all prefer to be helped in a way that suits us,

1.1 Encouraging individuals to communicate

Look around you at the people in the street or the office. What does the way they dress and groom themselves tell you about them? Do they pay attention to detail, or have they a more casual look, for example?

Think about your own appearance – what is important to you. How would you feel if you had to rely on another person to support you with your needs, preferences and beliefs about your personal care?

Look back at what you have learnt in this AC. How would you encourage an individual to communicate their preferences, beliefs and needs to you? Have you done this in your role? How could this/how has this improved your practice?

rather than feeling that our choices and preferences have been ignored.

There are a number of benefits to this as it can help you to build a therapeutic relationship with the individual. If they feel that you respect them you will foster trust and they are more likely to engage in the decision making process. This is all part of the person-centred approach to supporting people and ensuring their needs and wishes are at the centre of your practice. This also ensures that you are showing respect and consideration for their dignity, which again are all important aspects of your role and will allow you to improve your practice and be a better care worker.

The consequences of not doing so leads to a lower level of service and care that you will provide the individual. You also risk causing offence to them if you have not checked with them about their preferences and if do something that they may not have wanted you to do.

AC 1.2 Establish the level and type of support and individual needs for personal care

Ensure that you are familiar with the individual's plan of care and the agreed methods of support described. For example, it would be inappropriate to offer a bath if this has been assessed as unsafe.

Effective interactions with the individual ensure an active working partnership where the individual is very much at the forefront of the decision-making process.

You should consider the following:

The level of support an individual requires with personal care. This may also vary each day, depending on how they are feeling or if they have a different routine that day

Promoting independence and encouraging individuals to actively participate is key to supporting the individual. However, you should not let the person struggle, if this is not adding to their well-being. Equally, you should not take over, but rather take time with the individual so they can complete tasks in their own time.

Remember a person-centred approach is a fundamental part of your role. Check with the individual that nothing has changed and that the care plan does not indicate any changes. Some people will find it irritating to be asked every day about their personal care needs, and it is better to develop a respectful and open relationship with them so that they feel comfortable telling you if their needs are changing. Asking every day could suggest that you do not remember them very well – which is the opposite to person-centred care – it is better to be observant and ask more subtle questions, for example 'did you sleep well?', 'do you feel better than you did yesterday?' so that you have some understanding of how they are on any particular day.

An Occupational Therapist (OT) may be involved in an assessment of the individual, to look at the level of support they require in Activities of Daily Living (ADL) and to give advice and support about the how much support you offer and how you offer that support. They may also be able to advise on equipment that you should use, for example.

1.2 Level and type of support

Shirley is supporting Frank with his personal care. They have discussed his preference for Shirley to give him some time to himself while using the commode and when having his bath.

Consider how Shirley can support him, bearing in mind his independence is limited and he will need assistance in transferring. How should this be written in the care support plan?

AC 1.3 Agree with the individual how privacy will be maintained during personal care

Privacy and dignity go hand in hand. The Dignity in Care Campaign has a ten-point dignity challenge (**www.dignityincare.org.uk**, 21 March 2013), which includes the following values:

- Support people with the same respect you would want for yourself or a member of your family.
- Treat each person as an individual by offering a personalised service.
- Enable people to maintain the maximum possible level of independence, choice and control.
- Listen and support people to express their needs and wants.
- Respect people's right to privacy.
- Assist people to maintain confidence and positive self-esteem.

We all have a right to privacy and before undertaking any personal care **intervention** with the individual, you must ensure you have discussed and agreed with them how much they are able to do for themselves and covered this in their plan of care. This will help you to decide how much support you need to give them.

Show empathy

Ensure that you have a sensitive approach and empathise that this could be a particularly difficult situation and one where they may feel vulnerable or embarrassed.

Consider how to maintain their dignity

Leaving doors open while you rush out to find a towel is not acceptable – so be prepared as well! You should for example, ensure you knock and wait before entering the person's room.

Consider religious or cultural sensitivities

Some groups value modesty. You could talk to them beforehand to agree how much privacy they would like in personal care routines which could ensure you avoid causing any offence to them or their families. This should already have been noted in the plan of care so ensure that you have read this carefully and if you are concerned that these things have not been considered, discuss them with the individual and the person who wrote the care plan with the individual.

Consider risks

There may be risks involved in agreeing to allow individuals to carry out personal care routines unsupervised. This should also be included in the plan of care, and if you are concerned about the level of risk, refer to the person who wrote the care plan and undertook the risk assessment, or your manger/supervisor.

- When maintaining the individual's privacy, ask yourself: do the curtains need to be closed?
- Do you need to be with the individual at all times? Can you balance any risks against their right to privacy? For example, are they safe to be left unattended while they have a shower or use the toilet? If not, discuss the least **intrusive** way of supporting them. You may only be required to help the person get in and out of the bath and then you can wait outside within earshot while they wash.
- Do you have towels within easy reach so that you can ensure the individual is covered whenever possible?

Key terms

Intervention is an action taken when you change a situation, for example, helping an individual to change their clothes is an intervention.

Intrusive means to invade someone's privacy or personal space.

1.3 Privacy

Think about an individual you support with personal care. How do you manage to maintain their dignity? Have you discussed this with them recently? Do they think anything could be improved, bearing in mind independence, choice and control?

Research and investigate

2.1 Skin and infection

Use the internet to research and find out more about how the breaks in skin can lead to infection. You may want to research the structure of the skin and find out how breaks can be caused.

LO2 Be able to provide support for personal care safely

AC 2.1 Support the individual to understand the reasons for hygiene and safety precautions

There is a skill in being able to work with an individual in a person-centred way as well as provide support for personal care safely, taking into account hygiene and safety precautions.

Part of your role when providing support for personal care is to enable the individual to recognise the need to attend to their personal hygiene. We all have different standards and we should not impose our own standards on the individual. You should also bear in mind the way they have always managed their own personal hygiene – so for example, if they have never washed their hair more than once a week, their choice should be respected.

However, because of health and/or hygiene reasons (for example if the person is incontinent) it will be necessary for them to wash several times a day, something they may find difficulty in accepting this. In these circumstances it is your responsibility to work in a person centred way, within the plan of care to help the individual understand that you are there to help them stay healthy, and that you will respect their dignity at all times, particularly as they may feel embarrassed.

Similarly it is important to help the individual to understand the reasons for the safety precautions that you and they must take.

This is to ensure that any infections are not spread or that you or they are not injured in a procedure.

Skin care
Once skin becomes reddened and sore it is likely to break and infection is introduced. This is why we use preventative measures to help skin remain healthy. Good hygiene, drying the skin thoroughly and applying barrier creams (which should be prescribed by the GP) are all ways of keeping skin healthy; particularly when the person is frail or elderly. With age skin loses is elasticity and the layers of skin become thinner and can break down more easily. It is also important to keep the skin clean stop body odour caused by a build-up of bacteria.

Oral hygiene and care of teeth
Ill-fitting dentures can rub on the gums causing ulcers and introducing infection. If the person has their own teeth, lack of regular cleaning will lead to tooth decay, gum disease, infection and pain. It is important that you encourage individuals to clean their teeth properly to remove food; twice a day is usually recommended. All these factors have an effect on nutrition because the individual will find more difficulty eating if their mouth is sore. If the individual is unwell and not taking enough fluids their mouth can become sticky and their tongue dry. It is very important to get advice from a nurse or doctor about the right care in these circumstances.

Hair care
Head lice is probably more common in children. Advice should be sought from

the chemist or GP about effective treatment as head lice spread easily from one person to another. These treatments may include shampoos, and conditioners to prevent another instance of these. Conditioners also make it harder for lice to stay on the hair. Other treatments include fine toothcombs, electronic head lice combs, and head lice repellent sprays.

The individual can also be encouraged to maintain good hair hygiene by visiting the hairdresser regularly – this is usually seen as a treat. Make the experience as comfortable and quick as possible – use distraction techniques like playing music the individual enjoys if needed.

Nails

Some individuals are not comfortable having their nails cut and in fact may be used to having longer nails. However, long and dirty finger nails can give the impression of neglect as well presents a risk of introducing infection if the individual scratches their skin, or puts their fingers in their mouth.

It is best to cut fingernails after a bath when the nails are softer. Make it a pleasurable experience, using hand cream, offering to do a manicure etc. If it is unsafe to use scissors, try filing nails with an emery board. Remember, this should be done in line with the preferences of the individual – and if you do apply nail varnish ensure it is in keeping with the person's personal taste and that it is removed when chipped.

Like any procedure, also make sure you have been trained in cutting nails safely, and NEVER cut toe nails.

Promoting and demonstrating good practice

It is important to engage the individual in a discussion about the reasons for hygiene and safety precautions and that it is not simply

Evidence activity

2.1 Reasons for hygiene and safety precautions

You are helping Frank to have a bath. He is upset that you are wearing gloves and an apron and asks for someone else to bathe him. Frank has a skin condition which he constantly scratches. Consider:

● Did you discuss why you are wearing gloves and an apron?
● Have you considered if there are other options?
● How could you approach this situation the next time?

about preventing and controlling the spread of infection but also about increasing their self-esteem so that they feel good about themselves.

As a care worker, you should also promote and demonstrate good practice and be a good role model for individuals. For example, you should it was important in terms of infection control for you to wash your hands and wear an apron and gloves before assisting with some aspects of personal care. Consult with the individual about their experience. Have they enjoyed their bath or shower? Talk about how your support with personal hygiene and how this can helps them to feel better about themselves, and can add to their physical and mental well-being. You should remember to be sensitive to their feelings and needs when discussing the importance of good personal hygiene.

AC 2.2 Use protective equipment, protective clothing and hygiene techniques to minimise the risk of infection

It is essential to wear protective clothing and use appropriate hygiene techniques when dealing with bodily waste. This is because bacteria can spread very easily from one person to another if they are on your clothes or uniform. You will minimise the risk of infection by adhering to this procedures outlined by your workplace.

If you need to empty a commode, do so immediately and discreetly while wearing a disposable apron and gloves. The pan should be covered in transit and approved detergents used to clean it thoroughly. Once you have returned the pan, remove your gloves and apron and dispose of them in the approved way and wash your hands.

Personal Protective Equipment (PPE)

To protect the individual and ourselves it may be assessed as necessary to use Personal protective equipment – 'PPE.'

PPE is used to protect health and social care workers while performing specific tasks that might involve them coming into contact with infectious materials. PPE will only protect you and others from harm if you are able to put it on, use it, remove it and dispose of it in the correct manner. PPE includes disposable gloves and aprons and face masks.

Your policies and procedures will tell you when you need to wear PPE.

Disposable gloves

These should be worn if you are:

- performing or assisting in an intervention that involves a risk of contact with body fluids, broken skin and harmful substances such as disinfectants. This includes situations that involve: a risk of being splashed by body fluids (blood, saliva, sputum, vomit, urine or faeces, for instance)
- in contact with the individual's eyes, nose, ears, lips, mouth or genital area
- in contact with an open wound or cut
- handling potentially harmful substances, such as disinfectants.

Disposable gloves are not necessary for many parts of routine day-to-day care, like helping an individual to wash and dress. Disposable gloves should:

- fit you comfortably
- be changed between service users and between different tasks with the same individual
- never be washed or reused.

Disposable aprons

These are not required to carry out many normal aspects of day-to-day care with individuals, but you will need one when:

- performing or assisting in an intervention that might involve splashing of body fluids
- performing or helping the individual with personal hygiene tasks
- carrying out cleaning tasks in the individual's bedroom or bathroom.

Removal and Disposal

- If you need to empty a commode, do so immediately and discreetly while wearing a disposable apron and gloves.
- The pan should be covered in transit and approved detergents used to clean it thoroughly.
- Once you have returned the pan remove your gloves and apron and dispose of them in the approved way and wash your hands.
- After you have dealt with this waste, remove your apron and gloves by pulling them off gently by holding the cuffs.
- Dispose of these in the clinical waste bin and then wash your hands thoroughly in the approved manner.

Explain the reasons

When you are supporting the individual to go to the toilet it is very important that you explain to them the necessity of wearing gloves and apron. They may feel that you think they are 'dirty' and that you are protecting yourself. You must explain that the apron and gloves are as much to protect them and that you want them to be safe and comfortable.

Other hygienic practices

Toiletries, makeup and other items such as combs for example should never be shared. They are to some extent an expression of the person's individuality, choice and preference, and there is also the risk of infection. Sharing toiletries is also an institutionalised practice and not in keeping at all with person centred care.

Used incontinence pads should also be placed in the clinical waste bin.

Dirty or soiled clothing or bedding/sheets should be placed directly into a laundry basket and taken directly to be laundered – never leave them in bedrooms, sluices, corridors or on floors, because they could spread infection.

Your role

As a care support worker you must maintain your own personal hygiene. This is because you can act as a positive role model, it shows respect for the individuals you work with and the job you do. Observation of hand-washing and using appropriate protective clothing also ensures you are maintaining your own good health and safety. If you have long hair you should tie your hair back as this can get in way of individual or can get caught in equipment. Ensure you have clean nails as long finger nails and nail varnish can harbour germs. It is likely that if you work in a health setting you will also be required to wear minimal make up and jewellery, as this can harbour germs. You should avoid wearing uniform outside of the setting as this could risk spreading infection so you could make use of changing areas. Strong perfume and cigarette smoke are also offensive to some people so try and avoid this, particularly if they are unwell. You should ensure your uniform is clean, and keep a spare uniform with you in case of accidents in the setting.

AC 2.3 Explain how to report concerns about the safety and hygiene of equipment or facilities used for personal care

The Health and safety at Work Act 1974 places a responsibility on both the employer and employee to ensure a clean, healthy and safe environment, and to look after the safety of all the people in the setting. If you have any concerns about the safety and hygiene of equipment or facilities, you must immediately report these to your supervisor or manager. You may also be required to complete an incident form. It is your responsibility as an employee to report any incidents or equipment that is unsafe or a risk.

Equipment used for personal care includes:

- hoists
- slings for hoists
- commodes
- commode pans
- mattress protectors
- specialised baths and toilets
- disposal bags.

Facilities include:

- toilets
- bath and shower rooms
- 'wet rooms'
- sluices
- bin storage areas.

It is the manager's role to be responsible for:

- Ensuring you know how to use equipment correctly and can recognise when it is faulty.

It is important to understand how to use equipment safely so that you can identify any faults. Always check it is in good working order before using it and report any faults. Do not use faulty equipment and do not assume that because the equipment was OK yesterday, it is OK today.

All electrical equipment should have been tested before used. When electrical equipment has been 'passed' as safe to use it will have a label attached which states when it was tested and by who and when it will require retesting.

You should never use any equipment that you consider is faulty or dangerous. Make sure you report it to your supervisor and that it is removed or clearly marked as unsafe for use (this sign should be dated and signed). Ensure you act in accordance with your policies and procedures.

You should record and report depending on what your setting policy and procedures say.

What to report, when and to whom?
This includes:

- Accidents to self or others, including service users
- Faulty equipment (you should be trained in the use of all equipment and always check it before you use it)
- Security risks (faulty locks, for example)
- Poor practice of others (leaving soiled linen in corridors, for example).

All reporting should be done as soon as you come across the concern and should be reported to your immediate line manager or supervisor.

When reporting incidents employees should:

- Report any cases of their own ill health to their manager – they may have a potentially infectious condition.
- Let their doctor know about their work activities when they visit them. This will help the doctor assess the risk before they return to work. This is because their illness may have implications for the workplace in terms of infection – for example, diarrhoea and vomiting, or shingles.
- Report concerns immediately to the manager and work within accepted **codes of practice**. This might include recording all their concerns in detail in a log book. If these pose a risk to others the employee must also complete a health and safety sheet report form and a risk assessment.
- If the concern involves equipment it would need to removed and replaced.
- The facilities would have to be deep cleaned and any equipment sterilised or replaced.

Key term

Codes of practice are instructions and guidelines produced by your own or national organisations that guide you in best practice in your workplace.

Evidence activity

2.3 Reporting concerns
Make a tour of your establishment, looking at the areas used for personal care. Make a note of any causes for concern or any improvements you think you could make. Ensure you discuss this with your supervisor or line manager first. Make an action plan to share with the rest of the team.

If you work in the individual's own home think about an area that requires improvement. Discuss this with your manager or supervisor and the individual and consider how you could make some changes.

Write some guidance notes (ensure your manager is happy with them) explaining the main points when reporting concerns about the safety and hygiene of equipment used for personal care.

AC 2.4 Describe ways to ensure the individual can summon help when alone during personal care

This can be done through a variety of ways and will depend on a risk assessment as well as the individual's level of independence and **cognitive ability** (see page 322 for definition).

In care homes, the usual method of summoning help is a call bell, which registers at a central point. Call bells should always be treated seriously. Never ignore a call bell because it has been a false alarm in the past or because the individual uses the call bell all the time.

Risk assessments and deciding if the individual can be left alone

An individual can be left alone during personal care following a risk assessment. Do not assume they are 'safe' until you have clarified this. However, you should also consider how to maintain the individual's independence despite some assessed risks. For example, the risk assessment may indicate that the individual is unsafe to be left alone in the bath because they are unsteady, but they can sit on a chair and wash independently. The care plan should reflect this by indicating that the individual requires personal supervision during a bath, but can be left to have a wash in the morning, with her call bell.

Methods used to summon help

You must ensure that if and when an individual is left alone, that they are able to call for help and assistance. It is important that you are sure they know how to summon help before you leave them alone. In care homes, the usual method of calling for help is an electronic call bell, which registers at a central point. However, a simple hand bell may be used for example if you are working at the individual's home or they may verbally call for you. Call bells should always be treated seriously. NEVER ignore a call bell because it has been a false alarm in the past or because the individual uses the call bell all the time.

Your role

- Make sure the bell is in working order.
- Ensure it is within reach of the individual.
- Check each time that the individual remembers how to use the call bell.
- Agree a certain length of time before you will return. Do not just rely on the call bell – the individual might drop it or forget to use

it and so you need a **contingency plan**.

Some individuals may prefer you to stay close by so that they can call you when they are ready. Others will require regular monitoring checks every five minutes to ensure you are there when they need your help. This arrangement might be recorded on the care plan or you may need to negotiate with the individual on a daily basis. Communication with your colleagues is crucial.

- Make sure you stay alert and listen for their call. Ensure that you do not have the radio or television on so that this does not distract you.
- Respond quickly. This is very important in case individuals have hurt themselves. By responding as quickly as you can, you can also prevent further injury to the individual in case they hurt themselves even more.

Key terms

Cognitive ability – These are skills associated with the brain. They are to do with how we learn, remember, problem-solve, and pay attention. In this discussion they are taken to mean the ability to recognise the need to summon help, to be able to remember who can help and how to get that help.

Contingency plan is a plan made for an outcome other than in the usual (expected) plan.

Evidence activity

2.4 Summoning help

You are at handover and you have been allocated to support Gladys with personal care. She prefers someone to stay outside the door until she has used her commode. It has been assessed that this is safe and it also respects her dignity and privacy. You are working with your colleague, Ellen. While you are waiting for Gladys in the agreed way, you need to answer a call bell. You know Ellen is down the corridor and assume she will check on Gladys. When you return Gladys is very upset. She thinks you have left her – Ellen did not go in to check she was OK.

What has gone wrong in this situation in terms of managing Gladys' safety?

AC 2.5 Ensure safe disposal of waste materials

How can you ensure safe disposal of waste materials?
The definition of 'waste material' is offensive/hygiene waste which may include faeces, urine, incontinence or sanitary towels, catheter bags.

Hazardous waste
All staff should be aware of the (workplace) procedures to follow to minimise the risk of ill health and know what to do if unexpected hazardous waste is encountered.

All waste material should be wrapped and placed in a bag for disposal. Never put a soiled incontinence pad on any surface – place in a bag used for the purpose and then dispose of it in the approved manner. Your establishment should provide the appropriate facilities.

Remember that others will have to handle the waste after you so be considerate when disposing of waste. Don't overfill as this may be a problem for the person moving and handling the bag, it may for example split. There is also a risk that this may cause environmental issues to both people and the environment, for example overfilled bags may cause/attract vermin.

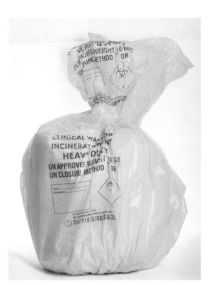

Figure 18.2 There should be clear procedures for disposal of waste

Offensive/hygiene waste should be identified and adequately contained by using colour-coded bags – yellow bags with black stripes ('tiger bags') are used for offensive/hygiene waste.

Why should you ensure safe disposal of waste materials?
Workplaces have to dispose of waste materials correctly by law. The main relevant legal requirements are contained in the Control of Substances Hazardous to Health Regulations 2002 (COSHH). These include assessing the risk from harmful substances and preventing or controlling exposure to them.

The hazards associated with offensive/hygiene waste can be:

● skin/eye infections
● gastroenteritis (symptoms include stomach cramps, diarrhoea).

There should be clear procedures for the:

● identification of waste
● segregation (isolation) of waste
● storage collection, transport, handling and disposal of offensive/hygiene waste.

How can you ensure personal hygiene when handling waste materials?
Good personal hygiene when handling offensive/hygiene waste is crucial and will reduce these hazards. It is important to:

● wash your hands before and after wearing gloves, or using the toilet
● have adequate hand-washing facilities, including mild soap
● select appropriate personal protective clothing
● ensure that people use it
● have training – all employees and managers should understand the risks through the correct training and supervision.

Evidence activity

2.5 Safe disposal of waste material
Write a list of the topics you would need to cover in training about the safe disposal of hygiene waste. Check that all staff are aware of these topics. You could do this as a training matrix to identify training needs.

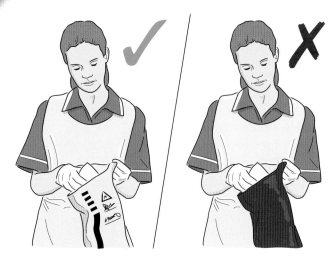

Figure 18.3 Offensive/hygiene waste must be put into yellow bags

LO3 Be able to support individuals to use the toilet

AC 3.1 Provide support for the individual to use toilet facilities in ways that respect dignity

Using the toilet is probably one of the most intimate aspects of personal hygiene. However, it may not always be possible for someone to use the toilet by themselves. For those individuals who require support on any level, it can be an embarrassing or humiliating experience, but you can make this less difficult by the way you approach the individual.

It is the care support worker's responsibility to work with the individual to ensure this experience is as comfortable as possible. Ensure that you have already built up a rapport with the individual. Remember that this activity is not simply a task, this is an intimate process that requires you to

> **Key term**
>
> **Toilet facilities** may include a toilet, commode, bedpan or urinal.

use discretion and the ability to maintain the individual's privacy and dignity at all times. The individual should feel as physically and emotionally comfortable as possible.

Providing support and methods to use toilet facilities

Portable equipment such as commodes, and bedpans should be used very discreetly. Never leave the person sitting on them longer than necessary and never wash and dress a person whilst they are sat on a commode. This will help you to show respect and dignity for the individual.

Clothing that has been specifically adapted for this purpose should be avoided as they are demeaning to the individual – it is better to be vigilant and support the person to use toilet facilities.

Toilet: Always close the toilet door and try to give the person as much privacy as possible, and make sure they have a call bell within reach.

Dos and don'ts

Do ask the individual discreetly if they need to use the toilet.

Do not discuss this over their head with other colleagues. Ensure others cannot hear you when you discuss issues to do with toileting.

Do look for body language if the individual cannot communicate their needs verbally – are they fidgeting in their seats or trying to adjust their clothing?

Do not refer to supporting the individual to use the toilet as 'toileting' – this is a dehumanising and non-person-centred term.

Do ensure that a risk assessment is in place and you use the plan to help you if the individual requires transferring onto the toilet.

Do not rush the individual.

Do ensure they are comfortable and have a call bell to hand if appropriate.

Do not leave the individual unattended unless it is safe to do so.

Do ensure the toilet door/curtain is closed at all times so there are no interruptions.

Respecting dignity

Respecting dignity means using empathy (walking in the person's shoes). Show that you are sensitive to the person's feelings and that you will give them as much privacy as is safe to do so.

Observe body language – not everyone is able to tell you they need the toilet, or may be embarrassed to do so. Observe body language and watch for patterns – people may prefer to go to the toilet at particular times.

- Be empathetic – understand that this is an embarrassing situation, so be sensitive to the feelings of the individual. You could explain that you understand the situation and that they should tell you when they need to use the toilet.
- If they are uncomfortable or embarrassed they may not go to the toilet or tell you when they need to, which could lead to other illnesses such as incontinence or constipation.
- Some may want workers of the same gender supporting them to use the toilet. Ensure you ask them about their preference beforehand, and ensure that you can cater for this. This is also important so that you do not cause offence. This should be in the care plan and if there are no members of staff of the same gender available it should be brought to the attention of your supervisor or line manager.
- Remember that the person should be at the centre and ensure you remember their well-being.

Evidence activity

3.1 Support for individual to use toilet facilities

Imagine you are unwell and cannot manage to use the toilet without help. Talk to your colleagues about how that makes you feel and how you would expect them to behave towards you when they were supporting you to use the toilet facilities.

Then put together a list of things you can do to support individuals to use toilet facilities that respect their dignity.

AC 3.2 Support individuals to make themselves clean and tidy after using toilet facilities

Because using the toilet is such an intimate process it is even more important to try to enable the individual to make themselves clean and tidy with as little intervention from you as possible. You must remember to find out beforehand how much support they will need, and you will need to wear protective clothing such as apron and gloves. Remember to explain to them why you are wearing this so that they are not offended or worried that you may think they are dirty. Emphasise that it is to protect them as much as you.

After you have checked that the individual has finished (if possible leave the toilet and stand outside and wait). Ask if you can re-enter. Close the door and ask the individual if they can manage on their own.

Have toilet tissues, wipes, etc. to hand. If the individual is struggling, hand them the tissue and assess whether they can manage on their own. Ensure they wipe correctly. Do this discreetly – do not scrutinise the individual. This respects the individual's dignity. If you assess that they may need some additional help suggest that you help a little so that they feel as comfortable as possible. You may want to discuss this beforehand.

If tissues have been used, ensure that they have cleaned thoroughly as any residue may cause sores or infections.

If you are aware that they require assistance do so gently and chat to the individual to minimise their discomfort or embarrassment. It is also important to explain what you are doing as you go along so they feel they are not out of control.

Some cultures may like to have running water to hand. Ensure that you provide a bidet or a jug of water. Remember that water should be warm, not too hot or cold.

Some females may like to use feminine wipes, ensure you are able to supply these being careful to choose suitable ones (e.g. non-irritant). They may also require assistance with replacing pads.

Help the individual to rearrange their clothes.

Encourage them to wash their hands. Water, soap and paper towels or a hand drier should be provided. Again, remember that water should be warm, not too hot or cold.

Ensure you dispose of any waste correctly.

Ensure you have also carefully washed your hands.

Evidence activity

3.2 Support individuals to make themselves clean and tidy

Write 'ten top tips' to help carers support the individual using the toilet.

Talk to a colleague about how you would feel if you had to receive intimate personal care. Think about what would be important to you, to ensure you kept your dignity and as much privacy as possible.

LO4 Be able to support individuals to maintain personal hygiene

AC 4.1 Ensure room and water temperatures meet individual needs and preferences for washing, bathing and mouth care

We need to take into account the following factors:

- Personal preference – we all have our own preference for the temperature of the bathroom and water but there are safety factors to consider. You could make a small memory card to carry with you, listing the correct temperatures.
- Safety – water temperatures: The individual may not be able to feel how hot or cold the water is and if this is the case you must make your own judgement and ensure you know the regulations for maximum water temperatures. If you work in a care home you may find that the water temperature is already controlled by thermostatic mixer valves. If it is not at the recommended temperature, you should report this. You should still check the temperature of the water before the individual gets in the bath with a thermometer.
Room temperatures: Generally, the room should be warm, ensure that heating is on, windows are closed and there are no drafts in the bathroom and it is at a comfortable temperature. This is important as individuals are likely to feel colder when they have just finished bathing and are wet.
- Ensure the door is kept closed for privacy.

Considerations for washing and bathing

- Be careful that the water is not too hot as this can be very dangerous and cause **scalding** (see page 327 for definition). It is therefore important that your run the cold water first. If a person is scalded this should be reported immediately once assistance and first aid support has been given.

Key term

Scald this is a burn or other injury which is caused by a hot liquid or steam.

- Provide warm clothes and towels but again, as with water ensure they are not too hot.
- Ask both yourself and the individual: you should also check the care plan and risk assessment to see if there is any guidance on the abilities of the individual.

Other things to consider are:

- Can the individual get in/out of the bath/shower?
- Can they sit up and wash themselves unaided?
- Are they able to make a decision regarding acceptable water temperature?

- Would they realise the water was too hot? This is important as if they cannot, they may be in danger if they are also unable to get out of the bath.
- Is the individual capable of calling for assistance if they need it?
- Will any lifting aids or medical equipment limit the patient's mobility in the bath?
- Could the patient get out quickly if the water was too hot?
- If using bubble bath, etc., ensure it does not make the bath slippery.

Risk assessments
Considerations for mouth care

A risk assessment should have been completed to determine:

- whether someone is at risk of scalds
- if they can get out of the bath with or without help

Evidence activity

4.1 Room and water temperatures

Figure 18.4 Dangers are lurking everywhere

Look at this illustration: list the issues and describe the solutions. Recap how you can ensure room and water temperatures meet individual needs and preferences.

- whether they require supervision in the bath
- what measures you need to take to reduce the risks.

AC 4.2 Ensure toiletries, materials and equipment are within reach of the individual

We need to make the bathing experience as enjoyable as possible. Think about how enjoyable a bath can be. Relaxing in warm water with bubble bath can give us a sense of well-being because it enhances our sense of smell and touch.

Toiletries, materials and equipment need to be in reach of the individual if it has been assessed that they are safe to use them.

- Promoting independence – make sure the individual is able to reach a sponge, toiletry bag etc. to wash themselves independently.
- Organise and ensure they know where everything is – ensure that everything is arranged so that the individual is able to easily reach items such as their glasses or prostheses, ensure they have all they may need but do not clutter or overcrowd the area which could also cause an accident if they have to pick up things. Explain where things are placed before you leave them.
- Offer choice – ensure the individual has preferred toiletries, etc. to hand.
- Offer support as and when the individual requires it. They may be able to manage certain things but need help to wash their back or feet, for example.
- Promoting choice – the individual can choose which soap, etc. to use.
- Care plan – work within the care plan and risk assessment.
- If necessary, ensure the hoist is positioned so that it is not in the way but.is easily accessible if you need to get the individual out of the bath quickly.

- Have towels within easy reach in case the individual becomes cold or they need to get out of the bath quickly.

AC 4.3 Provide support to carry out personal hygiene activities in ways that maintain comfort, respect dignity and promote active participation

Consult the care plan

You will need to find out how much an individual is able to do for themselves. You can find this information in the care plan, but the individual's condition can change so you should observe and record any changes which may affect how much support you offer.

Comfort:

- Ensure the room and water temperatures are safe and comfortable for the individual.
- Ensure that they are not in any pain, because this will affect their mobility and they may not want to take part in any personal hygiene activities. They may need to take prescribed painkillers before you carry out any personal hygiene activities
- You may need to use equipment aids such as hoists.
- Ensure you ask them if they would like to use toilet facilities before bathing or showering.

Respect dignity:

- Minimise the time you spend supervising the individual, bearing in mind the risk assessments.
- Ensure the bathroom door is closed at all times.
- Keep a discreet distance if possible.
- Promote active participation by encouraging the individual to do as much as possible for themselves. By enabling them to maintain their independence you can help them have a more positive and enjoyable experience. This can also add to their self-esteem as they will feel more in control of their personal care and demonstrates that you are respecting their dignity.

- Offer enough support to enable the individual to complete the task, but do not be tempted to 'take over'. Remember that the amount or level of support you may have to give could vary every day, depending on the health, energy levels or mood of the individual – to take this into account is truly person-centred care. You may require the advice of an Occupational Therapist.

Something to consider…

Supporting a person to have a bath can bring up other issues. Because it is an intimate activity and you may be spending a length of time in a one-to-one situation, the individual may seek the opportunity to talk to you. They may disclose information or ask you for advice. Remember, they are in a vulnerable situation and you must respect their privacy and safety.

If you observe any unusual or new bruising or marks you need to bring this to the attention of your supervisor or manager. They may not be a cause for concern but you have a duty of care to record your observations. Depending on the situation you may feel it appropriate to ask the individual if they know how they got the marks.

Evidence activities

4.2 and **4.3** Toiletries and personal hygiene activities

Mary has to be assisted in to the bath but can wash herself. She likes to take her time and tends to daydream and can forget to wash.

Write a plan of care for Mary. What do you have to consider in terms of risk and safety? How would you maintain her comfort, respect dignity and promote active participation?

Think about all of the things you have read about in this LO, and write a summary of the things you should consider to support individuals' personal hygiene. Think about this in terms of assistance, equipment, cultural and religious differences, and active participation.

LO5 Be able to support individuals to manage their personal appearance

AC 5.1 Provide support to enable individual to manage their personal appearance in ways that respect dignity and promote active participation

Personal appearance, promoting choice, individuality and respecting dignity

Personal appearance is subjective – we all have a particular style and taste in clothing. This must be recognised and respected in the individual. When supporting them to dress, we should enable them to choose their clothes for the day. It may not always be something you would choose but being person-centred means understanding that we should not impose our own tastes or ideas on the individual. You should encourage individuals to express their identity and individuality, and ask them or friends and families about their preferences for cosmetics and skin care, for example, so that they are making choices and **actively participating** in managing their appearance.

Intervening

Remember that if you are working with a person living with dementia, they may, if encouraged to dress independently, have problems putting on clothes in the right order, or may, for example, put on a cardigan inside out. You must use your judgement to decide whether you will undermine their

Key terms

Active participation – being able to join in and contribute to an activity, such as maintaining your personal appearance.

independence and self-esteem by rearranging their clothing or whether their dignity is affected. Similarly, you will have to use your own judgement about whether to intervene when you feel that clothes may not be appropriate for weather conditions for example. In many cases a little encouragement may be required, with good communication skills as discussed in SHC 21. Make sure you clearly explain the reasons for your suggestions.

Respecting religious and cultural preferences

Some people may have preferences for clothes based on their religion and culture and you should respect, support and encourage them to manage their appearance in relation to this. You should find out more about this by speaking to the individual or their friends and family.

Activities an individual may use to manage their personal appearance could include:

Hair care

This is personal choice but it is important to encourage the individual to attend to their hair daily and have it washed on a regular basis to keep it clean. If it is uncomfortable for them you will need to discuss whether hair washing is comfortable in a shower, bath or over a sink. You should consider religious and cultural expectations as some individuals may like to keep their hair covered; the role that hair can play in self-esteem and making people feel good about themselves; and raising their self-esteem; encouraging active participation so ensuring individuals have a say in the products and hair dressers that they like to use; and that the condition of hair deteriorates with ill-health.

Nail care

Although it is appropriate to help the individual with their fingernails, it is safer for the individual to seek the help of a chiropodist to cut their toe nails. You should check the policy of your setting, although this must happen if the individual is diabetic or has poor circulation. Also remember, to encourage individuals to keep their nails clean and trim. Consider whether individuals would like a manicure, and the best time to trim nails which is usually after a shower or bath when they are soft.

Shaving

You can promote active participation by checking if the person prefers electric or wet shaves. If you have never shaved someone do not do so without instruction as there is a technique which involves shaving in the right direction of the hair. You should also check with women whether they prefer to shave. wax or cream.

Skin care

Encourage females to use appropriate skin products. If you are applying cream ensure the skin is unbroken. You will not be required to wear gloves to apply face cream You can promote active participation by asking individuals about the products that they would like to use. Make sure you check with the individual or carers about anything that they may be allergic to so that you can choose and advise on products accordingly and wear gloves when you are applying skin products.

Use of cosmetics

These can be helpful for helping self-esteem, maintaining a feeling of personhood and pride in oneself. You may need to support the person and if cosmetics are important to them do not treat helping them put on makeup as an 'optional extra' – it is part of their person centred care plan. You should ensure that they have access to a mirror so that they can check on their appearance. You may want to give a magnified mirror to individuals who suffer from sight impairments and a full length one so that they can check whole appearance.

Use of prostheses and orthoses

You should be trained by experts to help the individual with prostheses or colostomy bags or catheters. Never attempt this without direction training and support.

See AC 2.1 for more information.

Evidence activity

5.1 Personal appearance

Write a care plan for yourself. What particular things about your personal appearance would you want to be respected?

Personal appearance is as much about grooming as it is about the clothes we wear. Think about some of your friends and family – the person with the well groomed nails or the person who always has a neat beard. This is their 'brand' or 'trademark' and is a significant part of their personal identity. Not to support the person to continue to manage their personal appearance is not respecting their dignity.

AC 5.2 Encourage the individual to keep their clothing and personal care items clean, safe and secure

Individuals should be encouraged to keep their clothing and personal care items clean, safe and secure.

Clean

- Keep hairbrushes and combs clean and free of hair.
- Encourage the individual to change clothing that is stained.
- Ensure clothes are washed at the correct temperature.
- Work in a person-centred way to help the individual to choose new clothes.
- Using a person-centred approach means that you respect the individual's rights and preferences. You should not impose your own values on them.

Safe

- Pay attention to any damage or repairs.
- Ensure clothes are hung in the wardrobe and are easily accessible to the individual.
- Throw away old creams and cosmetics as they can contain germs, and spread infections, but you must consult with the individual first as these products are their property.

- Ensure any razors and other equipment are working and safe to use. Ensure you use the correct razors, they should be clean, not blunt. Ensure you find out about the correct ones to use. The wrong type could cause discomfort or pain, and damage skin and again cause infection.
- Ensure they have the appropriate items for dental care.

Secure

- Keep toiletries in the individual's own room – never share toiletries, creams, etc.
- Consider labelling clothes although this is an institutionalised approach and you should consult with the individual and their family first about the best way of doing this discreetly.
- Ensure they are stored safely in wardrobes and drawers.
- Consider labelling clothes although this is an institutionalised approach and you should consult with the individual and their family first about the best way of doing this discreetly.
- Ensure they are stored safely in wardrobes and drawers.

Time to think

5.2 Clean, safe, secure

Think about why it is important to encourage the individual to keep their clothing and personal care items clean, safe and secure.

How would you feel if your clothes and personal care items were not looked after properly? How would it make you feel about yourself?

Evidence activity

5.2 Clean, safe and secure

Look at some care plans in your place of work. Is there enough information in them about the care of clothing, toiletries and equipment? Amend a care plan to include this or write a new one that supports the individual. Ensure you have discussed these additions with the individual.

LO6 Be able to monitor and report on support for personal care

AC 6.1 Seek feedback from the individual and others on how well support for personal care meets the individual's needs and preferences

Feedback is vital because it helps us to provide the right service to the individual, to understand what has gone well and to ensure we make improvements or respond to problems or decline in the individual's health and well-being. In turn, this will allow you to develop your knowledge and practice and be a better worker.

Formal and informal feedback

Formal feedback can include questionnaires to users of the service or their family. The NHS is currently using a 'Friends and Family Test' which asks patients if they would recommend the service they receive to friends or family and if not, why not.

Care reviews are also a good way of seeking feedback because they involve the individual, their family or advocate and people involved in supporting them.

The Care Quality Commission inspects and regulates health and social care providers. During the inspection they usually ask for feedback from service users and carers.

Informal feedback can be as simple as 'checking' with the individual and their family that they are happy with the support they are receiving by introducing the topic into a conversation.

You may need to ask others for feedback, including health and social care professionals – this may be a more formal approach, by using a letter, for example.

It is important to communicate feedback in a way that the individual will understand and find helpful – so think about the different types of communication techniques you can use. See SHC 21 for more information on communication.

> **Time to think**
>
> **6.1 Feedback**
>
> Think about a time when you were not consulted about something that was important to you and changes in your circumstances were not acknowledged. How did it make you feel? Think about how this must feel for the user of your service. How can you ensure that you involve them and their family as much as possible in feedback about their care and support?

> **Evidence activity**
>
> **6.1 Feedback, comments and complaints**
>
> Look for leaflets in your organisation that explain how people can make complaints and comments. Are they written in a 'user-friendly' way?
>
> Look at the complaints procedure. Ask your colleagues if they are aware of how to deal with a complaint or comment. Design an information sheet with step-by-step instructions on how to deal with comments and complaints.

AC 6.2 Monitor personal care functions and activities in agreed ways

When you monitor personal care functions and activities you should consider:

- The assessed needs of the individual.
- Do they still match with what is said in the care plan?
- The feedback the individual gives you.
- The feedback family and friends give.
- What have you observed?
- Are there changes that should be taken account of?

● Changes might include bodily functions – is the person drinking and eating enough? Have their appetite and eating habits changed? You will need to observe, monitor and look for changes.

Faeces

If you notice a change in the appearance of the individual's faeces, or you are aware their bowel habits are changing, it is also important to inform your line manager or supervisor. Infrequent bowel movements could mean constipation which is potentially serious. Poor diet and lack of fluids can lead to constipation; severe constipation can cause confusion and even poor mobility. It is likely that if the situation does not improve medical advice will be needed.

Faeces that change in colour and become darker can be an indication of the presence of blood – again it is vital that a medical opinion is asked for.

Diarrhoea is also a problem if left untreated, particularly in children and the frail elderly. It can lead to dehydration and the individual can become drowsy or dizzy. Diarrhoea is due to infection, virus, food poisoning or medical conditions like irritable bowel syndrome. Medical advice should also be sought if the diarrhoea is persistent.

Urine

A change in the appearance and consistency of urine and faeces can indicate a change in the individual's health, or diet. It is important that you report any change to your manager or supervisor, but equally that you know what is 'normal' for the individual.

If urine becomes dark and cloudy and smells offensive it can mean that the individual has a urine infection. They may have blood or protein in their urine. Your manager or supervisor may ask you to collect a urine specimen (you should have training in this first). Always wear a protective apron and gloves and ensure you keep the dignity and privacy of the individual uppermost in your practice.

Remember that normally, urine should be straw like in colour and not have a strong odour. It should be clear and the individual would not usually experience pain passing urine.

Menstruation

Report any observed changes in cycle such as missed periods and and blood flow or increased discomfort or distress. This could be signs of other things like anaemia and menopause, pregnancy, which may need to be investigated further. You should also report bleeding after menopause.

Sleeping patterns

Has their sleeping pattern changed? Do they have more difficulty going to sleep? Do they wake earlier or sleep later? Do they sleep more during the day?

Washing and dressing

Are they more or less able to manage personal care tasks like washing and dressing, Are they more or less motivated to do as much as possible for themselves?

Record your observations accurately and objectively, and ensure you have informed your supervisor or line manager. In some circumstances, especially when the changes are sudden and are causing the individual pain or distress, it is important to deal with them as soon as possible and ensure they are part of the process.

Evidence activity

6.2 Personal care functions

You notice that an individual you support has some changes to their eating and sleeping patterns – they are eating less and having trouble sleeping.

What do you think this might be a symptom of? Should you be concerned? How would you respond and who would you inform?

How might you help the individual?

AC 6.3 Record and report on an individual's personal care in agreed ways

The personal care plan should guide you to deliver care in the most appropriate person centred way. It should be written with outcomes for the individual and they should be asked on a regular basis if they feel these outcomes are still being met.

When recording and reporting you must remember to ensure this is done:

- accurately
- in a person-centred way
- by not giving a personal opinion unless you can justify it
- by keeping your observations objective, using dates and times if appropriate.

You should record:

- on the amount and nature of the support given
- the observations and changes you have noticed
- the individual's observed response to the care and support given
- the feedback from the individual, family and friends.

It is important to record and report using agreed ways of working so that you are working within the law and are able to justify your comments. You should respect confidentiality and use non-judgemental language. If your organisations have processes for recording including standardised forms and care plans these should be used. You should sign and date each entry.

The consequences of not working within agreed ways of working might include:

- Distress to the individual or their family if you have not behaved in a professional way.
- Not working within the law which makes you and your organisation vulnerable – you could receive complaints or be investigated by a regulatory body like CQC, or both.
- Risk to the individual if you have failed to record important information about them.

Evidence activity

6.3 Recording and reporting

Investigate the relevant procedures for recording in your own organisation. Write a bullet point 'pocket' guideline that you and your colleagues can carry with them to remind you of the principles of the agreed ways of recording and reporting.

Legislation

Health and Safety at Work Act 1974

Control of Substances Hazardous to Health Regulations 2002 (COSHH)

Useful resources

Websites

The Dignity in Care Campaign

www.dignityincare.org.uk

Friends and Family Test

www.england.nhs.uk/ourwork/pe/fft

Unit HSC 2028

Move and position individuals in accordance with their plan of care

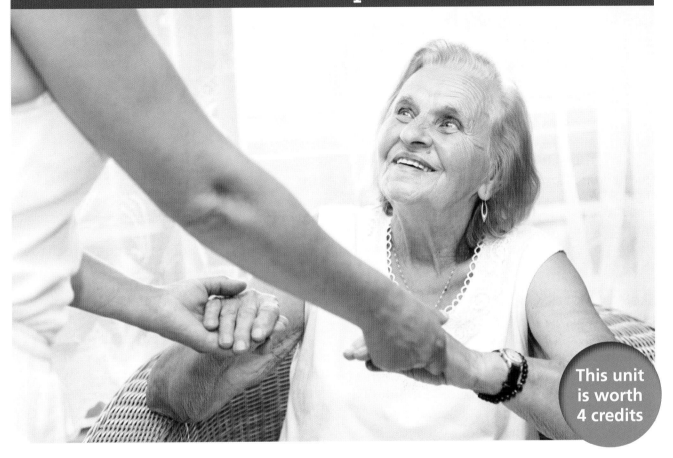

This unit is worth 4 credits

What are you finding out?

The level of assistance required for moving and positioning an individual will be different for each service user and it is essential that these people are supported in a safe way. Incorrect moving and handling techniques can lead to injury, both to the person being supported and the staff who are supporting them. Legislation aims to protect the health and safety of everyone involved in moving and handling activities through policies, guidelines and risk assessments and through procedures and agreed ways of working that are written into each person's care plan.

This unit will help you to develop and demonstrate your knowledge about moving and positioning individuals in accordance with their plan of care.

These skills and knowledge can be used in a wide range of health and social care settings.

By the end of the unit you will:

1 Understand anatomy and physiology in relation to moving and positioning individuals
2 Understand legislation and agreed ways of working when moving and positioning individuals
3 Be able to minimise risk before moving and positioning individuals
4 Be able to prepare individuals before moving and positioning
5 Be able to move and position an individual
6 Know when to seek advice from and/or involve others when moving and positioning an individual.

LO1 Understand anatomy and physiology in relation to moving and positioning individuals

AC 1.1 Outline the anatomy and physiology of the human body in relation to the importance of correct moving and positioning of individuals

As part of your role as a health or social care worker, you will be required to assist people to **reposition** and **mobilise**. It is therefore important that you have some understanding of basic **anatomy** and **physiology** so that you can take steps to reduce the risk of injury and harm to yourself and others when you are involved in moving and handling tasks.

The musculoskeletal system is the system of muscles, **tendons**, bones, joints and **ligaments**. Its purpose is to move the body and maintain its form.

Skeletal muscle
Skeletal muscles are voluntary muscles, which means we can control what they do. For example, the muscles in the hand won't allow our fist to clench unless we want it to. Skeletal muscles, along with the skeleton, form the musculoskeletal system. Together, the skeletal muscles work with the bones to give the body power and strength. Skeletal muscles are

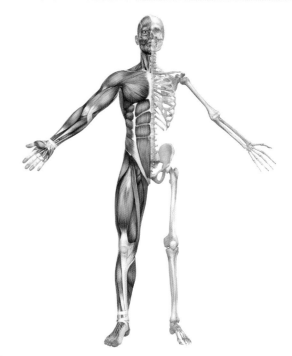

Figure 19.1 The musculoskeletal system

held to bones by tendons. Tendons are made of tough tissue and are attached so well that when we contract a muscle, the tendon and the bone move along with it.

Some of the biggest, most powerful skeletal muscles are in the back, near the spine. These muscles help to keep us upright and stop us from slumping over. Skeletal muscles also give the body the power required to lift and push things.

Skeletal muscles are like levers: they are grouped together in pairs on the skeleton and allow the bones at a joint to work like a hinge. When one muscle contracts, the other muscle relaxes. Skeletal muscles pull in one direction only. For this reason they always come in pairs. When one muscle in a pair contracts, to bend a joint for example, the opposite muscle then contracts and pulls in the opposite direction to straighten the joint out again. Without this arrangement we would not be able to straighten our legs when we walk, or bend our fingers to grip something.

The spinal column
The spine is the major supporting structure of the body.

Key terms

Reposition refers to the times when a person needs assistance to change position in accordance/in line with their plan of care.

Mobilise refers to the act of moving from one place to another.

Anatomy is the physical structure of the body.

Physiology is concerned with the functions of the body.

A **tendon** is a band of tissue that connects a muscle with a bone.

A **ligament** is a band of tissue that connects bones, typically to support a joint.

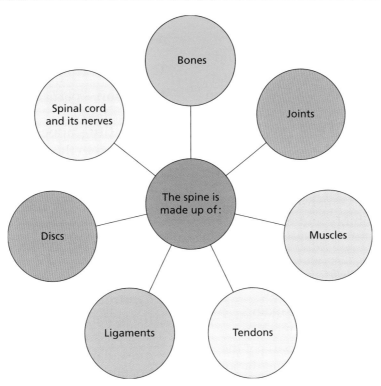

Figure 19.2 Different parts of the spine

Bones

The bones of the spine are known as vertebrae. These bones consist of 24 moveable vertebrae and 9 fixed vertebrae, all of varying sizes. The top 24 vertebrae are separated by discs and these act as 'shock absorbers' as they stretch and relax during movement. The spine also encloses and protects the spinal cord. So, in total, there are 33 vertebrae, which are divided into sections of the spine:

- cervical (neck): 7 bones
- thoracic (upper back): 12 bones
- lumbar (lower back): 5 bones.

The remaining two segments of the spine are fused to each other and provide little movement. They are the sacrum, which is attached to the pelvis, and the coccyx (the final segment of the vertebrae, tail bone).

Joints

A joint is where one bone meets another. The joints of the spine are called facet joints. There are two facet joints at the back of each vertebra that connect a vertebra to the one below it. As well as joining bones, facet joints along with the spinal discs and muscles control movement of the spine and limit the amount and direction of movement.

Muscles

The main functions of the muscles are to provide support and assist in movement. The abdominal muscles support the spinal muscles and can often be felt contracting when lifting. Without muscular support the spine would be unstable. Movement is initiated and controlled by the contraction of muscles.

Tendons

The tendons connect the muscles to the bones and also facilitate movement.

Ligaments

Ligaments are strong bands of fibres that attach bone to bone at the joints. They allow movement between bones but protect the joints from excessive movement. Each vertebra of the spine is strongly bound and joined to each other by ligaments. They help to support and stabilise the spine in position and prevent any abnormal movements

Intervertebral discs

Each vertebra is connected to a vertebral disc. These discs provide cushioning between the vertebrae, acting as an absorber. They also allow some flexibility and movement of the spine.

Spinal cord and nerves

The spinal cord runs through a space in the centre of the spine. It is the main communication cable and takes messages between the brain and different parts of the body. The spinal cord branches off at the joints between each of the vertebra into various nerves which supply different parts of the body.

The spine has four main functions:

1 **Support** – particularly the weight of the upper body.
2 **Mobility** – upper and lower limbs are attached to the spine through a series of joints. Muscle, ligaments and tendons connect parts of the spine to each other as well as to other limbs and allow a diverse range of movements.
3 **Housing and protection** – the spine houses and protects the spinal cord and nerves as they pass from the brain to the upper limbs.
4 **Control** – the movement of each segment of the spine is controlled, actively by muscles and passively by ligaments. Without muscular support the spine would become unstable.

Evidence activity

1.1 Anatomy and physiology

Complete the following table to show your understanding of how incorrect moving and positioning of individuals can affect the musculoskeletal system and cause injury.

Moving and positioning technique	Possible effect on the musculoskeletal system
Pulling, jerking	
Pushing	
Gripping, clasping	
Twisting	
Any technique that requires a weakened individual to bear their own weight, for example standing	
Any technique that carries risk of a fall	
Any technique that uses equipment	
Any activity that prevents the body assuming its natural 'S'-shaped curve	
Any technique that forces a joint beyond its normal range of movement	

AC 1.2 Describe the impact of specific conditions on the correct movement and positioning of an individual

Many people who use health and social care services will require help and support to move and change position. A range of moving and positioning activities is shown in the table below. Organisations that provide support in this way are obliged to have in place procedures and agreed ways of working that describe exactly how each manoeuvre must be carried out. These procedures and agreed ways of working will be detailed in your organisation's moving and handling policy;

but each manoeuvre must be detailed in every service user's care or support plan.

Research and investigate

1.2 Moving and positioning

Check out your workplace's safe moving and handling procedures for three individuals with different needs.

How do they compare?

In what ways are they different?

Why are they different?

Moving and positioning activities

Table 19.1 Aims and objectives of activities

Aim of activity	Objectives of activity
Support an individual to sit, stand and walk	Move forwards and backwards in a chair.
	Move from sitting in a chair to standing, and vice versa (doing something and then reversing it the other way round).
	Move from sitting on the edge of a bed to standing, and vice versa.
	Walk.
	Prevent from falling and raise from a fall.
Support an individual to move in bed	Get in and out of bed and turn in bed.
	Lie at an angle.
	Sit up from lying and onto the edge of the bed.
	Slide up and down when lying and sitting.
	Maintain the correct posture and appropriate position.
Support an individual to move laterally (side to side)	From bed to trolley, and vice versa.
	Standing and seated transfers from bed to chair, and vice versa.
	Transfer from chair to chair.
	Transfer from chair to commode or toilet, and vice versa.
Hoisting	Fitting a sling with the individual in bed or in a chair.
	Fitting a sling with the individual in bed or in a chair using glide sheets.
	Hoisting from bed to chair, and vice versa.
	Hoisting from the floor.
	Transferring to the toilet or bath using sling-lifting or a stand aid hoist.

1.2 Mrs Hopwood

Mrs Hopwood requires support with moving and handling. She is a lady who has had a stroke and has a right-sided weakness.

She experiences pain when moving and needs to take pain management medication. She uses a wheelchair but is able to transfer with support.

How would this impact on her requirements for moving and handling?

Evidence activity

1.2 Impact of specific conditions

Think of four individuals that you work with that have different conditions. Describe the impact their conditions have on the correct moving and positioning procedures. Talk to two people you support. How do they feel their condition impacts on the way they are moved? How do they think this could be improved? Write ten top tips/ guidance for your colleagues.

There are a number of conditions that can impact on a person's mobility and on the support they need to move and reposition. For this reason, moving and handling procedures must be adapted and agreed ways of working put in place that meet each person's specific needs. Tailored moving and repositioning activities must be devised for people who:

- have bone and joint conditions, such as rheumatoid arthritis, in which the joints become inflamed and painful; osteoarthritis, in which the cartilage of the joints becomes worn, stiff and painful; and osteoporosis, in which the density of the bones is much reduced, increasing the risk of fracture
- have a physical disability that affects movement and mobility, such as amputation, muscular dystrophy, multiple sclerosis, stroke, Parkinson's disease, Huntington's disease, cerebral palsy and epilepsy
- have a sensory impairment, such as impaired sight or hearing, which may affect their ability to hear how to help in a manoeuvre or to see where to move
- have attachments, such as a feeding tube, urinary catheter or oxygen therapy
- have variations in capabilities during the day and night – for example, an individual may be able to move themselves during the day but may not be able to move at all at night

- have issues with tissue viability, which is to do with the ability of the skin to remain intact and healthy. Reduced tissue viability manifests as skin breakdown and pressure ulcers. Skin breakdown is caused by failure to care for skin exposed to moisture from urine, sweat and exudate, while pressure ulcers are due to pressure (of the body on the bed or chair), shear (pressure created by pushing and pulling in a lateral direction) and friction (created by two surfaces moving over each other)
- are paralysed and unable to move
- are unconscious – someone who is comatose is unable to change their own position.

LO2 Understand legislation and agreed ways of working when moving and positioning individuals

AC 2.1 Describe how legislation and agreed ways of working affect working practices related to moving and positioning individuals

Unsafe moving and handling techniques can result in injury to health and social care workers and also to the people who are being supported to move or be repositioned. In order to protect people and reduce the risk of injury, all health and social care workers have a duty to comply with health and safety legislation.

The purpose of this legislation is to protect the health, safety and well-being of all people in the workplace, including staff, service users and visitors. Health and safety policies set out the arrangements that an organisation has for complying with legislation, and health and safety procedures and agreed ways of working describe how work activities must be carried out for policies to be implemented and the law obeyed.

There are a number of pieces of legislation that aim to protect everyone involved in moving and repositioning activities. If your job requires you to support people to move or reposition, whether manually or with the help of equipment, you should familiarise yourself with the legislation and your workplace's policies, and ensure that you are working in line with these.

Since the Health and Safety at Work Act (1974) many other health and safety laws have been introduced. These are presented in the form of Regulations. The following Regulations in their entirety offer a systematic approach to manual handling.

The Health and Safety at Work etc. Act 1974

This piece of legislation does not specifically cover moving and repositioning activities. However, it requires employers to:

- write health and safety policies and procedures, including ones that relate to moving and positioning activities, and make employees aware of them
- ensure everyone's health, safety and welfare, as far as is reasonably practicable.

In addition, it requires employees to:

- take reasonable care of yourself and anyone else who may be affected by your activities
- co-operate with your employer in relation to health and safety issues, including those related to moving and repositioning
- not interfere with or misuse anything provided in the interest of health and safety, for example equipment used for moving and repositioning.

The Manual Handling Operations Regulations 1992 (amended 2002)

This legislation defines manual handling operations as:

'Any transporting or supporting of a load (including the lifting, putting down, pushing, pulling, carrying or moving thereof) by hand or bodily force'.

A load is defined as 'anything which is moveable', e.g. an inanimate object, person or animal.

These Regulations apply wherever people or objects are moved by hand or bodily force. They impose duties on both the employer and the employee.

The employer's duties are to:

- avoid the need for hazardous manual handling as far as is reasonably practicable
- assess the risk of injury from any manual handling that cannot be avoided
- reduce the risk of injury from hazardous manual handling as far as is reasonably practicable

Time to reflect

2.1 Legislation

What health and safety legislation affects the way that you carry out moving and positioning activities within your place of work?

What policies does your employer have in place to ensure that you comply with the law when carrying out moving and positioning activities?

Where are moving and positioning procedures stored in your workplace? When did you last look at them to make sure that your work practice is accurate?

- review to ensure that changes are made to an assessment when required.

The employee's duties are to:

- follow appropriate systems of work that have been laid down for their safety
- make proper use of any equipment that has been provided to minimise the risk of injury
- co-operate with their employer on health and safety matters to protect themselves and to protect others.

The Lifting Operations and Lifting Equipment Regulations (LOLER) 1998

This piece of legislation aims to reduce health and safety risks due to using lifting equipment such as hoists and slings. Employers are required to ensure that lifting equipment used for moving and repositioning activities is:

- strong, stable and marked to indicate safe working loads
- safely positioned and installed to minimise any risks
- used safely and appropriately by trained and supervised employees
- maintained and inspected by competent people.

The employee's duties are to:

- follow any training and comply with their employer's instructions regarding safety
- report any faults to their employer
- always use appropriate personal protective equipment.

The Provision and Use of Work Equipment Regulations (1998) (PUWER)

These Regulations cover all equipment used at work, including manual handling equipment such as slide sheets and handling boards. The Regulations require that equipment provided for use at work should:

- be suitable for the intended purpose
- be safe for use, maintained in a safe condition and inspected at regular intervals

- be used only by people who have received adequate information, instruction and training
- have suitable safety measures, e.g. markings and warnings.

The employer's duties are to:

- ensure that equipment is suitable for use
- maintain equipment in a safe condition so that people's health and safety are not put at risk
- ensure that equipment is inspected so that it continues to be safe for use – inspection should be carried out by a competent person
- maintain records of all inspections.

The employee's duties are to:

- follow any training and comply with their employer's instructions regarding safety
- report any faults to their employer
- always use appropriate personal protective equipment.

Case study

2.1 Legislation

A care home group was fined £57,000 after a service user in their care died when she fractured her neck in a fall during a moving and handling transfer.

A carer in the home was in the process of assisting the service user with her personal hygiene as well as transferring her from her bed to her shower chair when the service user fell to the floor. The carer, who had very recently taken up employment within the home, was unaware that a care plan and manual handling risk assessment stated that two people were required to transfer the resident.

The care home group admitted that they had failed to review and update the risk assessment for the resident, and had also failed to provide adequate people handling training and instruction, as well as staff supervision, for those workers within the home who were expected to undertake moving and handling activities. How had the care home group breached legislation and which pieces of legislation had they breached?

AC 2.2 Describe what health and safety factors need to be taken into account when moving and positioning individuals and any equipment used to do this

There are a number of health and safety factors that need to be considered when moving and positioning people. It is therefore important to be aware of these and to ensure that any moving or repositioning task is carefully planned.

Within this section we will look at the health and safety hazards or risk factors that need to be taken into account when moving and repositioning individuals:

- the environment
- the person being moved or repositioned
- yourself and others
- the activity or task being undertaken
- equipment that may be used.

The environment

Before undertaking a moving or positioning activity it is important to consider the environment and the hazards that might be present within it. You will need to consider the following:

- How much space is available? Does the environment or space in which you work constrain your posture? For example, do obstructions or a lack of space restrict your movements or make movement uncomfortable? Postural constraint is a further cause of musculoskeletal disorders (MSD).
- Is the floor level and free from slip and trip hazards?
- Is there sufficient lighting? Can you see what you are doing, or is lighting dazzling or insufficient?
- Can you hear, or is background noise distracting, preventing you from hearing instructions accurately?
- Is there a comfortable working temperature, neither too hot nor too cold?
- Is ventilation comfortable, not too draughty or humid?
- Is the environment clean?

The person being moved or repositioned

The person being supported with moving and repositioning will be at the centre of the activity. It is therefore essential that they contribute to the move as much as possible.

Before attempting to help an individual move or reposition, it is important to be aware of factors such as:

- what the person can do for themselves
- how much support the person will need
- the person's ability to communicate and understand what is required
- the person's skin condition
- the person's weight and height
- any health conditions that may affect the moving or repositioning task, for example if the person is in pain

- any medical devices that might be attached to the person, such as catheter bags or feeding tubes.

Yourself and others

Before supporting a person to move or reposition it is vital to consider the capability of the person or the team undertaking the activity. It is therefore important to consider the following points:

- Are you trained and confident in your ability to do the activity safely?
- Are your clothing and footwear appropriate, or do they restrict movement?
- Are you fit and strong enough to undertake the activity?
- Does your health status affect your ability – for example, are you pregnant or do you have an musculoskeletal disorder (MSD)?

- Are you able to give the activity the time it requires, or do high job demands, time constraints, fatigue and stress tempt you to cut corners?
- Do you need to take precautions against the risk of cross infection, for example by using personal protective equipment (PPE)?
- Are you trained and confident in your ability to report and record any accidents and injuries?

The activity

When considering the activity, there are several factors that need to be taken into consideration. For example:

- Does the activity need to be undertaken?
- Does the activity involve particular hazards to posture?

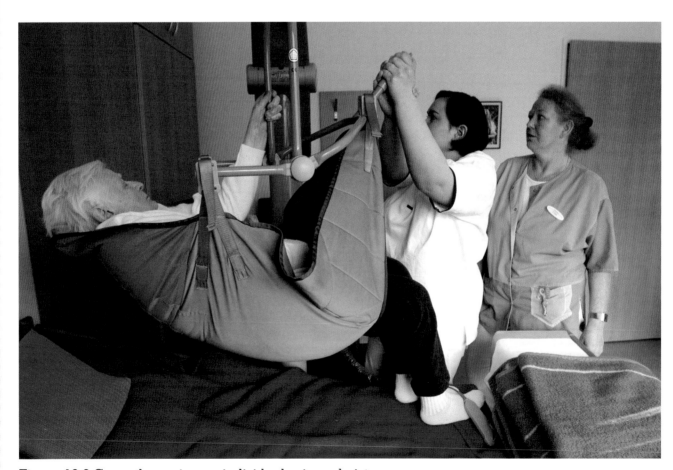

Figure 19.3 Correctly moving an individual using a hoist

- Is the activity repetitive?
- Is there sufficient time for recovery?
- Is there enough time to undertake the activity?
- If you require another person to help you, are they available?
- If you require equipment, is it available?

Equipment

When undertaking moving and handling activities, you may be required to use equipment, for example a **hoist** or a **slide sheet**. Before using the equipment you should always consider the following:

- Is the equipment available?
- Is the equipment in good working order and has it been checked as safe to use?
- Has the equipment been maintained?
- Is the equipment clean?
- Are you trained to use the equipment?
- Is the equipment appropriate for the activity being undertaken?

Key terms

Hoist is a mechanical or electrical device used to move or transfer a person from one area to another from one position to another. An example of this is transferring a person from a bed to a chair.

A slide sheet might be used to assist in the movement of an individual in bed, but you must be cautions that they do not damage frail skin.

Evidence activity

2.2 Health and safety

Think about two individuals you need to help to move and position, one of which requires the use of equipment.

For each individual, make a list of the health and safety factors you need to consider when helping them move and position, including those that relate to the equipment that is used.

LO3 Be able to minimise risk before moving and positioning individuals

AC 3.1 Access up-to-date copies of risk assessment documentation

Risk assessments are required to identify risks and appropriate measures to reduce risks associated with certain activities. Health and safety legislation that relates to moving and positioning requires that any moving and handling activity is assessed for risks, and that steps are taken to eliminate or minimise any risks. The results of risk assessments must be recorded, manually and/or electronically, and everyone involved made aware of the health and safety procedures.

Risk assessment records should be stored in filing cabinets or electronic storage systems in a clearly known and accessible location, for example a staff room or office, so that everyone can keep themselves familiar with their content. Anyone who carries out an activity must follow to the letter the procedures described in the risk assessment.

Risk assessments need to be routinely reviewed and updated, to take account of, for example, changes in legislation and developments in moving and handling techniques and equipment. Good practice dictates that you keep up to date with the law and the latest moving and handling procedures.

Evidence activity

3.1 Risk assessment documentation

Where are moving and handling risk assessments kept within your workplace?

How do you access the risk assessments?

Why is it necessary to review the risk assessments?

How do you know the risk assessments are up to date?

AC 3.2 Carry out preparatory checks using:

- **the individual's care plan**
- **the moving and handling risk assessment.**

Risk assessments record procedures for carrying out moving and handling activities. Care plans contain information about an individual's abilities and needs, including instructions for moving and handling activities that are specific to them. It is therefore essential to access up-to-date information about a person's requirements for moving and handling before supporting them to move or reposition. This is important because the person's requirements may have been reassessed and updated since you last carried out the activity.

The two documents that you should check are the person's support or care plan and their moving and handling risk assessment. These documents will tell you about:

- the level of support the person requires
- how the person usually mobilises
- any goals relating to mobilisation
- how often the person should be repositioned
- the equipment required to mobilise.

Failure to follow procedures laid out in care plans and risk assessments flies in the face of best practice and will put the service user, yourself and others at risk.

Evidence activity

3.2 Preparatory checks

Think about three people you help to move and position.

What documentation describes the moving and handling activities in which they need support?

Where is this documentation stored?

Why is it important to follow the procedures described in this documentation? Why is it important to check you have the most recent documentation?

AC 3.3 Identify any immediate risks to the individual

Every person who requires support with moving and handling should have a moving and handling support or care plan and risk assessment. However, it is important to be aware that risks change constantly and just because you have read a person's risk assessment and support plan doesn't mean that all risks will have been identified, or indeed that they have not changed. It is therefore important that you informally assess risks associated with moving and handling before you undertake any procedure.

Questions you should ask yourself prior to carrying out any moving and handling activity include the following:

1 Is the activity appropriate? Changes in an individual's physical health, for example their weight, mobility, balance, tendency to fall, sight, hearing and tissue viability, can put health and safety at risk. Similarly, changes in their mood and mental health, such as level of dependency, understanding, behaviour and ability to help in the manoeuvre, can affect health and safety.
2 Is the working environment free from obstruction and noise, and is it well lit?
3 Is the equipment you are going to use appropriate, and are you confident and competent in its use?
4 Is there evidence to show that equipment is safe and well maintained?
5 Are you and any others involved in the manoeuvre appropriately trained, fit and healthy, sufficiently strong and appropriately dressed?
6 Is there any possibility of cross infection? Infection is a major cause of illness and hospitalisation among people living in residential care homes, and health care associated infections (HCAIs) may be serious, even life threatening.

AC 3.4 Describe actions to take in relation to identified risks

It is very difficult to eliminate risks. The aim of risk assessment is to create procedures to reduce risks 'to the lowest level reasonably practicable'. Once risks have been identified, control measures must be put in place. As a health or social care worker it is important that you follow the control measures that have been put in place. Failure to do so could result in injury to the person you are supporting, yourself and others.

The table on the next page outlines how to minimise risks associated with moving and positioning.

AC 3.5 Describe what action should be taken if the individual's wishes conflict with their plan of care in relation to health and safety and their risk assessment

Although you have a duty of care towards the people you support, they also have a right to make their own choices and decisions about the support they receive and the way they would like to live their lives. There may be times when you find yourself in a position where a person's wishes conflict with their care plan and risk assessment in relation to the way they wish to be supported with moving and handling. For example, a person who has been assessed as requiring a hoist to be moved and repositioned may not want to be hoisted. Instead they may insist that staff lift them manually. Another example could involve a person who refuses to be supported with moving and handling. They may insist they don't need assistance with walking despite being at high risk of falling. They might choose to engage with staff throughout the manoeuvre, even though their **active participation** would promote their independence and would help and protect staff, or they might decide they do not want to move at all, putting themselves at risk of developing **pressure ulcers**.

Although you might see these decisions as eccentric or unwise, everyone has a right to make decisions that carry an element of risk to themselves, and you have a responsibility to support individuals in exercising their right o take risks. The only exception is where a person has been deemed as lacking the capacity to make decisions and best interest decisions need to be made on their behalf.

However, you also have a responsibility to protect their health and safety as well as your own and that of any colleagues involved. In the event of a seemingly unwise decision, it is therefore important to discuss the safety implications with everyone concerned and point out your duty of care to follow safe procedures and

Key terms

Active participation is when a person takes an active rather than a passive role in their own care and support.

Pressure ulcers are a type of injury that breaks down the skin and underlying tissue. They are caused when an area of skin is placed under pressure.

Table 19.2 Risk factors and actions to take to minimise the risks

Risk factor	Action to take to minimise the risks
Activity	Don't carry out any activity unless you have been trained. Don't carry out any activity unless you are sufficiently strong, fit and healthy. If an activity puts great pressure on you, request the support of a team. If a manual activity poses a risk, consider using equipment instead. Don't use equipment unless you have been trained. Use equipment that is appropriate to the activity and the needs of the individual. Inspect equipment before use to make sure it is safe and well maintained. Follow procedures within care plans and risk assessments. Report any concerns.
Load	Prior to the activity, assess individuals for changes in their physical and emotional condition that could affect the manoeuvre. Know what can affect their behaviour so you can plan for unexpected movements. Know their weight in order to decide whether you are strong enough to help in the manoeuvre and that any equipment you intend to use can carry them safely. Take into account their size and shape when planning how to grasp or support them. Report any changes in the individual that impact on moving and positioning. Report any concerns.
Working environment	Don't carry out any activity if there isn't sufficient space for you to move in comfort. Don't carry out any activity if there isn't sufficient space to use equipment properly. Don't carry out any activity if the light, noise, ventilation and temperature could compromise comfort and safety. Report any concerns.
Capabilities	Ensure that you are trained in moving and handling, including using equipment. If you work in a team, know your responsibilities and commit to developing teamwork skills. Ask for supervision to check that you are competent and work safely. Wear appropriate clothing, including PPE if necessary. Stay fit and healthy and let your employer know if you are pregnant or if a manoeuvre causes you pain or discomfort. Report concerns related to high job demands, time constraints, fatigue and stress that you think could interfere with your ability to work safely.
Other factors	Follow procedures for working with people who are infected. Follow procedures if you think that you may have an infectious disease. Follow procedures for reporting accidents and injuries related to moving and handling.

comply with health and safety law. Make every attempt to explain to the person the importance of following their care plan or the relevant risk assessment, while at the same time indicating your wish to respect and promote their rights.

If, having discussed the possible consequences of their decision, the person is insistent on continuing with an unsafe activity, you will need to escalate your concerns to your manager or a more appropriate member of the wider team, such as an Occupational Therapist, so that the person can be assessed and appropriate solutions can be found. You should never put yourself or the person at risk by undertaking unsafe moving and handling procedures. It is also important to record any discussions about their wishes and choices and the actions taken.

It is worth remembering that conflicts can be prevented if people are involved in contributing to their care plans and risk assessments. Care plans and risk assessments should focus on the needs of the person and the person should be placed at the centre of the care planning process. The wishes of the person must always be balanced against the health and safety of staff. This will help to promote the person's right to make decisions, their independence, dignity and autonomy.

Evidence activity

3.5 Wishes and health and safety

Check out your workplace's policy for accommodating individuals when their wishes conflict with the health and safety procedures you are required to follow.

Use your findings to produce an information sheet or poster for colleagues whom you feel need support in dealing with situations that could become difficult.

AC 3.6 Prepare the immediate environment ensuring:

- **adequate space for the move in agreement with all concerned**
- **that potential hazards are removed.**

In order to reduce the risk of injury from undertaking a moving or repositioning activity, it is important to ensure the immediate environment is prepared before the procedure. The environment should be incorporated as part of the risk assessment, but it is essential that you check the environment prior to every moving and repositioning activity in order to minimise any risks. Even if you have supported the person to move several times a day for the past six months, you should still assess the risks on each occasion.

When preparing the environment you should take into account all of the following factors:

- Is there enough space to undertake the activity?
- Is the surface of the floor safe? Are there wet or slippery patches, or is there anything you could trip over?
- Does the environment give the person privacy and can the person's dignity be maintained throughout the activity?
- Is the environment suitable for any equipment required to undertake the activity?
- Have you got everything you need before you carry out the activity? This could include staff and equipment.

Make sure you remove or reduce the risks associated with these hazards 'to the lowest level reasonably practicable'.

Adequate, accessible space is vital for a normal range of joint and muscle movements. Working in cramped, cluttered conditions will lead to unsafe movements such as twisting, leaning sideways, stooping, overreaching and turning in a small area. Unsafe movements put pressure on the spinal column, overstretching muscles and joints and leading to MSDs, for example a **prolapsed disc** (see page 350 for definition), joint injury, sprains and strains. MSDs are very debilitating. Apart from long periods of reduced mobility and pain that can affect everyday activities and the ability to sleep, they can also affect your job prospects.

3.6 **Preparing the immediate environment**

Complete the following table to show how you ensure that the environment in which you carry out three moving and handling activities is as free from risk as possible.

Description of moving and handling activity	How I ensure that there is adequate space for the move	Details of other hazards that I remove
1		
2		
3		

Working in cramped conditions increases the risk of accidents, so before carrying out any moving and positioning activities, make sure that everyone involved has enough space to move freely and comfortably and that there is enough space to use equipment properly. Assess the area for obstructions that could restrict movement, such as furniture, wheelchairs, televisions, shelving, cupboards, even curtains and curtain rails, and deal with them to make the space as tidy and free from clutter as possible. If you are working in a team, co-ordinate your tasks so that you don't restrict each other.

AC 3.7 Apply standard precautions for infection prevention and control

Helping someone to move or reposition requires close body contact and, on occasion, contact with blood and body fluids. Standard precautions are the practices adopted by health and social care workers when there is a chance that they may come into contact with blood or body fluids. They are a set of principles designed to minimise exposure to and transmission of a wide variety of **pathogens**.

When supporting people with moving and repositioning activities you will need to assess risks associated with infection as this will determine the precautions you will be required to take. The standard precautions required will depend on the level of risk and the activity being undertaken – for example, if you are supporting a person to walk to the dining room, as a minimum you must ensure you wash your hands before and immediately after the activity. If you are supporting a person to use the toilet, there is a high risk that you may come into contact with body fluids, so you will need to ensure you wear an apron and gloves.

Key term

A **prolapsed disc** occurs when one of the discs of the spine is ruptured and the jelly-like substance inside leaks out, putting pressure on the spinal cord. It causes intense back pain as well as pain in other areas of the body.

Pathogen is a disease-producing micro-organism such as bacteria, fungus, virus or a parasite.

Evidence activity

3.7 **Standard precautions**

Explain and apply the standard precautions required when supporting people with moving and handling activities. How can you minimise risk, using standard precautions when moving and handling an individual? What would your immediate course of action be if you realised their needs had changed and the usual precautions were insufficient to move them safely?

LO4 Be able to prepare individuals before moving and positioning

AC 4.1 Demonstrate effective communication with the individual to ensure they:

- understand the details and reasons for the action/activity being undertaken
- agree the level of support required.

The use of effective communication is really important when supporting people with moving and repositioning activities so that they are involved in the process and understand the details and reasons for the activities.

You also need to reach an agreement with them about the level of support they require. Human nature is such that we want to stay as independent as possible for as long as we can. Taking away someone's independence takes away their control, prevents them from doing what they want to do when they want to do it, and destroys any feelings of self-worth. Reassure the individuals you work with that you don't intend to 'take over'; that you want to work with them, in a partnership; that you respect what they can do; and that you value their active participation, especially since that makes your job easier and more enjoyable!

Many people find it difficult to admit to needing help and support, especially with everyday activities. Asking for help and support can be embarrassing and can challenge their pride and status. It is therefore important to talk with them about what they can do and what they would like to do. Read between the lines and watch their body language for clues as to where support would be appreciated. For example a person may tell you they do not need help but they may actually be reaching out to you for support.

Agreeing the level of support you give will empower individuals to maintain their independence, autonomy and dignity. It promotes partnership working and people's right to be cared for in a way that meets their needs and takes account of their choices.

Case study

4.1 Mr Bennett

Mr Bennett has been diagnosed with Alzheimer's disease and needs a little longer to take in any information that is being communicated to him. Some staff say he is aggressive and nasty and he lashes out. However, some staff say they have not experienced this. This has been brought to the attention of the manager of the care home and she decides to observe the interactions of staff with Mr Bennett. She soon comes to the conclusion that staff who rush Mr Bennett and do not give him time to think are experiencing problems. One day she hears one member of staff saying to Mr Bennett. 'Come on I have five other people to get out of bed.' She rushes him and does not give him time to respond. Every instruction is rushed.

Does it ever occur to you that the individuals for whom you provide care and support may be frightened, or they may not understand what is required of them? They may feel they have lost independence and control, and that what they have to undergo takes away their pride and self-respect?

If you were in their shoes, how would you like to be treated?

Time to think

4.1 Help and support

Think about the people you work with who find it difficult to admit to needing help and support. How do they show their feelings? Are they defensive, embarrassed, apologetic?

How do you reassure them that it is OK to receive help and support? Why do you think it is important to give this reassurance?

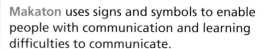

Evidence activity

4.1 Effective communication

Talk to two or three of the individuals you work with. Ask them for feedback on how you can improve your ability to:

- communicate to them the details and reasons for your work with them
- agree with them the level of support they need.

AC 4.2 Obtain valid consent for the planned activity

As we have discussed, every service user has the right to be cared for in a way that meets their needs and takes account of their choices. Therefore, before carrying out a caring activity or procedure, you must obtain the person's consent.

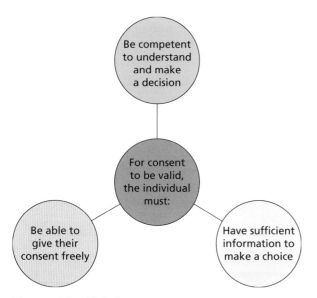

Figure 19.4 Valid consent

To obtain consent, you will need to explain what you are planning to do, how you plan to do it and any risks that might be involved. Consent should be obtained using a form of communication with which the individual is most comfortable, for example it may be spoken or written, or be non-verbal, such as British Sign Language or **Makaton**.

Key term

Makaton uses signs and symbols to enable people with communication and learning difficulties to communicate.

Evidence activity

4.2 Obtaining valid consent

Explain the factors you take into account to ensure consent is valid before supporting people with moving or repositioning. How would you give your consent if you were the person receiving care?

The consent you get from people for supporting them with moving and positioning does not have to be written, consent will usually be obtained verbally or through physical signs. Failure to obtain consent could result in allegations of assault being made against you.

People who are unable to give their consent, perhaps because they lack the capacity to make a decision about being moved or positioned, such as some people with dementia, should not have their care needs ignored. People who are deemed to be incapable of giving valid consent should be protected under the Mental Capacity Act 2005. This will allow staff, in consultation with the individual's family to make best interest decisions for the individual.

LO5 Be able to move and position an individual

AC 5.1 Follow the care plan to ensure that the individual is positioned:

- **using the agreed technique**
- **in a way that will avoid causing undue pain or discomfort.**

Moving can be painful and uncomfortable. Bone and joint conditions, strains, sprains and pressure ulcers can make even the slightest movement distressing. Everyone needing help and support to move should be risk assessed to identify techniques that either eliminate the risk of pain and discomfort or reduce it to an absolute minimum. And once the individual concerned has agreed those techniques, they must be written into their care plan and routinely reviewed.

By following the information in the person's care plan you can reduce the risk of causing undue pain and discomfort.

AC 5.2 Demonstrate effective communication with any others involved in the manoeuvre

Many moving and positioning activities require team work, particularly when the individual concerned is heavy or requires a high level of care. Effective team work will help to protect the health and safety of everyone involved.

Ideally, team members should be similar in height and strength in order to:

- avoid unsafe movements, such as overreaching – you read earlier that awkward movements can cause MSDs
- ensure that the individual's weight is evenly shared – being overloaded and unbalanced can also cause an MSD
- keep the move as smooth and comfortable as possible for everyone concerned.

An effective team needs a good leader whose experience is worthy of respect and in whom the rest of the team has confidence. Apart from setting a good example by carrying out moving and positioning activities according to agreed techniques, a leader must be able to communicate effectively to:

- ensure everyone involved, including the individual concerned, understands the reason for the manoeuvre and their specific role in enabling it to take place safely
- work with everyone to agree commands, such as 'Ready, steady, slide'
- issue commands during the manoeuvre
- evaluate the manoeuvre and how it could be improved.

AC 5.3 Describe the aids and equipment that may be used for moving and positioning

There are many aids and equipment to help individuals move, reposition and retain a comfortable posture. These include:

- mobility scooters and wheelchairs
- walking frames, trolleys and sticks
- manual and electric mobile hoists, which are used to move people from bed to chair, wheelchair to car, etc.
- wall and ceiling track hoists, which consist of a rail or track fixed to the wall or ceiling, along which a seat or sling is moved

- sling lifts and bath hoists, which are fixed to the floor and have either a sling or a chair seat to lower and raise people into and out of the bath
- stand aids, to help a person from sitting to standing and to transfer a short distance
- slide sheets, for repositioning a person in bed or moving them from bed to trolley – their low friction surface prevents the shearing that can lead to pressure ulcers; some slide sheets have a non-slip area that allows the person to get a heel grip and turn themselves over
- monkey poles and bed ladders, to help a person move from lying down to sitting up
- inflatable lifting cushions and backrests, to enable people to stand up from a chair and sit up in bed respectively
- swivel aids, turntables and turn disks, for transferring people from one sitting or standing position to another
- transfer boards, for lateral transfer, for example bed to chair, chair to wheelchair, wheelchair to car
- handling belts, for gripping a person prior to a move, often used in conjunction with swivel aids, transfer boards and slide sheets
- leg lifters.

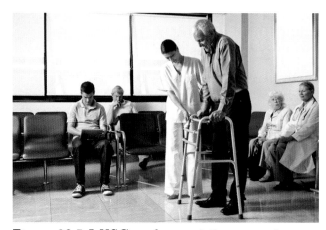

Figure 19.5 A HSC worker assisting a service user using an aid

Evidence activity

5.3 **Aids and equipment**

Copy and complete the table below.

Aids and equipment used in moving and positioning activities at my workplace	Function

AC 5.4 Use equipment to maintain the individual in the appropriate position

Because some people are unable to maintain a stable posture, they require frequent repositioning, aided or unaided. This can be tiring and uncomfortable, disrupt their concentration on their current activity, affect their quality of life, compromise their dignity and cause pressure ulcers.

Frequent repositioning can be avoided by using equipment that maintains the appropriate position, for example:

- support chairs, standing frames and wheeled walkers that have head, arm, knee

Evidence activity

5.4 **Equipment and posture**

What equipment is available at your workplace to help individuals maintain a stable, comfortable posture?

and foot supports and straps; chest and hip pads, all of which can be adjusted for comfort and safety

- positioning wedges, such as those used to prop someone into position when in bed
- orthopaedic supports, braces and immobilising slings
- glide and lock sheets that allow movement in one direction only, helping people who tend to slide forwards or to the side to stay upright.

AC 5.5 Encourage the individual's active participation in the manoeuvre

Active participation is a way of working in which people using health and social care services are regarded as active partners in their care or support, as opposed to being passive recipients. There are many ways in which you can encourage individuals to actively participate when supporting them with moving and positioning, and it is important that you do so, to ensure they stay as independent as possible for as long as possible and to protect your own health and safety.

Before you carry out a moving and positioning activity, ask the individual how they think they can help and what help they think they would like. Answers will vary from day to day, and in some cases hourly, depending on mood, motivation, level of confidence, fear of falling, fear of pain, physical health status and so on. It is important to remind the person that you are there to provide support but that you want them to be in control.

Figure 19.6 Active participation

AC 5.6 Monitor the individual throughout the activity so that the procedure can be stopped if there is any adverse reaction

Throughout any moving and handling activity, it is important that you continually observe the individual being supported to move or reposition, and that you stop and get help if they show any adverse reaction. Adverse reactions could include:

- distress due to fear, pain, discomfort, a lack of confidence in the handler and anxiety about relying on equipment
- a failure to follow instructions, due to difficulty in hearing or understanding, or a change in the ability or desire to co-operate

Key term

Muscle tone is the tension or resistance to movement in a muscle that enables us to keep our bodies in a certain position.

Evidence activity

5.6 Monitoring and adverse reactions

Think about three moving and positioning activities that you stopped because of an adverse reaction.

What caused the individual involved to react in these ways?

What have you learned from these experiences?

- a change in **muscle tone**, unexpected movement, loss of balance
- sprained joints, trapped fingers and limbs, and dislodged health care attachments, due to poor positioning
- changes in medical status, for example a drop in blood pressure, loss of consciousness, restricted ability to breathe.

It is important to be on the alert for adverse reactions throughout every moving and handling activity you undertake. If you detect any risks to health and safety, you should stop what you are doing and get help without delay.

AC 5.7 Demonstrate how to report and record the activity noting when the next positioning manoeuvre is due

It is important that you follow your workplace's procedures for reporting and recording any moving and positioning activities you undertake, including accidents, incidents and near misses. Verbal reports should be made to the relevant person and written records should be made in care plans and on appropriate accident/incident report forms.

Research and investigate

5.7 Reporting and recording

What does your workplace's policy require of you with regard to reporting and recording:

- moving and handling activities?
- the timing of moving and handling activities?

It is important to report and record any adverse reactions you observe while undertaking the activity and any actions that were taken. This will trigger a review of the manoeuvre to ensure that the situation does not recur. Use care plans to record details of every manoeuvre that is carried out and when the next is due. Failure to reposition someone, in bed or in a chair, to transfer them when necessary to the toilet or bath, and to generally help them keep moving as much as possible, amounts to neglect. Skin breaks down after a prolonged period of exposure to urine, sweat and **exudate**, and pressure ulcers can develop after lengthy periods of sitting or lying in the same position. So it is important that you and your colleagues know when to reposition the people you are supporting.

Reporting hazards

Any hazards you identify with the manoeuvre, the individual concerned, aids and equipment and the working environment must be reported and recorded without delay. Similarly, any accidents, incidents and near misses must be reported and recorded. Unless hazards, accidents, incidents and near misses are reported, their cause cannot be investigated and they will continue to put health and safety at risk.

Finally, make sure your colleagues and line manager know about any personal factors such as MSDs, illness or pregnancy that might affect your ability to carry out manoeuvres in the future.

Evidence activity

5.7 Report and record

Produce an information sheet for use in a training session that tells your colleagues how to report and record any moving and positioning activities they undertake, and the importance of noting when the next positioning manoeuvre is due.

LO6 Know when to seek advice from and/or involve others when moving and positioning an individual

AC 6.1 Describe when advice and/or assistance should be sought to move or handle an individual safely

Time to think

6.1 Help and advice

In what circumstances do you currently get help or advice to carry out moving and handling activities?

Why might you not seek help?

What might be the outcome if you carried out an activity for which you didn't feel 100 per cent confident or competent?

If you are pregnant, feel yourself coming down with an infection, have an MSD or are concerned that you are not physically big or strong enough to participate in a particular moving and handling activity, get advice from your manager about whether or not you should carry out the move or handling technique.

It is important that you receive training to enable you to carry out moving and handling procedures safely. If you have not received this training you will need to speak with your manager. Working outside the boundaries for which you have been trained may result in injury or harm to the person you are supporting or to yourself.

Evidence activity

6.1 Advice and assistance

Make a list of the occasions when, because of fears for safety with regard to moving or handling an individual, you have sought advice or assistance. Investigate the policies and procedures in your workplace that help and advise you to carry out moving and handling procedures. Design a brief guide using the most helpful tips and guidelines.

If you are asked to help in a moving and handling activity that:

● is outside the confines of the care plan,
● is not within the scope of your job role,
● you know could cause injury,

it is important to speak to your manager if you cannot reach a compromise that will enable you to work within health and safety guidelines.

If, despite being trained, you are not confident that you can carry out a manoeuvre competently, you should seek advice from an experienced colleague. Ask them to supervise you and help where necessary until you can demonstrate the required level of competence.

If you have concerns that a moving or repositioning activity is no longer appropriate for the individual, for example because of a change in their health or ability to understand instructions, it is important to get help. The activity may need to be reviewed and adapted.

If you have concerns that a piece of equipment is not sufficiently clean or well maintained, get help. Never put health and safety at risk by using unsafe equipment.

AC 6.2 Describe what sources of information are available about moving and positioning individuals

Sources of information about moving and positioning individuals can be found:

● within each person's care plans and risk assessments – these will provide person-specific information

- within your organisation's moving and handling policy – this will give you more general information about the way in which you should support people within your organisation
- from the Health and Safety Executive (HSE) – this organisation provides a wide range of material relating to moving and handling
- from the National Back Exchange – the Association exists to develop, disseminate and promote evidence-based best practice in moving and handling.

It is important that you consult every person's care plan and risk assessment prior to supporting them with moving and handling. Circumstances can change in such a short space of time and you will need to ensure you are working in line with the most current plan of care.

Evidence activity

6.2 Sources of information

Produce a list of sources of information about moving and positioning individuals, which can be retained within care plans and risk assessment records.

Legislation

Health and Safety at Work etc. Act 1974

Manual Handling Operations Regulations 1992, amended 2002

Lifting Operations and Lifting Equipment Regulations (LOLER) 1998

Provision and Use of Work Equipment Regulations (PUWER) 1998

Useful resources

Websites

Health and Safety Executive

www.hse.gov.uk

Royal College of Nursing

www.rcn.org.uk

National Back Exchange

www.nationalbackexchange.org

Index